Science

IDEAS AND APPLICATIONS

10

The Wiley Intermediate Science Program

Science Ideas and Applications 9

Science Ideas and Applications 9 Teacher's Guide

Science Ideas and Applications 10

Science Ideas and Applications 10 Teacher's Guide

Science Explorations 9

Science Explorations 9 Teacher's Guide

Science Explorations 10

Science Explorations 10 Teacher's Guide

Science
IDEAS AND APPLICATIONS

SERIES EDITORS
E. Usha R. Finucane
H. Murray Lang

AUTHOR TEAM

Carol A. Caulderwood
St. Ignatius of Loyola High School

E. Usha R. Finucane
Central Technical School

Don Galbraith
Faculty of Education, University of Toronto

Alan J. Hirsch
Brampton Centennial Secondary School

Craig Johnson
Bendale Secondary School

Barry McCammon
Newtonbrook Secondary School

Thomas E. Trotter
Riverdale Collegiate Institute

Doug Wrigglesworth
Sir Sandford Fleming Secondary School

Mary Kay Winter

John Wiley & Sons
Toronto   New York   Chichester   Brisbane   Singapore

Canadian Cataloguing in Publication Data
Main entry under title:

Science ideas and applications 10

For use in secondary schools.
Includes index.
ISBN 0-471-79665-4

1. Science. I. Finucane, E. Usha R.
II. Lang, Murray (Harold Murray), 1922-
III. Caulderwood, Carol A.

Q161.2.S26 1988   500   C88-093250-3

Designer: Julian Cleva
Typesetter: CompuScreen Typesetting Ltd.

Printed and bound in Canada.

 3 4 5 BP 98 97

Contents

Acknowledgements

This textbook has been reviewed by science teachers at several stages in the developmental process. In addition, each unit in the textbook was class tested in typical science classrooms. Our thanks to Mary Kay Winter for organizing the class testing.

We would like to express our appreciation to the following reviewers and class testers who, as science teachers and educators, have provided us with many useful suggestions and comments on the manuscript at various stages of its development. Many of their recommendations have been incorporated in the textbook, but for the final content, we alone are responsible.

Marcel Agsteribbe, Weston Collegiate Institute
Cecil Ball, Birchmount Park Collegiate Institute
Dan Blum, St. Ignatius of Loyola High School

Victoria Brooks-Johnson, Earl Haig Secondary School
Jim Complak, St. Ignatius of Loyola High School
Ivor Furtado, Father Henry Carr Secondary School
Nicholas Gomez, Brother Edmund Rice Secondary School
Penny McLeod, Unionville High School
Terry Weatherill, Birchmount Park Collegiate Institute
Ron Wilson, Wexford Collegiate Institute

We would also like to thank our developmental editors, Jonathan Bocknek and Mary Kay Winter, who provided valuable support and suggestions during the writing of this book.

We would especially like to thank Gerry Sieben, author of Unit IV from **Science Probe 8** for material used in Unit I and H. Murray Lang, author of Unit 6 from **Life Probe** for material used in Units One and Three.

Science Ideas and Applications 10 and its companion textbook, **Science Ideas and Applications 9**, have been written with a specific goal in mind—to provide learning resources that are completely appropriate for students who are most likely to begin their working careers with the completion of grade 12, or who will receive post-secondary technician/technology training.

Our textbooks are designed to provide a general introduction to science that will help students prepare for their role as citizens in an increasingly technological society. We have strived to prepare materials that will be relevant to the daily lives of your students. Our very title reflects this goal of relating science ideas to practical applications. Please note below the features of the textbook that we think you will find most useful in implementing your course.

FEATURES OF THE TEXT
- **Science Ideas and Applications 10** employs a mosaic approach to the study of science, an approach that emphasizes the breadth of science and ensures that students are exposed to a variety of science disciplines. The textbook contains six units, each representing a separate topic of scientific enquiry.
- Each chapter opens with a brief summary of the *Key Ideas* of the chapter, followed by a motivational introduction.
- Reading level has been carefully controlled so that material is appropriate for the grade 10 students for whom this textbook has been developed.

- Activities have been included in the textbook. Distinctive logos identify each activity as either a *Laboratory Experiment,* a *Thought Experiment,* or a *Teacher Demonstration.*
- Instructions for the safe use of equipment and materials are emphasized throughout the textbook. The *Safety Rules* section should be read carefully at the onset of the course and referred to as needed. In each activity, notes of *Caution* occur whenever there are procedures or techniques that require special care or attention.
- *Self-check* questions, occurring at the end of most numbered sections in the textbook, are provided to allow the student or the class to review short sections of content and to consolidate ideas and applications covered.
- *Challenges*, interspersed throughout the textbook, stimulate students to think about ideas and/or applications presented and to extend their knowledge beyond the limits of the required course material.
- *Ideas and Applications*, likewise found throughout the textbook, provide examples, in addition to those included in narrative passages, of the relevance to life and society of a science idea.
- Each unit contains a feature called *Science and Technology in Society*. As the title suggests, this feature focusses on the science behind, and the societal implications of, a particular technological invention or event.
- Each unit contains a *Science at Work* feature that spotlights the work of a Canadian scientist or group of scientists, and the relation of that work to a key concept or concepts in the unit.

- Newly defined terms, in **boldface** type, are also found in the *Words to Know* section at the end of each chapter. These terms are defined in the *Glossary* at the end of the textbook.
- The end of each chapter contains the following:
  * *Chapter Objectives* to provide students with a checklist of the ideas and applications they should know by the time they have completed their study of the chapter (these are keyed to appropriate sections if the students require review)
  * *Words to Know*, a listing of words which the student should now be able to define and/or use in a sentence
  * *Tying It Together*, a series of chapter review questions
  * *Applying Your Knowledge*, a selection of questions that involve applications of the ideas covered
  * *Projects for Investigation*, questions which involve library research

- Each unit concludes with a two-page self-review and/or class review called *How Well Have You Understood....* This feature contains a matching exercise, 10 multiple choice questions, 10 true/false questions, and a case study.
- Appendices on *The Metric System*, *Graphing*, and *Practical Tips on Microscope Use* may be found at the end of the textbook.
- The accompanying *Teacher's Guide* contains many helpful teaching suggestions, including a rationale for teaching each unit, ways to help stimulate interest, advance preparation and planning, answers to all questions, additional activities and questions, and lists of resource materials.

We hope you and your students have a successful year of ideas and applications.

The Authors

The title of our textbook, **Science Ideas and Applications 10**, shows that the ideas of science are often put to use (applied) in everyday life. In this course you will have an opportunity to learn about the changes that are occurring in our environment and their effects on that environment. You will learn about the basic principles of magnetism and electricity as well as other energy forms. You will also study the human body and its systems. As well, you will have an opportunity to learn about how characteristics are passed from one generation to another.

Science and its applications are essential to our lives. Changes that can affect our lives are continuously happening in our world. These changes may be natural or caused by humans, harmful or beneficial. For example, the development of nuclear energy technology occurred because of the increased demands of a growing world population for alternative energy sources. However, the waste products from this industry are hazardous. Technicians, technologists, and researchers are needed to determine what are our present and future needs and how these needs will affect us as human beings. It is also important that our politicians, historians, and the public in general should have a good understanding of science, its ideas, and its applications to our lives.

Many of the applications of science ideas suggest ways of making a living. If you enjoy science and the applications of science to the machines and instruments of modern life, you may also enjoy an occupation that puts science to work. The pictures show several examples of people whose jobs use (directly or indirectly) skills and knowledge you will gain in this course. You will also find references to other science-related jobs throughout the book.

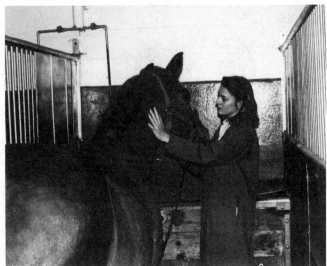

But what if you're not interested in a science-related job? Does science have anything else to offer you? To answer this question, think about the headlines shown below.

MAPLE TREES THREATENED
BY AIR POLLUTION

Salmon will be Added to River this Spring

INVESTIGATORS SEEK SOURCE
OF RIVER POLLUTION

Man-Powered Flying Machine
Achieves New Distance Record

Smoking is Prohibited in
Public Buildings in Toronto

Why is it necessary to protect the purity of the air around us? What effect will the salmon have on the rivers? What forms of energy can be developed to reduce the use of non-renewable energy resources? These are the kinds of questions that a knowledge of science will help you answer. We hope that, by the time you finish your studies, you will feel you have a better understanding of the world and events that affect you every day.

Your school laboratory, like your kitchen or shop, need not be dangerous. In these places, understanding how to use materials and equipment and following proper procedures will help you maintain an accident-free environment.

Care has been taken to ensure a safe environment for all activities in this textbook. Take special note of the word CAUTION associated with certain activities. This alerts you to the fact that you will be working with potentially dangerous equipment, such as Bunsen burners and scalpels, or using chemicals that require special care.

Follow the guidelines and general safety rules listed below. Your teacher will give you specific information on additional safety procedures recommended in your province and on routines that apply to your school. You will also be informed about the location and proper use of all safety equipment.

1. Read through each activity before you begin.
2. Clear the laboratory bench of all materials except those you are using in the activity.
3. Learn the location and use of the safety equipment available to you, such as safety goggles, protective aprons, fire extinguishers, fire blankets, eyewash fountains, and showers. Find out the location of the nearest fire alarm.
4. Do not begin an activity until you are instructed to do so.
5. Do not taste any material unless you are asked to do so by your teacher.

6. When you are instructed to smell a chemical in the laboratory, follow the procedure shown below. Only this technique should be used to smell chemicals in the laboratory. Never sniff a chemical by placing it close to your nose.

7. Use flames only when instructed to do so. Read the special Bunsen burner safety rules that follow.
8. When using dangerous chemicals, wear safety goggles.

9. When heating materials, wear safety goggles. Make sure the test tubes you use are Pyrex and are clean and not cracked. Always keep the open end of the test tube pointed away from other people and yourself. Move the test tube through the flame so heat is distributed evenly.
10. Handle hot objects carefully. If you suffer a burn, immediately inform your teacher.
11. If any part of your body comes in contact with a harmful chemical, inform your teacher. Wash the area immediately and thoroughly with water. If your eyes are affected, do not touch them, but wash them immediately and continuously for at least ten minutes.
12. Wash your hands after you handle chemicals, biological specimens, and micro-organisms that your teacher has instructed you to use.
13. Clean up any spilled chemicals immediately, following instructions given by your teacher.
14. Never pour harmful substances into the sink. Dispose of them as instructed by your teacher.
15. Clean all apparatus before putting it away.
16. Always unplug electric cords by pulling on the plug, not the cord.
17. Watch for sharp or jagged edges on all apparatus. Do not use broken or cracked glassware. Place broken glass only in special marked containers.
18. Report to your teacher all accidents (no matter how minor), broken equipment, damaged or defective facilities, and suspicious looking chemicals.

BUNSEN BURNER SAFETY RULES

If a Bunsen burner is used in your science classroom, make sure you follow the procedures listed below. (Note: hot plates should be used in preference to Bunsen burners whenever possible.)

1. Do not wear scarves or ties, long necklaces, or earphones suspended around your neck. Tie back loose hair, and roll back and secure loose sleeves before you light a Bunsen burner.
2. Obtain instructions from your teacher on the proper method of lighting and using a Bunsen burner.
3. Never heat a flammable material (for example, alcohol) over a Bunsen burner.
4. Be sure there are no flammable materials nearby before you light a Bunsen burner.
5. Never leave a lighted Bunsen burner unattended.
6. Always turn off the gas at the valve, not at the base of the Bunsen burner.

WHAT TO DO IF A FIRE OCCURS

Your teacher will review procedures for fires. Always follow those instructions.

1. Shut off all gas supplies at the desk valves.
2. Notify your teacher immediately. Since every second is vital, move quickly to provide help in an emergency.
3. Here are some other recommendations for action.
    (a) If clothing is on fire, roll on the floor to smother the flames. Use a fire blanket to smother the flames if a fellow student's clothing has caught fire.
    (b) A small fire can be smothered by using sand or a small container such as an inverted large beaker or can.
    (c) Make sure you know how to operate the fire extinguishers in order to assist your teacher.
    (d) If the fire is not quickly and easily put out, leave the building in a calm manner.

The student of science seeks for knowledge about nature. The scientist asks questions and looks for ways to interpret and apply the solutions before asking more questions. Science involves political, social, economic, and technological problem solving. It also involves the seeking of answers about events and natural phenomena. A knowledge of science and its language will help you improve life on earth— not only your own life but the lives of others around you.

In some countries and even in your own city or town, mealtime may not always be a satisfying event. How are food resources made available and distributed to the needy? What can you do to help make sure that everyone has enough food to eat and sufficient water that is safe to drink? What scientific information is necessary to solve some of these problems? What are some of the political, social, economic, and technological factors that make these problems difficult to solve?

You have probably used the *scientific method* of problem solving in earlier science courses. Table 1 shows the steps used in the scientific method. This method works with simple problems as well as difficult social or economic issues. You may not always follow all these steps in this order. Sometimes information you obtain may not lead to the conclusions that you may have expected or wanted. Then you will need to go back and investigate a new hypothesis or idea to explain your results.

The most important step in the scientific method is *communicating*. New knowledge should always be shared with other people. This should be done simply and effectively, and it should be based on knowledge that you have obtained through scientific enquiry. In this way, other people can benefit from your knowledge.

The problem of food resources and their distribution is universal. Use the scientific method to investigate the issue of food shortage. Complete the problem by discussion or group work. What research will you do? How will you communicate your findings to other people? Can *you* make a difference?

Table 1 *Using the Scientific Method to Solve a Problem*

STEP NUMBER	THE SCIENTIFIC METHOD	USING THE SCIENTIFIC METHOD
1	*Observe* an unexplained object or event.	Some people do not eat a satisfying meal every day.
2	Identify a *problem*.	I would like everybody to eat enough every day.
3	Pose a *question*.	How are food resources made available and distributed to the needy?
4	Collect *data* (information).	What is a satisfying meal? Where is food available for the needy? What food is available? How can I help?
5	Suggest a *hypothesis*.	
6	Conduct *experiments* or do *research* to test this hypothesis.	
7	Draw some *conclusions* from the results of the experiments.	
8	*Communicate* the conclusions to others.	

Community Ecology

Our home, planet earth, is the only known planet in our solar system where life exists. Yet even that existence is limited to no more than ten kilometres above and below the oceans. This can be compared to the thin skin that covers and protects an apple. It is a very small area.

All life on earth exists within this small area called the biosphere. In the biosphere, no living thing can live alone and survive. How, then, do living things affect one another? What is the relationship between living things and the biosphere? And how do human beings affect other living things and the biosphere? In this unit, you will come to see the earth as more than just a home for people. Instead, you may see it as a kind of greenhouse where *all* life exists together. Perhaps only then can we begin to develop into truly responsible members of the biosphere.

1

Living Together

Key Ideas

- Ecology is the study of relationships among organisms and between organisms and their environment.
- An ecosystem is made up of interacting biotic and abiotic components.
- A population is the number of individuals of a species living in the same area at the same time.
- Population size is determined by three factors: birth rate, death rate, and migration rate.

Plants and animals have been living together for millions of years. They depend on each other for their survival. How do plants depend on animals? How do animals depend on plants? Who benefits most—plants, animals, or both? In this chapter, you will investigate several types of relationships found in nature. You will also discover how the natural world is organized. Finally, you will find out how living things interact in order to survive.

The Science of Ecology

You are a special person. Many people around you depend on you, and you in turn depend on them. This is called a **relationship**.

In nature, relationships are much the same. Every plant and animal is special, no matter how large or small it is. What are the relationships between plants and animals? Not only do plants and animals live together, they depend on each other for survival. The most obvious dependency is for food. But plants and animals depend on each other in other ways as well. Look at the photograph of the bee and flower at the beginning of this chapter. The bee uses the nectar and pollen of the flower for food. This food gives the bee energy to perform its daily routine. The flower depends on the bee to transfer pollen from one flower to another. This transfer of pollen is an essential part of the reproductive process of plants. In this relationship each living thing is helping the other to survive.

Besides studying the relationships of plants and animals, we must also be concerned with their surroundings. An organism's surrounding is called the **environment.** See Figure 1.1.

Figure 1.1 *What makes up the environment of an animal such as a raccoon?*

The environment is made up of two parts—a living portion and a non-living portion. The living part of the environment includes animals, plants, micro-organisms, and fungi. All of these living things are called the **biotic components**. The non-living part of the environment includes water, sunlight, soil, and climate. These are the **abiotic components**. See Figure 1.2.

The science that explores the relationships among living things and the abiotic components of their environment is called **ecology**.

Figure 1.2 *Small plants on the forest floor. Their environment consists of sunlight, soil, temperature, minerals, water, gases, plus the organisms that affect them.*

Challenge

Look carefully at the other photographs that began this chapter. Describe how one living thing in each picture depends on the others for its survival.

Ecosystems

Together, the interacting biotic and abiotic components of a particular environment make up an **ecosystem**. This can be summarized as follows:

An ecosystem = Biotic Components + Abiotic Components

An ecosystem may be as small as a puddle formed after a rain shower. In a short time the puddle may be teeming with micro-organisms. Or an ecosystem can be as large as a lake where fish constantly search for food. No matter what size the ecosystem is, biologists can find out about the factors that are important in each ecosystem. For instance, they might be concerned with the factors that determine the size of the animal population. They might want to know what factors allow the micro-organisms that live there to reproduce successfully. Even though ecosystems exist in many different sizes, there is one common element found in all of them: the relationship of biotic and abiotic components. The fact that organisms depend on each other for survival is common to every ecosystem.

Challenge

Land has become available for development in your neighbourhood. What will happen to the ecosystem if it is to be used for
1. parkland?
2. an apartment building?
3. a shopping centre?
4. single family dwellings?

In this activity, you will set up a model ecosystem similar to the one in Figure 1.3. In this way you can find out how an ecosystem works. The model ecosystem you are about to make is called a *closed* ecosystem.

Problem

How can a self-contained water ecosystem be made?

Materials

large clear glass jar with lid (mason jars work well)
2–3 very small fish such as guppies or sticklebacks
green plants such as *Elodea* or eel grass
coarse sand or aquarium gravel
pencil crayons: red, green, blue
sheet of paper
lamp with 40 W bulb   ruler
3–5 snails   scissors
strainer   tap water

Procedure

1. Wash the jar thoroughly with warm water. Do *not* use soap or detergent.
2. Place the coarse sand in the strainer and wash the sand three or four times.
3. Place the washed sand in the jar so that it is about 5 cm deep in the front and 7 cm deep in the back.
4. Cut or fold a piece of paper so that it covers the sand in the jar. Gently pour water onto the paper so that the sand is not disturbed. Stop pouring when the water is 5 cm from the top of the jar.
5. Remove the piece of paper. Be careful not to disturb the sand. Let the water stand at least 48 h before adding anything else.
6. Place the green plants carefully into the jar. Allow some to float on the surface and plant a few in the sand.
7. Carefully add the snails and the fish, then screw the lid on the jar very tightly. Once the jar is closed, do not open it.
8. Set the lamp 30 cm away from the jar and turn on the light.
9. In your notebook make a table similar to Table 1.1 on page 6. Observe the jar once a day for at least two weeks and record your data every day.
10. After two weeks, make a graph similar to Figure 1.4. Plot the number of individuals of each organism on the same graph. Use a red pencil for the snails, blue for the fish, and green for the plants. Discuss with your teacher how successful your closed ecosystem has been.

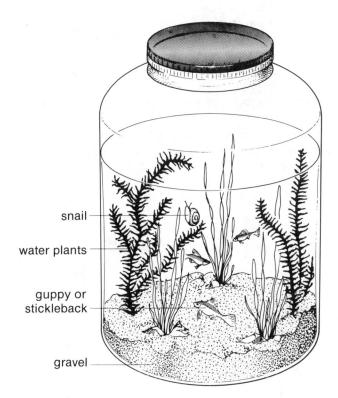

Figure 1.3 *A closed ecosystem*

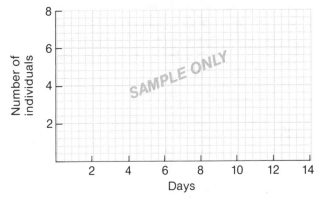

Figure 1.4 *Your graph should be set up like this.*

Observations

Table 1.1 *Ecosystem Information Chart*

DAY	NUMBER OF		NUMBER OF PLANTS	WATER CLARITY	CHANGES
	SNAILS	FISH			
1					
2					
3					
4					
5					
Etc.					

Questions

1. Why did you let the water stand for two days before adding anything else?
2. Why was the sand washed before placing it into the jar?
3. In this ecosystem
   (a) what are the biotic components and
   (b) what are the abiotic components?
4. What do you think will happen over the next few weeks?
   Note: Answer the rest of the questions when you have completed at least two weeks of observations.
5. The type of ecosystem you have constructed is called a closed ecosystem. Nothing was added after sealing the jar.
   (a) What did the fish eat?
   (b) What did the snails eat?
6. In some instances, the model ecosystems may continue for several months. Others may fail after just a few days or a few weeks. What might cause a closed ecosystem to fail?
7. Explain why each of the following is necessary to the ecosystem:
   (a) snails
   (b) green plants
   (c) fish
   (d) the lamp
   (e) the water
8. (a) Does the number of plants increase or decrease?
   (b) Does the number of animals increase or decrease?
   (c) Does this pattern change after some time has passed?
   (d) What does this tell you?
9. How do you think your model ecosystem compares with a natural ecosystem? Explain.

Ecosystems in Nature

Your model ecosystem is similar to ecosystems in nature. The plants and animals in the jar play roles similar to those they play in nature. The fish will eat the plants. The plants, in turn, will gain nutrients for growth from the waste products of the fish. The plants are providing materials and energy for the fish, and the fish are providing materials and energy for the plants. As a result, a balance usually exists in an ecosystem. If an ecosystem is balanced, the plants and animals in it can continue to grow and thrive over a long period of time.

Self-check

1. In your own words, define the following:
   (a) ecology
   (b) environment
   (c) ecosystem
2. (a) What is meant by a biotic component of an ecosystem?
   (b) What is meant by the abiotic component of an ecosystem?
   (c) List three biotic and three abiotic components that might be found in a pond.
3. What is the purpose of setting up a classroom or laboratory model such as the one you constructed in Activity 1A?

The Living Things in an Ecosystem

Activity 1A gave you an opportunity to make and observe a self-contained ecosystem. The ecosystem contained several individual plants and animals. To understand the effect of living things on each other, you should consider the plant and animal populations. A **population** is a group of organisms of the same kind (species) that live in an area.

Population Size

All natural populations tend to be a certain size. The size of the population is the number of individuals in that area. Population size is determined by three major factors:

1. **Birth Rate**: This tells us how fast new individuals are being added to a population. For plants, the birth rate is the number of new plants that germinate and grow.
2. **Death Rate**: This tells us how many individuals die in a population.
3. **Migration Rate**: This tells how many individuals move into or move out of the area.

A combination of these factors allows you to determine if a population increases, decreases, or remains the same.

In this activity, you will investigate an imaginary population. This will show you the effect that birth rate can have on a **hypothetical population**.

Problem

What effect does birth rate have on population growth?

Materials

graph paper

Procedure

1. Make a table similar to Table 1.2 in your notebook.
2. Read the following information. Then answer the questions.

Table 1.2 *Data for Activity 1B*

YEAR	NUMBER OF PARENTS	BREEDING PAIRS	NUMBER OF OFFSPRING
0	2	1	4
1	4	2	8
2	8		
3			
4			
5			

After a severe rain storm, a small lake is formed in an abandoned quarry pit. Soon, two beavers—one male and one female—move into the new lake. There is plenty of food. There are also no other animals that can affect the two beavers. The beavers build a home and produce four offspring. This population of beavers will grow under the following conditions:

(a) Every spring, each pair of beavers produce four offspring, two female and two male.
(b) All the parents die each winter. Only their offspring survive to reproduce.
(c) None of the offspring die during the winter.
(d) None of the beavers migrate.
(e) There is an ample supply of food for everyone.

Observations

1. Determine what the population would be in the spring three, four, and five years later. Use your copy of Table 1.2 to record your calculations.
2. (a) Make a graph similar to Figure 1.5. Plot the number of offspring on the *y*-axis and the years on the *x*-axis.
   (b) Describe the pattern of growth of the beaver population.

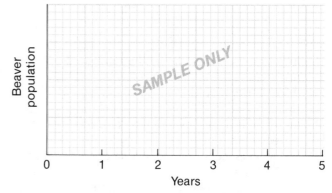

Figure 1.5 *Graph for a hypothetical population*

Questions

1. Do you think actual populations of organisms in nature grow like this hypothetical beaver population? Explain.
2. What do you think would happen to the growth pattern of this population if condition (e) stated that there was only enough food to support 50 beavers? Explain.
3. What would happen if another similar animal was added to the population?

Population Steady State

A real population rarely grows like the beaver population in Activity 1B. In nature, population sizes vary because of changes in the birth rate, death rate, and migration rate. These rates interact to keep the population in balance with its environment. This balance is called a **steady state**. In a steady state, a population will change or fluctuate (Figure 1.6).

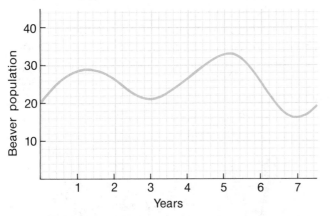

Figure 1.6 *This population of beavers is in a steady state. The size of the population remains within the limits that the environment can support.*

What might cause the birth rate, death rate, and migration rate to change? There are several environmental factors that can affect them.

1. Food supply: As a population continues to grow, it will soon become larger than the amount of available food.
2. Disease: In a large population, individuals tend to live close together. This allows disease to spread among them very easily.
3. Overcrowding: All organisms need room to reproduce and care for their young. As a population increases, the amount of available living space decreases.

4. Other organisms: When a population increases, populations of other organisms may also increase. For example, when a population of field mice increases, the population of snakes that feed on the mice may also increase.
5. Weather: Poor weather conditions can reduce a population's food supply. Severe storms can kill many individuals in a population.

The effects of these factors usually work together to control the size of a population. In general, a population will increase until it becomes so large that the environmental factors begin to reduce it.

Challenge

Consider a population of field mice that live in an open meadow near a forest. What effect will each environmental factor have on controlling the size of this population?

Population Samples

You have just been given a summer job by the Ministry of Natural Resources. Your first task is to count a population in a community. A **community** is the place where many different populations live together.

You wouldn't actually have to count each and every member of the population. Instead, you could measure small parts or samples of a population in a community. For example, you might choose samples that measure one hundredth (1/100) of the area of a community. Then you could multiply the count by 100. This gives a fairly accurate estimate of the total population.

To avoid choosing an especially good sample, or a very bad sample, you could take your samples at random. **Random samples** are samples chosen by chance from a large area. Figure 1.7 shows one method for sampling a caribou population. In the next section, you will learn a technique that is useful for measuring populations.

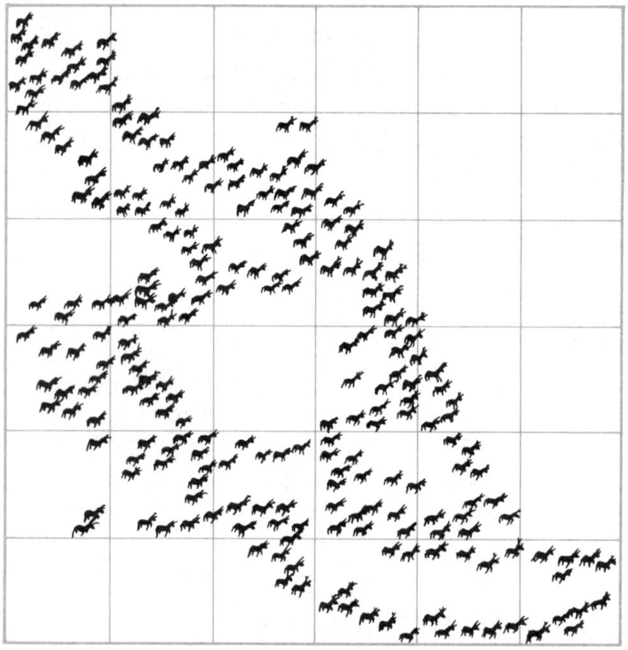

Figure 1.7 *A pipeline is planned for the far north to transport oil to the south. Many people question how the pipeline may affect the wildlife. To find out how many caribou live in the area, for example, biologists will take a random sample of the population. The animals shown here were first photographed from an airplane. A drawing was made from the photograph. To make the sampling easier, the whole area was divided by a grid. To find out the total number of caribou per square kilometre, the biologist randomly picks a certain number of squares shown. He or she then counts the caribou in each selected square, adds them together, and multiplies by the number of squares it would take to represent one square kilometre. This technique will give an estimate of the number of caribou per square kilometre.*

1.4

Population Sampling: A Field Study

To count a population in a community, you need to measure a convenient area. An area of one square metre (1 m^2) is useful for laboratory work. Such a sampling area is called a **quadrat**.

A simple population to measure is a dandelion population. Dandelions are easy to recognize. They appear as weeds in many lawns and fields (Figure 1.8).

Why would someone want to count the number of weeds in a lawn? One possible reason is to find out whether dandelions are increasing in number and crowding out the grass. Another possible reason is to measure the effectiveness of a certain brand of weed spray in controlling the dandelion population.

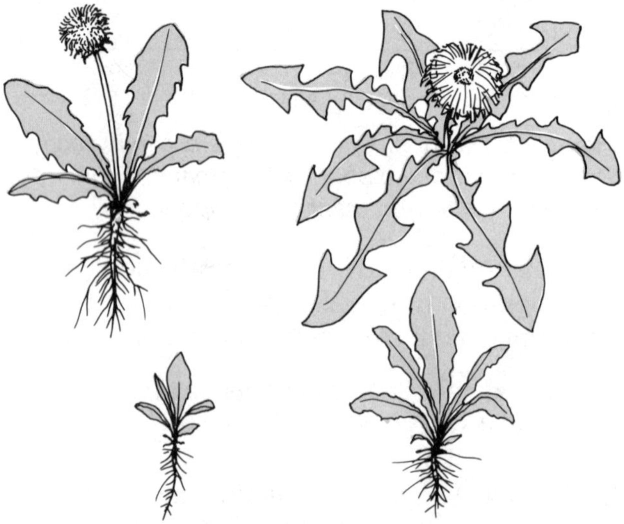

Figure 1.8 *How to recognize a dandelion. There are two varieties of dandelion plants. Both produce the familiar yellow flower head. The plants differ in the shapes of their leaves. One variety has huge "teeth" that divide the leaf almost to the midrib. The "teeth" curve back toward the base of the leaf. The second variety has broad oval leaves with a few very small "teeth." Very young dandelions look like the second variety.*

Problem

How can you estimate the dandelion population living in a lawn or playing field?

Materials

4.5 m length of string
4 large eye bolts (see Figure 1.9)
50 m or 100 m measuring tape
clipboard
small colourful objects to use as markers
pen or pencil

CAUTION

1. Never taste or eat unknown plants.
2. If you have any allergy to plants, tell your teacher.
3. Wash your hands after handling plants and soil.

Figure 1.9 *Equipment used to mark a quadrat*

Procedure

1. Figure 1.9 shows the equipment used to mark quadrats. At 1 m intervals, tie loops in the string. These will form the corners of the quadrat.
2. Copy Table 1.3 onto loose-leaf paper, and clip it to your clipboard. You and your partner will work as a team. One of you will record the observations in the field. The other will look after the materials.
3. Choose a suitable part of the lawn or playing field. The part you choose should be typical of the lawn or field so that your sample can truly represent the whole area.
4. Toss a colourful object onto the lawn or field in the part you selected. Where it lands, place the nearest corner of your quadrat.
5. Carefully screw the bolts into the ground to fasten the four corners of the quadrat. Make sure that the corners are square. The quadrat should cover 1 m^2.
6. Count all the dandelion plants in your quadrat (Figure 1.10). If a plant lies on the boundary line, count it only if half or more than half of it lies inside the quadrat. If the roots of the plant are inside the boundary, then you count it.

Figure 1.10 *These students are carefully counting a species of plants in their quadrat.*

11

7. Record the number of dandelions in your table.
8. Repeat steps 4–6 at least four more times in different parts of the lawn or field.
9. One team should measure the total area of the lawn or field. Record the total area in your table.
10. To estimate the total population of dandelions in the lawn or field, add the total number of dandelions from each of your five quadrat samples. Divide this total by the area of the quadrats (5 m^2). This will give you the average number of dandelions per square metre. Finally, multiply this number by the area of the lawn or field. This will give you the estimated total population of dandelions in the lawn or field. Here's an example:

Dandelion count in 5 quadrat samples: 13, 15, 16, 12, 15
Total number of dandelions in 5 quadrats: 71

$$\text{Average} = \frac{\text{total number of dandelions}}{\text{total area of quadrats}}$$

$$= \frac{71 \text{ dandelions}}{5 \text{ m}^2}$$

$$= 14.2 \text{ dandelions per square metre}$$

Estimated total population of dandelions in the field

= average number of dandelions × area of field
= 14.2 dandelions × 1000 m^2
= 14 200 dandelions

Observations

(see Table 1.3)

Questions

1. Were there more or fewer dandelions in the study area than in most lawns in the neighbourhood? What might be the reasons for any difference?
2. Are there any indications that suggest the population is changing?
3. Why is it important to choose your sample areas at random?

Table 1.3 *Observation Sheet*

Quadrat Sample: A Population of Dandelions

Date _____ Team Members _____
_____
_____
_____

Location of study area_____
Description of study site_____
Total area of lawn or field _____ m^2
Area covered by our quadrat _____ m^2
Number of organisms counted within our quadrat:

SAMPLE NUMBER	NUMBER OF DANDELIONS PER QUADRAT
1	
2	
3	
4	
5	
Total	
Average	

Calculations
Average number of dandelions
 per square metre = _____
Estimated total population of
 dandelions in the field community = _____

SAMPLE ONLY

Self-check

1. In your own words, define the word population.
2. What three factors determine population size?
3. How would you describe a population that fluctuates?
4. List the five environmental factors that affect population growth.
5. Describe a technique that can be used to estimate population sizes.

Communities and Ecosystems

You know that different populations living together make up a community. There are three different types of communities that exist throughout the world. In *terrestrial communities* the environment consists mostly of land. Examples include a woodlot, meadow, field, or alley way. Examples of *freshwater communities* include ponds, marshes, streams, and lakes. Another kind of community also involves water. A salt water community is called a *marine community*. Areas along the ocean shore and salt marshes are two examples of marine communities.

Individuals, populations, and communities all exist in a very organized pattern or system in nature. Several communities existing together in a particular area make up the ecosystem for that area. Thus, scientists tend to call ecosystems on land **terrestrial ecosystems**. Ecosystems in water are called **aquatic ecosystems**.

No two ecosystems are exactly the same. Differences in abiotic components such as temperature, moisture, and sunlight all combine to make each ecosystem unique. In Activity 1D, you will use equipment such as that shown in Figure 1.11 to compare two ecosystems.

Challenge

Make a list of three different communities found near your school. List the different populations that are contained in each community.

Figure 1.11 *Equipment for a field study: clipboard, psychrometer, air thermometer, soil thermometer, plastic collection bottles, tape measure*

Problem

What abiotic components make one ecosystem different from another ecosystem?

Materials

compass
soil thermometer
anemometer to measure wind speed
light meter
metre stick or measuring tape
psychrometer to measure humidity
air thermometer
trowel
clipboard

CAUTION

1. Never taste or eat unknown plants.
2. Wash your hands after handling plants and soil.
3. If you have any allergy to plants, tell your teacher.

Procedure

1. Copy Table 1.4 onto a piece of paper and clip it to the clipboard. This will allow you to record your measurements at the site.
2. When you arrive at the first site selected by your teacher, sit down quietly for 10 min and observe the area. Look for animals or any evidence of animal life.
3. Sketch a diagram of the area. Mark the direction "north" on your sketch.
4. The class may be assigned to work in teams at a different area. When you reach your area, mark the location on the sketch.

5. Conduct the following tests and record your results in Table 1.4.
   (a) Measure light intensity.
   (b) Measure the air temperature.
   (c) Measure the humidity.
   (d) Measure the wind speed and direction.
   (e) Measure the soil temperature at (i) the surface and (ii) 15 cm below the surface.
   (f) Measure the soil moisture content by taking a scoopful of soil in your hand and squeezing to see if it holds together (moist) or falls apart (dry).
6. At the next site, look around, listen to the sounds, and smell the air. Mark your location on your sketch.
7. Repeat step 5. Compare your team's results with those from other teams.

Observations

Table 1.4 *Data for Activity 1D*

Team Members _____ Date_____
  _____
  _____
  _____
Weather Conditions_____

ABIOTIC COMPONENTS	SITE 1	SITE 2
1. Light		
2. Air Temperature	_____°C	_____°C
3. Humidity		
4. Wind Speed		
5. Wind Direction		
6. Soil Temperature:		
surface	_____°C	_____°C
15 cm	_____°C	_____°C
7. Soil Moisture		
Animals		
Distance Between Each Plant		

SAMPLE ONLY

Questions

1. At which of your sites was
   (a) light intensity greatest?
   (b) temperature highest?
   (c) humidity highest?
   (d) soil temperature lowest (i) at the surface and (ii) 15 cm deep?
2. Which site had the (a) wettest soil and (b) driest soil?
3. What types of plants were found at (a) site 1 and (b) site 2?
4. List the abiotic components that made it possible for the plants to survive at (a) site 1 and (b) site 2.
5. What evidence of animals did you find at (a) site 1 and (b) site 2?
6. List the (a) biotic components and (b) abiotic components that allowed these animals to live at site 1 and site 2.
7. Which abiotic factors were the same at both sites?

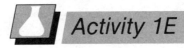

Activity 1E

The information you acquired from Activity 1D will allow you to set up a terrarium. A **terrarium** is a model that represents a terrestrial ecosystem. This is an *open* ecosystem.

For this activity you will work in groups. It will be up to the group to decide what type of terrarium to assemble. Will it be a woodlot, meadow, field, or forest floor? Once a decision has been made, the abiotic components must be considered.

Will you need soil, clay, humus, moss, or a combination of these things for the ground cover? How much light will the terrarium require? What is the best range of temperature (lowest to highest temperature)? How moist should the ground cover be?

Next, your group will need to consider biotic components. What types of plants will you put in the terrarium? How many will you use? Which animals will be placed in it? Are the plants suitable for the animals chosen? How many animals will there be? (Too many animals will cause overcrowding.)

Problem

How can you set up a terrarium?

Materials

terrarium case, aquarium, or large jar
clean gravel
glass cover or lid
lamp and 60 W bulb
thermometer
string
abiotic components
biotic components

Procedure

1. Place 2–3 cm of the gravel in the bottom of the terrarium. This will provide drainage.
2. Place enough of the ground cover so that it will be at least 4–5 cm deep in the terrarium.
3. To give it a realistic look, sculpt in a hill or ridge.
4. Carefully add the plants.
5. Carefully place the animals in the terrarium.
6. Hang the thermometer in the corner of the terrarium.

Table 1.5 *Data for Activity 1E*

Ecosystem _____				
DATE	TEMPERATURE (°C)	NUMBER OF PLANTS	NUMBER OF ANIMALS	CONDITIONS (HUMIDITY/SOIL)
1				
2				
3				
4				
5				

SAMPLE ONLY

7. Set the glass cover on the top of the terrarium. Leave a 1 cm space on one side of the terrarium so that air can circulate.
8. Place the terrarium in an area of the room where it will receive enough light. If there is not enough light, place a lamp about 30 cm from the terrarium and turn it on. One caution: Be sure that the temperature does not go above the ideal range.
9. Copy Table 1.5 into your notebook and record the data once every 5 d.

Observations

(see Table 1.5)

Questions

1. Why is it important to keep a record of the data for the terrarium?
2. How can you tell if the humidity in the terrarium is too high or too low? How would you correct the condition?
3. What are the animals eating in the terrarium?
4. List three abiotic components of the terrarium.
5. Why is it important that the terrarium receive light?
6. How similar is this model to the sites investigated in Activity 1D?
7. How long do you think this terrarium will last? What changes must be made to ensure that all the organisms in the terrarium will survive for a long period of time?

Self-check

1. What is a community?
2. Name three types of communities. Give one example of each type.
3. For what would you use each of the following pieces of equipment:
   (a) anemometer
   (b) psychrometer
   (c) air thermometer
4. What is a terrarium?

Challenge

Using your terrarium, adjust one of the abiotic factors such as raising the temperature. Maintain recordings over a two week period. What changes occurred in the ecosystem? Did these changes improve conditions for the organisms in the terrarium? What abiotic changes occurred?

Beyond Ecosystems: Biomes and the Biosphere

So far in this chapter, you have considered the following levels of biological organization:

- population: a group of individuals of the same species that live in an area
- community: different populations living together in an area
- ecosystem: several communities living together in an area

The next level of biological organization above the ecosystem is the **biome**. In many ways, a biome can be thought of as a large ecosystem. A biome has a relatively constant climate and soil, and a characteristic group of plants and animals.

The last level of biological organization is the **biosphere**. See Figure 1.12. The word biosphere is made up of two Greek root words: "bio" means life and "sphere" means a ball or globe. Thus, biosphere means literally "globe of life." The biosphere is made up of all the materials essential for life and all forms of life itself: bacteria and other single-celled organisms, fungi, plants, and animals, including humans.

The biosphere is an integrated system. All parts of it are related. Each part affects the others. The loss of even a single organism has some effect on other organisms. Keep this in mind as you continue your studies of ecology in Chapters 2 and 3.

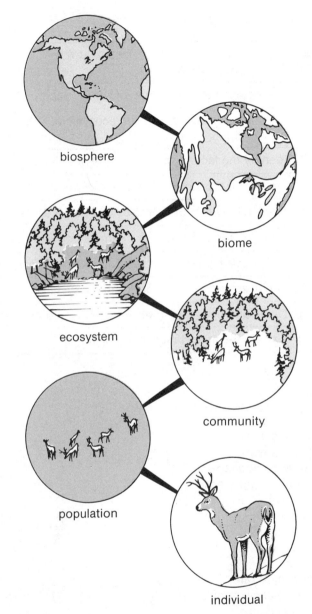

biosphere

biome

ecosystem

community

population

individual

Figure 1.12 *The levels of biological organization*

Chapter Objectives

NOW THAT YOU HAVE COMPLETED THIS CHAPTER, CAN YOU DO THE FOLLOWING?	FOR REVIEW, TURN TO SECTION
1. Distinguish between biotic and abiotic components of an ecosystem.	1.1
2. Organize and set up a closed ecosystem, and explain how such a model relates to a real ecosystem.	1.2
3. Identify the factors that determine population size.	1.3
4. Graph the growth of a hypothetical population.	1.3
5. Explain how random samples can be used to estimate the size of a population.	1.3
6. Use a quadrat to measure a sample population, and estimate the total size of the sample area.	1.4
7. Conduct a field study in two ecosystems to examine different abiotic components.	1.5
8. Organize and set up a terrarium ecosystem.	1.5
9. Name and define the levels of biological organization.	1.6
10. Explain the importance of the biosphere.	1.6

Words to Know

relationship
environment
biotic component
abiotic component
ecology
ecosystem
population
birth rate
death rate
migration rate
hypothetical population
steady state
community
random sample
quadrat
terrestrial ecosystem
aquatic ecosystem
terrarium
biome
biosphere

Tying It Together

1. (a) What are the different parts of an ecosystem?
   (b) Give two examples of each.
2. What makes up the environment of an organism?
3. Copy the following words into your notebook. State whether each is a biotic or abiotic component of an ecosystem.
   (a) rain
   (b) wind
   (c) bacteria
   (d) humidity
   (e) rotting leaves
   (f) turtle eggs
   (g) snow
   (h) population of mosquitoes
4. List four different examples of ecosystems.
5. Name the three factors that determine population size.

6. Describe at least two environmental factors that prevent a population from constantly increasing in size.
7. Name three types of biological communities.
8. Decide whether each of the following refers to a community, a population, or an individual.
   (a) a deer grazing in a field
   (b) all the different plants in a meadow
   (c) the white pine trees in Northern Ontario
   (d) a worm burrowing into the soil
   (e) the fish and ducks that live in a marsh
   (f) the honeybees swarming around a hive
9. (a) What is a quadrat?
   (b) Why are quadrats useful?
10. Calculate the population of cattails in a marsh 500 m long and 150 m wide if the quadrat counts of the cattails were 50, 56, 54, 60, and 55. The area enclosed by the quadrat was 1 m².
11. On a field study, what equipment would you need to measure the following?
   (a) air temperature
   (b) wind speed
   (c) humidity
   (d) light intensity
12. Name four populations you would find within two blocks of your school.
13. What is a biome?
14. How is the biosphere related to all other levels of biological organization?

Applying Your Knowledge

1. A field is 200 m long and 100 m wide. The cows that graze in the field are not producing enough milk. The farmer knows that the cows will not eat buttercups. The farmer has a quadrat that covers 1 m². In six quadrat samplings of the field, the farmer counts 24, 31, 29, 25, 24, and 27 buttercups.
   (a) What is the total area of the field?
   (b) What is the estimated total population of the buttercups in the field?
   (c) What can the farmer do to make the field produce more food for the cows?

2. By the year 2000, human beings may be living in an orbiting space laboratory for extended periods of time. What biotic and abiotic components will they need in order to survive in space?
3. What similar types of animals would you expect to find in both an aquatic ecosystem and in a terrestrial ecosystem? Why do you think they can be found living in both environments?
4. A student tries to set up a closed ecosystem. It contains a few plants, a snail, and several micro-organisms, but too many fish are placed in the jar.
   (a) What will happen to the fish if the jar remains sealed?
   (b) Which population will probably increase?
   (c) Do you think that all the organisms in the closed ecosystem will eventually die? Explain.

Projects for Investigation

1. What is meant by the term *population explosion*? Which countries are experiencing this problem? Has there been a population explosion in a plant population? What were the results?
2. Insect populations tend to be very large. Research techniques that can be used to estimate the size of an insect population.

2

Food Chains and Food Webs

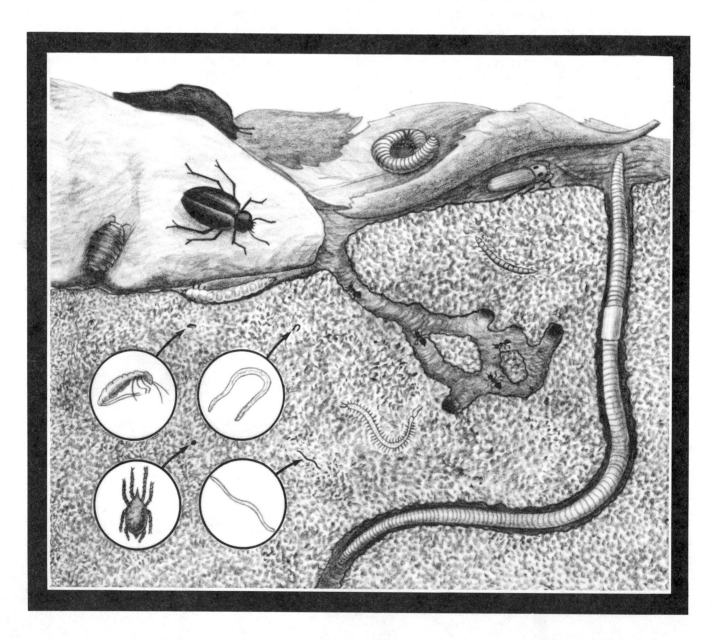

Key Ideas

- Food chains show the flow of energy through ecosystems.
- Food webs show the complex interrelationships among food chains in a community.
- All matter is cycled in an ecosystem.

All organisms need energy to stay alive, grow, and reproduce. For example, the soil organisms shown here may eat plants, other animals, or micro-organisms. A bird, in turn, may well eat some of these soil organisms to obtain the energy it needs to survive. Where did this energy originally come from?

Feeding relationships and the flow of energy are important parts of any ecosystem. In this chapter, you will investigate the flow of energy in ecosystems. But first, you need to find out more about the feeding relationships of organisms.

Energy in Ecosystems

Plants are organisms specialized to produce their own food. In the process of photosynthesis, a plant needs the raw materials, carbon dioxide, and water in order to make its own food. The energy to combine these materials comes from the sun. Green plants are, therefore, direct users of the sun's energy. They are able to capture and store this energy because of a chemical known as chlorophyll. Chlorophyll not only gives leaves their green colour but also enables plants to absorb the sun's energy.

Green plants have the ability to capture light energy and change it into chemical energy (food). We call these plants **producers**. A maple tree, clover, marsh grasses, and a berry bush are all examples of producers.

Animals do not have the ability to make their own food. Since they must eat to obtain their food, they are called **consumers**.

Food Chains

Figure 2.1 shows two living things that are eaten by other living things in a woodlot ecosystem. This series of organisms—each organism eating the other named before it—is called a **food chain**.

sun → grass → rabbit → fox

Figure 2.1 *An example of a food chain in a field*

The sun is the original source of energy in the food chain. The sun's energy is shown by a wavy line with an arrow. The arrows show the direction in which the energy moves. All activities—hunting for food, reproducing young, building a shelter—require energy. This energy is obtained from food. In Figure 2.1, the rabbit gains energy from the grass. In other words, the consumer (rabbit) feeds on the producer (grass). Now, can you explain the transfer of the energy from the sun to the fox?

Consumers, such as rabbits, that eat only plants are called **herbivores**. Deer, hamsters, and caterpillars are typical herbivores. Consumers that eat other animals are known as **carnivores**. Examples of carnivores are hawks, foxes, and northern pike. Finally, there are consumers that eat both plants and animals.

These consumers are known as **omnivores**. A grizzly bear, housefly, and most humans are omnivores.

Figure 2.2 shows two other examples of food chains found in different communities.

Other Organisms in Food Chains

Food chains all begin with a producer. The producers are constantly using energy from the sun and nutrients from the soil. How are these nutrients replaced? Every community has its own special "clean-up" squad of consumers. These special organisms perform two main tasks:

1. They "clean up" garbage, sewage, and dead plants and animals.
2. They return nutrients to the community for use by the producers.

Figure 2.2 *Other examples of food chains*

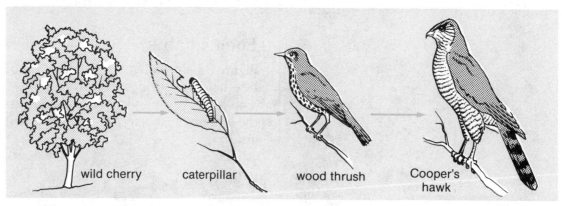

wild cherry   caterpillar   wood thrush   Cooper's hawk

(a) *Food chain in a forest*

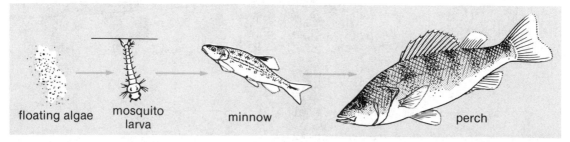

floating algae   mosquito larva   minnow   perch

(b) *Food chain in a pond*

Decomposers

When an organism dies, the nutrients that are part of it are not useful to the producer until they are decomposed (broken down chemically). Organisms called decomposers perform this task. **Decomposers** are the organisms, such as moulds and bacteria, that penetrate dead material and digest it. As they decompose dead material, they return valuable nutrients to the soil. These nutrients can then be used again by plants (producers) to help them grow (Figure 2.3). In this way, useful materials are being recycled in the community. There is little waste.

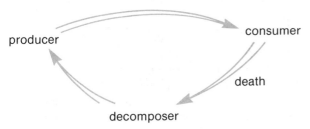

Figure 2.3 *A summary of how materials are returned to the producer*

Scavengers

Another type of clean-up organism in the community is the scavenger. A **scavenger** is an organism that eats dead or decaying plant and animal matter. Snails act as scavengers in an aquarium when they eat dead fish. However, snails are also herbivores when they eat living plants and algae. Ring-billed gulls act as scavengers when they eat the dead material washed up along a beach. Gulls are also carnivores when they hunt and eat earthworms in a freshly ploughed field. Thus, you can see that the same organism can have more than one "job" in the community.

Habitat and Niche

Organisms can be found living in a wide variety of areas. Some make their homes in a rotting log, a meadow, or a hole in a river bank. Others make their homes in a deep ocean. Obviously, there are many different places where organisms can live. The place where they live is called their habitat. The word **habitat** means the physical space where a species is found. It provides a general description of the particular type of environment in which an organism can survive. More than one population can share the same habitat.

The word **niche** refers to an organism's role or job in a community. For example, the niche of a beaver is to feed on young trees, fertilize the soil with its wastes, become food for wolves, build dams to control water levels (thus preserving its habitat), and so on (Figure 2.4).

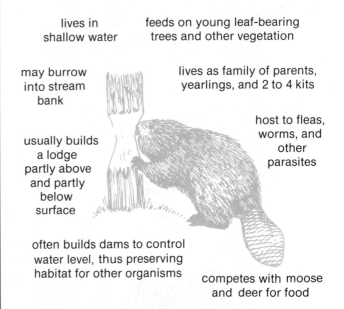

Figure 2.4 *The niche of the beaver involves its interaction with the biotic and abiotic components in its habitat.*

There are other animals, like muskrats, moose, and deer, with the same life requirements as beavers. If they shared the same habitat with beavers, they would be competing with them for food. There might not be enough available food and space for all of them. For this reason, it is unusual for two or more life forms with the same niche to live in the same habitat for long.

Challenge

Some animals live in a relationship in which neither is harmed. This is called mutualism. The figure below shows some of the organisms that can live together for mutual benefit. Find out more about mutualism and the animals that live together in this manner.

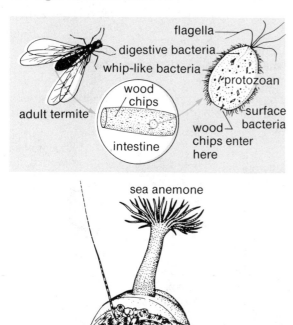

Self-check

1. (a) What is a producer?
   (b) Give three examples of producers.
2. (a) What is a consumer?
   (b) Give three examples of consumers.
3. What is the difference between a carnivore, a herbivore, and an omnivore?
4. Why are decomposers important to an ecosystem?
5. What is a scavenger?
6. In your own words, define the word habitat.
7. Describe the niche of a gull.

Ideas and Applications

Have you ever wondered why you rarely see a dead carcass in a natural environment? Burying beetles are organisms that help get rid of carcasses. These little creatures dig under the bodies of dead animals, causing them to sink into the ground. Then they lay their eggs in the carcass. When the young hatch, they have a plentiful supply of food.

Burying beetles at work

Food Webs

Most organisms eat several kinds of food. Thus, they are part of several food chains. These connected food chains make up what is called a **food web**. Figure 2.5 shows a food web in a pond community. All of the organisms in this community depend on others for their survival. The floating plants provide food for the insects, which in turn provide food for the minnows. The perch depends on the minnows for its food. Activity 2A will give you an opportunity to observe the relationships in a food web.

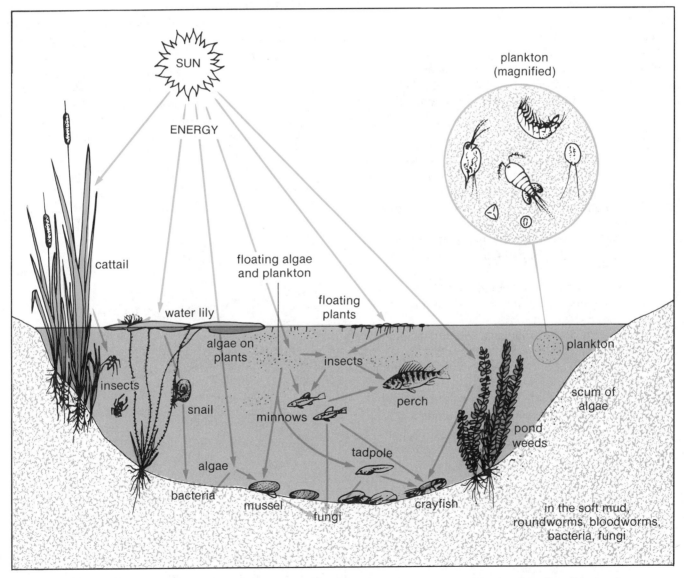

Figure 2.5 *Very few simple food chains exist in nature. Most organisms eat or are eaten by other kinds of organisms. They are all part of a food web.*

Problem

How can we show the flow of energy in a community?

Materials

ball of string
straight pins
paper (6 cm × 3 cm)
scissors
cardboard (60 cm × 60 cm)
list of organisms: grass plants, fox, skunk, toad, rabbit, bee, bear, field mouse, squirrel, deer, robin, snake, oak tree, caterpillar, bobcat, woodpecker, blackfly, worm, chipmunk, owl, sparrow, ant

Procedure

1. Choose one producer and ten consumers from the list. Write the name of each of your organisms on a separate piece of paper.
2. Pin the name of the producer to the middle of the cardboard.
3. Pin 2 or 3 other animals around the producer. Hint: Leave a minimum of 6 cm between each name.
4. If one animal could eat another, join them with a length of string tied to the pin to show the flow of energy.
5. Add the rest of the organisms and connect them with the string.
6. Draw a sketch of this food web in your notebook to remind you of its structure.
7. Repeat steps 2, 3, 4, 5, and 6 using the same names but show the animals consuming a different meal.
8. Repeat steps 1–6 using the name of a different producer and ten new consumers.

Observations

1. List the consumers found in your food web.
2. What is the original source of energy for your food web?
3. Name the herbivores, carnivores, and omnivores in your food web.

Questions

1. How many separate food chains did you produce?
2. Draw a neat diagram to represent three separate food chains.
3. Which way does the energy flow in the food web?
4. Consider the food web shown in Figure 2.6. What would happen to the community if (a) all of the hawks were to disappear, (b) all of the rabbits were to vanish, (c) all of the grass plants died, and (d) all of the decomposers vanished?

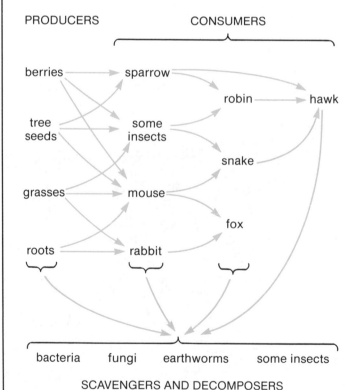

Figure 2.6 *A food web typical of many terrestrial ecosystems*

Challenge

A student observes several organisms in a terrestrial community over a period of one month. She constructs a food web similar to the one shown here. One year later, she discovers that all of the foxes have been killed by hunters. Explain what effect the loss of the foxes would have on populations of (a) grass, (b) rabbits, and (c) deer.

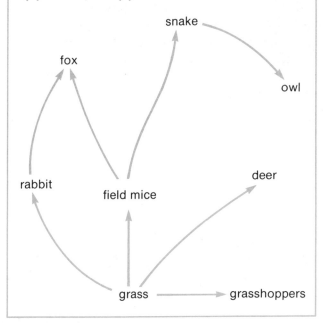

Nutrient Cycling

Matter in nature moves in a cycle. In an ecosystem, material moves from the producer to the consumer. Eventually some of that material is returned to the producer by decomposers. Many of the nutrients in nature follow a similar cycle. Examples of these nutrients are water and carbon.

The Water Cycle

Long before organisms existed on earth, there was water. The earth is the only planet in our solar system that contains liquid water. Figure 2.7 shows the **water cycle**.

Figure 2.7

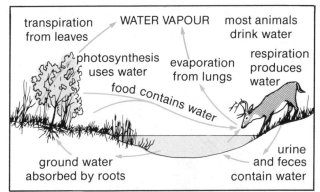

(a) *The importance of the water cycle to organisms*

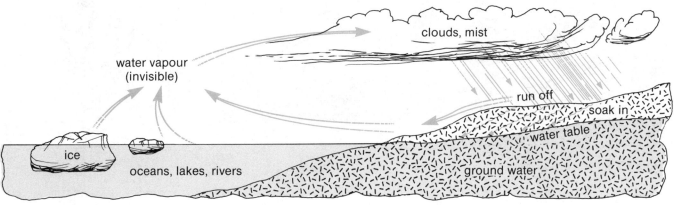

(b) *The water cycle*

Ideas and Applications

When the smoke from large industries mixes with the water vapour in air, a dangerous chemical change takes place. The precipitation that results is acidic. Acid precipitation can be very damaging to all ecosystems. In an aquatic ecosystem, for example, it kills water plants. Numbers of lakes become uninhabitable for many kinds of fish. The effect on terrestrial ecosystems is similar. Acid precipitation damages leaves, reducing plant growth. Roots are also damaged. The overall result can be a decrease in the productivity of farms, forests, and sport industries such as fishing and hunting. Governments around the world are studying the effects of acid precipitation to find a solution to the problem.

The Carbon Cycle

Carbon is an important element in all organisms. It is the vital building block for the chemistry of cells. Green plants obtain carbon from the carbon dioxide in the atmosphere. All other organisms must eat plants or plant-eating organisms to get their own supply of carbon. The life processes of both plants and animals also release carbon dioxide into the air. In addition, the activity of decomposers releases carbon dioxide. Imagine that you could label a single carbon atom in a molecule of carbon dioxide before it entered a green plant. You would be able to follow it through the **carbon cycle** shown in Figure 2.8.

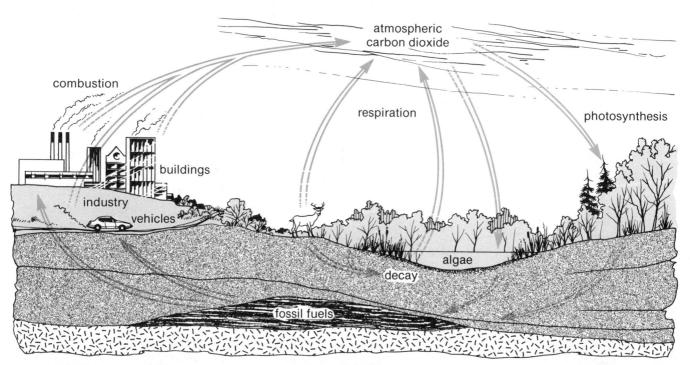

Figure 2.8 *The carbon cycle*

Self-check

1. What is a food web?
2. List five distinct food chains found in the food web shown in Figure 2.5.
3. Construct a food web using organisms found locally around the school.
4. List three ways that organisms take part in the water cycle.
5. Describe, in simple terms, the water cycle. Explain its importance to nature.
6. (a) How do plants use carbon?
   (b) How is carbon returned to the air?

Feeding Relationships

Predator-Prey

In every food web there are different ways in which organisms get their food. A very common feeding relationship is the predator-prey relationship. A **predator** is a carnivore that hunts and kills for food (Figure 2.9). A lion stalks a Thompson's gazelle. A northern pike attacks a golden shiner. A robin pulls a worm from its hole. These are all examples of a predator-prey relationship.

Predator and prey are both part of a food web. The prey is necessary to the predator. It is a source of food. Is there any benefit to the prey from this relationship? Activity 2B will allow you to analyze these two populations to determine why they change over several years.

Figure 2.9 *This antelope was killed by a predator, the cheetah.*

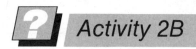

Activity 2B

Problem

How do a predator and its prey control each other's population?

Materials

graph paper
blue and red pencil crayons

Table 2.1 *Populations of Snowshoe Hare and Canada Lynx*

YEAR	POPULATION OF HARE × 1000	YEAR	POPULATION OF LYNX × 1000
1845	12	1848	28
1850	76	1853	8
1855	68	1858	24
1860	8	1863	4
1865	152	1868	60
1870	16	1873	8
1875	84	1878	32
1880	12	1883	16
1885	120	1888	72
1890	60	1893	20
1895	20	1898	36
1900	8	1903	4
1905	64	1908	40
1910	28	1913	4
1915	12	1918	24
1920	8	1923	2
1925	72	1928	28
1930	12	1933	8
1935	80	1938	32

Procedure

1. On the graph paper, plot the information concerning the number of snowshoe hare. Locate the population on the *y*-axis and the years on the *x*-axis. Graph this population with a blue pencil.
2. Use a ruler to join all the plotted points.
3. On the same graph, plot the data for the Canada lynx. This time use a red pencil.
4. Use a ruler to connect the points for the lynx.

Observations

1. What length of time is represented on the graph?
2. During this time what is the largest population of the (a) lynx and (b) hare?
3. (a) Why might the hare population increase?
   (b) Why might the hare population decrease?
4. (a) Why might the lynx population increase?
   (b) Why might the lynx population decrease?

Questions

1. Why do changes in the lynx population follow the changes in the hare population?
2. How can both predator and prey be said to control each other's population?
3. If there were no lynx controlling the hare population, what would eventually happen to the population of snowshoe hares?

Parasite-Host

A **parasite** is another type of consumer. A parasite uses another living thing as a home and a source of food. It may not kill the organism. The organism affected by the parasite is called the **host**. Table 2.2 lists some examples of parasites and their hosts. Each parasite gains the necessary nutrients for survival from its host.

Table 2.2 *Examples of Parasites and Their Hosts*

PARASITE	HOST	RESULT
Tapeworm	Cat	Lives in cat's intestines and uses partially digested nutrients to grow. Cat may become ill.
Mosquito	Human	Needle-like mouthparts penetrate a person's skin to drink blood. Red, itchy welt appears on the skin.
Flea	Dog	Burrows into the dog's skin to feed on the flaking skin. Dog scratches irritated area.

Energy Relationships in Aquatic Ecosystems

Figure 2.10 shows that over 70% of the earth is covered with water. You can also see in Figure 2.10 that this water can be either salt water or fresh water. Canada contains 25% of the earth's fresh water. Lakes, ponds, and streams all contain fresh water. This abiotic component is essential to all life on earth. Organisms need water for nourishment, growth, and (for many) a place to live.

The lakes, ponds, and streams in Canada all contain unique ecosystems. Activity 2C will give you an opportunity to examine some of the relationships that exist in aquatic ecosystems. You will perform your investigation by using an aquarium as a model aquatic ecosystem.

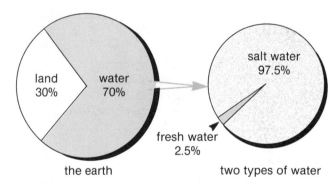

Figure 2.10 *Amount and types of water on earth*

Before beginning the activity, you should decide on the type of aquatic ecosystem you will set up. Will it be a freshwater or marine (saltwater) ecosystem? What abiotic components (amount of light, water temperature, etc.) will affect your ecosystem? Biotic components will have to be chosen carefully. What are the most suitable plants for the animals chosen? How many plants and animals will you need? Will the plants float at the surface or be fixed at the bottom? Will your ecosystem need a decomposer?

Problem

How can you set up a model aquatic ecosystem?

Materials

aquarium or large jar   thermometer
clean gravel   abiotic components
aquarium light, or lamp   biotic components
aquarium filter (optional)

CAUTION

1. Use only CSA-approved electrical equipment with the aquarium.
2. Unplug any electrical equipment before making any adjustments to the aquarium.

Procedure

1. Choose an area of the room for your aquarium. You will not be able to change its position later because once it is full of water, it will be too heavy to move. Place 2–3 cm of the gravel in the bottom of the aquarium.
2. Fill the aquarium with water so that it will be at least 2–3 cm from the top. Note: If tap water is being used, be sure to allow the water to sit in the tank for at least 24 h before continuing.
3. Carefully add the plants.
4. Carefully place the animals into the aquarium.
5. If there is not enough light, place a lamp about 30 cm from the aquarium and turn on the light. One caution: Be sure that the temperature does not go above the ideal range.

6. If a large aquarium tank (30 L or more) is being used, put in an aquarium filter.

Observations

1. Design a data chart to record daily observations of biotic and abiotic components.

Questions

1. Why is it important to keep a record of the data for this ecosystem?
2. What is the source of energy for the producers in this ecosystem?
3. List three abiotic components of the ecosystem.
4. Which organisms are (a) producers, (b) consumers, (c) scavengers, (d) decomposers? What niches do these organisms occupy?
5. List two food chains in the ecosystem.
6. How long will this ecosystem last? What changes must be made to ensure that all the organisms in the aquarium will survive for a long period of time?
7. What would happen to this ecosystem if
   (a) the producers began to reproduce very quickly?
   (b) the decomposers died?
   (c) one large predator was added to the ecosystem?

Challenge

In Chapter 1, you made a terrestrial ecosystem. Construct a chart to compare your aquatic and terrestrial ecosystems. Include in the chart for each ecosystem
1. the abiotic requirements
2. the biotic requirements (plants and animals).
What are the basic similarities between the two ecosystems? What are the basic differences between the two ecosystems?

Activity 2D

In this activity, you will investigate a natural aquatic ecosystem. Some of the equipment you will use is shown in Figure 2.11.

Problem

What types of food chains and food webs exist in natural aquatic ecosystems?

Materials

sieve
sorting trays
thermometer
boots or hip waders
metre stick
plastic collection jars
dip net
clipboard
hand lens
compass

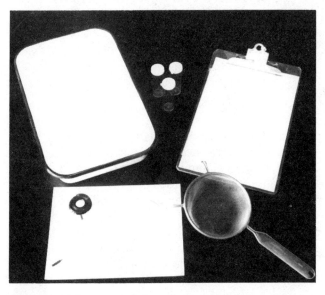

Figure 2.11 *Some useful equipment for an aquatic study*

Procedure

1. Copy Table 2.3 onto a piece of paper and clip it to your clipboard. This will allow you to record your measurements at the pond.
2. When you arrive at the ecosystem sit down quietly for 10 min, and observe the area. Note evidence of animal life on or in the water.
3. The class may be assigned to work in teams at different sites. When you reach your site make a sketch of the area. Mark the direction "north" on your sketch.
4. Record the air temperature on the observation sheet. Briefly describe the appearance of the water. Is it clear or cloudy? Is the bottom muddy, sandy, or rocky? Is the water moving or still?
5. Record the temperature of the water at the surface and one metre below the surface.

CAUTION

1. Be careful not to place yourself in an awkward position that might cause you to fall into the water.
2. Do not drink the water.
3. After all of your observations have been made, wash your hands thoroughly.

---

6. Reach to arm's length with the sieve, scoop up material from the shore, and place it in the tray. Examine any organisms with the hand lens. Count and record the number of each organism.
7. Take samples from other areas using the dip net. Carefully place some of the organisms you have caught into the collection jars for closer observation. Be sure to collect a few of the plants from the water.
8. On Table 2.3, sketch three food chains using the organisms that you observed.
9. Draw a food web that shows the relationships among these organisms.
10. After all of the observations have been completed, return the organisms carefully to the water.

Observations

Table 2.3 *Aquatic Ecosystem Chart*

Team members_____   Date_____

_____   Air temperature ___ °C

_____

_____

Location_____

Appearance of water_____

Temperature
(i) at the surface ___ °C   (ii) to a depth of 1 m___ °C

Types and numbers of animals:

_____

Types and numbers of plants:

_____

Food chains:

_____

Food web:

SAMPLE ONLY

Questions

1. What are the producers in this ecosystem?
2. (a) Which organisms are the consumers?
   (b) How many different consumers did you find?
   (c) What structures of these animals allow them to be (i) herbivores, or (ii) carnivores?
3. Is there any evidence of scavengers or decomposers in this ecosystem? Explain your observations.
4. What are the abiotic components that make this ecosystem different from other ecosystems?
5. What might happen to this ecosystem if
   (a) the water became polluted?
   (b) the precipitation in the area was mainly acid rain?
   (c) all the herbivores died?

Applying Our Understanding of Aquatic Ecosystems: Aquaculture

A better understanding of aquatic ecosystems has led to a new type of farming in Canada. **Aquaculture** is the cultivation of fish and shellfish in a controlled environment.

Throughout Canada, several of these farms are in operation. These include farms in Nova Scotia where bluefin tuna are fattened in cages and farms in New Brunswick where oysters, Atlantic salmon, and trout are raised. In Quebec and Ontario, restaurants and many grocery stores are supplied with trout and salmon raised in large ponds by private companies. On the prairies and in British Columbia, farmers and government organizations are raising salmon, walleye, and whitefish to stock rivers and lakes.

Aquaculture will help support both the sport and commercial fishing industries. At the same time, it will help protect *natural* populations of fish from the effects of overfishing.

Self-check

1. (a) What is a parasite?
   (b) Name three examples of parasites.
2. What is the difference between a parasite-host relationship and a predator-prey relationship?
3. What are the basic abiotic components of an aquatic ecosystem?
4. (a) What is aquaculture?
   (b) How do you think aquaculture can help natural populations of fish?

Science in Your Life

Worldwide estimates suggest that there may be between 5 million and 10 million different plant and animal species. On the following pages are photos of plants and animals which live in Canada. Using a geography textbook, locate the biomes of Canada. Decide which biome or biomes each plant and animal belongs to.

It is the responsibility of all who are alive today to accept the trusteeship of wildlife and to hand on to prosperity, as a source of wonder and interest, knowledge and enjoyment, the entire wealth of diverse animals and plants. This generation has no right by selfishness, wanton or intentional destruction, or neglect, to rob future generations of this rich heritage. Extermination of other creatures is a disgrace to humankind.

WORLD WILDLIFE CHARTER

Do you agree that it is everyone's responsibility to preserve the diversity of plants and animals? What does "intentional destruction" mean? What can you do to preserve the plants and animals in Canada for future generations?

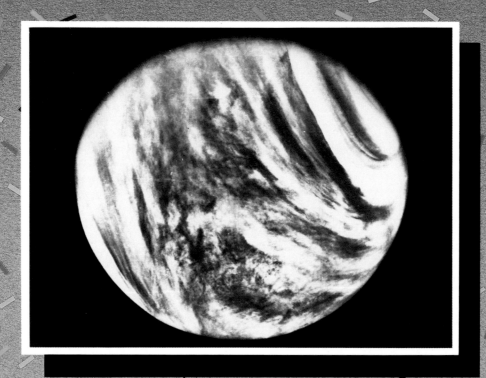

Chapter Objectives

NOW THAT YOU HAVE COMPLETED THIS CHAPTER, CAN YOU DO THE FOLLOWING?	FOR REVIEW, TURN TO SECTION
1. Explain the importance of the sun as the original source of energy in an ecosystem.	2.1
2. Explain the energy transfer in a food chain.	2.1
3. Define and give examples of the following: producer, consumer, herbivore, carnivore, and omnivore.	2.1
4. Describe the importance of decomposers and scavengers.	2.1
5. Describe and give an example of habitat and niche.	2.2
6. Design a food web, using a list of organisms.	2.3
7. Describe the water cycle and the carbon cycle, and explain the importance of both.	2.4
8. Describe the relationships of predator-prey and parasite-host.	2.5
9. Organize and set up a model aquatic ecosystem.	2.6
10. Conduct an ecological investigation of an aquatic ecosystem.	2.6
11. Explain the use of aquaculture in Canada.	2.6

Words to Know

producer
consumer
food chain
herbivore
carnivore
omnivore
decomposer
scavenger
habitat

niche
food web
water cycle
carbon cycle
predator
parasite
host
aquaculture

Tying It Together

1. What is the difference between a producer and a consumer?
2. (a) How are food chains and food webs alike?
    (b) How are food chains and food webs different?
3. For each of the organisms in Figure 2.5, state whether it is a herbivore, a carnivore, or an omnivore.
4. (a) Ferns and shrubs, trees, slugs, insects, birds, and garter snakes are all part of a food chain. From this list, identify the producers, consumers, scavengers, and decomposers.
    (b) Give an example of an animal that is both a consumer and a scavenger.
5. What is the original source of energy in a food chain or food web?
6. Use the following list of organisms to draw a food web: owl, minnow, mayfly, algae, crayfish, bass, frog, snake.
7. Why are decomposers important to an ecosystem?
8. Why are scavengers important to an ecosystem?
9. Describe how carbon is recycled in an ecosystem.

10. List three different predator-prey relationships that you might find in an aquatic ecosystem.
11. What would happen in an aquatic ecosystem if all of the decomposers were removed?

Applying Your Knowledge

1. In Activity 1A in Chapter 1, you constructed a closed ecosystem. List all of the organisms in that ecosystem and explain the importance of each one. Then draw a food web to show the relationships in the ecosystem.
2. Imagine a small Pacific island that has active volcanoes on it. Clouds of volcanic ash are constantly thrown into the air. These clouds are so dark that they block out 90% of the sun's energy for two years. What effects would this have on the ecology of this tiny island? Explain.
3. List all of the food that you ate at dinner last night. Then draw a food chain to show how you obtained the energy that originated from the sun. Compare your food chain with those of your classmates.

Projects for Investigation

1. Find out if there are any communities that exist without the energy from the sun. Describe these communities. What types of organisms are found there?
2. An erupting volcano is a natural disaster. In May 1980, Mount St. Helens, in the state of Washington, erupted. What immediate effect did this have on the ecosystem? How has this ecosystem changed since 1980?
3. Animals are not the only organisms that are consumers. There are several kinds of plants that eat animals. Among these plants are the sundew, the pitcher plant, and the Venus fly trap. Find out where these plants grow and how they consume animals.

Changes in the Environment

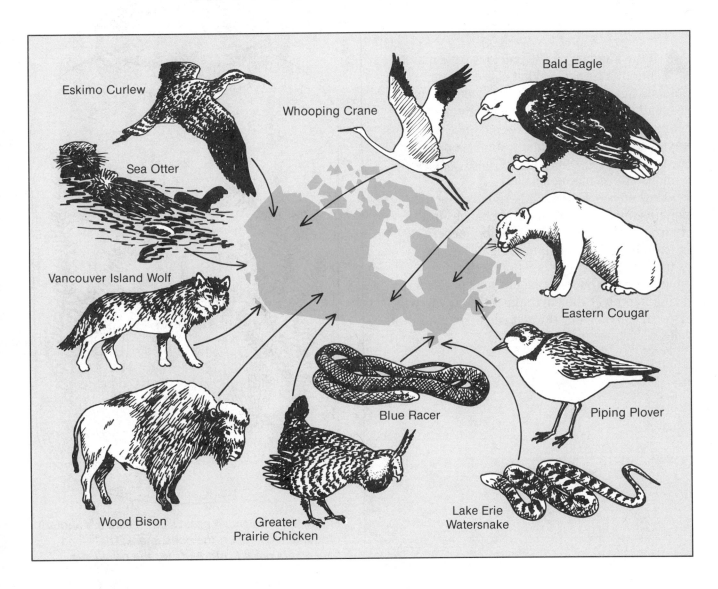

Eskimo Curlew

Sea Otter

Whooping Crane

Bald Eagle

Vancouver Island Wolf

Eastern Cougar

Wood Bison

Greater Prairie Chicken

Blue Racer

Piping Plover

Lake Erie Watersnake

Key Ideas

- Change is a natural part of all ecosystems.
- Humans directly and indirectly affect ecosystems.
- Many plants and animals are endangered species.
- All ecosystems exist in a delicate balance that can be easily upset.

A ll the animals on the previous page may be found in Canada. What else do these animals have in common? Their populations are so small that they are in danger of dying out completely. They would never again be seen anywhere on earth. Humans are responsible for the fact that the populations of most of these animals are becoming smaller.

How do people affect ecosystems? Should humans interfere with natural changes in the environment? Do we have a choice in every case? In this chapter, you will investigate several examples of human interaction with the environment. You will find out how people are trying to protect the environment. And you will also learn about the efforts made to maintain the delicate balance in ecosystems.

Balance in Ecosystems

The model ecosystem shown in Figure 3.1 is similar to the one you made in Activity 1A in Chapter 1. This ecosystem should continue to

Figure 3.1 *A balanced ecosystem. There are enough producers to support the consumers. The consumers provide nutrients for the producers.*

thrive if the following conditions are met:

- There are enough producers to provide food for consumers.
- There are enough consumers to provide nutrients for producers.
- The abiotic factors remain favourable to the producers and consumers.

In other words, the ecosystem should continue to thrive if there is a balance between the biotic and abiotic components.

This type of balance exists in natural ecosystems. But all ecosystems are affected by change. Every living thing alters its own environment and that of its neighbours in the same community. There can be small changes. For example, a tuft of grass might shade a small area of soil. There can be large changes. For example, every year in a forest, tonnes of leaves are dropped to the ground. Each change—small or large—alters the environment of each organism as time passes.

Activity 3A

Problem

How can biotic or abiotic changes affect a balanced ecosystem?

Materials

Procedure

1. Your teacher will divide the class into six groups. Each group will examine Figure 3.1 and be assigned one of the following changes to discuss:
   (a) What would happen if six more fish were added?
   (b) What would happen if all the snails died?
   (c) What would happen if two crayfish (carnivores) were added?
   (d) What would happen if soapy dish water were added?
   (e) What would happen if the light source burned out?
   (f) What would happen if all the fish were removed?
2. Discuss the effects these changes could have on the balanced ecosystem.

Observations

1. Make a report to the rest of the class on the results of your discussion.

Questions

1. Does the change you discussed involve biotic or abiotic components? Explain.
2. What effect can the change have on the populations of the following:
   (a) plants
   (b) fish
   (c) snails
3. Describe the effect of each change on the balance of the ecosystem.

Natural Changes in Ecosystems

There is a special pattern of change in ecosystems. This pattern of change is called **succession**. Succession occurs when organisms change the environment. Organisms occupy a particular environment, change it by their activities, and then are "forced out" by new species of organisms that are better suited to the changed environment. Succession ends when various populations continue to live and reproduce in an environment, in balance. Figure 3.2 shows the stages of succession in one kind of environment.

Once succession in a particular environment has ended, the ecosystem remains stable or unchanged unless there is a disturbance. Examples of two such disturbances are volcanic eruptions and forest fires. Forest fires are especially devastating. They occur quite often in many ecosystems. Forest fires often start when lightning strikes dry vegetation. Such fires may leap quickly from treetop to treetop. Or the fire may burn at ground level, destroying trees, soil, and many habitats.

The next activity will let you determine the effects of fire on ecosystems that support a pine tree called the jack pine. This tree grows in many vacation areas throughout Ontario.

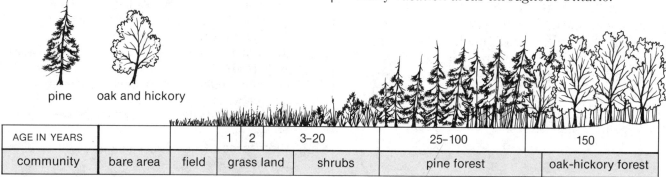

AGE IN YEARS			1	2	3–20	25–100	150
community	bare area	field	grass land		shrubs	pine forest	oak-hickory forest

Figure 3.2 *The first organisms to grow in a bare area such as sand are grasses and weeds. The grasses and weeds hold the sand in their roots. When they die, their decomposition begins to change the sand into soil. Small shrubs can become established, and insects and small mammals begin to appear. Over time, fast-growing trees such as pine become established. Their seeds have been carried to the area by the wind and small animals. But the shade caused by adult pine trees prevents the growth of seedlings. Species better adapted to shade, such as oak and hickory, begin to grow beneath the pines. The oak and hickory trees eventually take over and become the dominant species in the area. Shade-tolerant ferns, shrubs, and small vines are able to live underneath the taller trees. The process of succession has ended.*

Problem

What effects does fire have on the plant life in an ecosystem?

Materials

Procedure

1. Study Figure 3.3 carefully.
2. Use the pictures in Figure 3.2 to answer the questions below.

Observations

1. What are the distinctive structures of the jack pine shown in Figure 3.3 (a)?

2. As a fire develops and burns, what changes occur to the pine trees? See Figure 3.3 (b).

Questions

1. What would happen to the following animals during a fire?
   (a) deer
   (b) rabbits
   (c) birds
   (d) insects
2. When fire burns an area, several species of plants will die. What will happen to these dead plants?
3. Describe what has happened in Figure 3.3 (c) and (d).
4. How would you describe the overall effect of the fire on this ecosystem? (Hint: Recall what you have learned about succession.)

Figure 3.3

(a) *May 4, 1975*

(b) *May 13, 1976*

(c) *June 24, 1985*

(d) *May 4, 2063*

Altering the Pattern of Change

Humans have a tremendous ability to alter their environment. Consider a park near where you live. What will happen if it is not frequently mowed, watered, fertilized, and weeded? It will eventually be replaced by the next stage of succession that is typical of the area in which you live. The efforts of gardeners slow down succession.

The human practice of keeping large stocks of grazing animals is another example of human impact on the course of succession. Grazing by wild herbivores is part of the natural process of succession. Wild grazers choose certain plants to eat, and move over large areas. Succession continues around them and continues after they have moved on. Grazing animals, which are kept by humans in the same location, have a totally different effect. The eating of vegetation by these animals can halt the normal succession of rangeland to forest. Thus, soil, local climate conditions, and habitats can be drastically affected.

Responsibility for Altering the Pattern of Change

Our increased understanding of ecosystems and succession has resulted in improvements in land use planning. Knowing about the stages of succession in a particular area helps us to make decisions that will work *with* rather than against this natural process. See Figure 3.4.

We can't deny our ability to influence the life around us. No other organism has been able to "step out" of the process of succession, let alone alter or reverse its progress. We enjoy considerable power over the patterns of life around us. Humans must accept the great responsibility that goes with such power.

Figure 3.4 *How is replanting trees an example of working with the process of succession? Does it matter what kind of tree species is replanted in a certain area?*

Self-check

1. What is meant by an ecosystem having balanced biotic and abiotic components?
2. (a) What is succession?
   (b) How does succession affect ecosystems?
3. (a) Name two natural disasters that may affect ecosystems.
   (b) Choose one of these two changes, and explain how it affects ecosystems.
4. Why do humans have such a tremendous ability to affect ecosystems?

Ideas and Applications

In the early days of the forestry industry, over 150 years ago, loggers cut the trees, sent the wood to mills, and moved on to cut new areas. Vast expanses of land were left without trees. Today, foresters recognize the need for proper forest management. To keep forests productive and to supply trees for industry, better forestry methods have been established. After selective cutting, the forest is replanted. Populations of trees are thinned out to prevent overcrowding and to control fire and disease. This type of human intervention ensures large, healthy forests for generations to come.

Wildlife Extinction and Preservation

Imagine that you are one of 50 people left on earth. The conditions for your survival are becoming worse every day. This is the reality for many different plant and animal species around the world.

When a species is forced out of its natural habitat, it must seek a new, suitable one. If it can't find a new habitat, the species will eventually die and become **extinct**. The word extinct is a harsh word. Its meaning is clear and simple—a species has died out. When a species becomes extinct, it can no longer be found anywhere in the world. The illustration at the beginning of this chapter shows some animals in Canada that are in danger of extinction. They are endangered species.

Biologists try to determine which species of organisms are in danger of becoming extinct and try to make plans to save them. The concern is not simply for the endangered species itself. When a species becomes extinct, the organisms that depend on it for food will also be affected. The balance in the ecosystem will be upset. Whole food webs may suffer.

Extinction is a natural process. Throughout the history of life, many species have become extinct. Dinosaurs are one familiar example. But the action of humans has increased the extinction process. When people clear the land for agriculture, for example, they are destroying wildlife habitats. Plants and animals always lose in this competition with humans for land.

More alarming is that in this century alone, over 200 plant and animal species have become extinct because of human interaction. Now, concerned people are taking steps to save the organisms that are endangered.

Protecting Wildlife: The Whooping Crane

The whooping crane is one of North America's largest bird species (Figure 3.5). Whooping cranes once lived in marshlands from Alberta to Iowa. As humans took over these areas for farming and ranching, the number of cranes fell drastically. Another contributing factor to their population decline was that hunters were allowed to kill cranes for sport. In 1964, there were only 50 cranes left alive.

To try to save the whooping crane and other endangered species, scientists and governments worked together to establish **wildlife sanctuaries**. These are areas where wildlife is protected. The Wood Buffalo National Park on the Alberta-Northwest Territories border is an area where the whooping cranes can now nest safely (Figure 3.6).

Today, many hazards still face the "whoopers." Their greatest danger is their 3900 km migration. The migration occurs twice a year. The path leads from their breeding ground in Wood Buffalo National Park to the salt flat marshes of the Aransas National Wildlife Refuge in the United States, on the Texas coast. If there are places where they can nest and reproduce safely, the cranes have a better chance of survival. Along their migration route, the "whoopers" are protected by law from hunters. Today, the crane population is on the increase.

In 1986, biologists reported a record 20 chicks survived the breeding season. By the fall of 1987, the crane population had increased to 130. The whooping crane is now in less danger of extinction. Protective measures can work!

Figure 3.5 *The majestic whooping crane is a tall, white bird that stands almost 1.5 m high. On its forehead is a crimson band. It has black legs and black feathers on its wing tips. Its wing span can reach 2 m.*

Figure 3.6 *The migration route of the whooping crane*

Self-check

1. In your own words, define the word extinction.
2. Why is it important to preserve an organism's habitat?
3. What is a wildlife sanctuary?
4. Why did biologists and governments work together to establish wildlife sanctuaries?
5. Explain how the whooping crane is being saved from extinction.

Pests, Pesticides, and the Environment

At the turn of the century, American cabinet makers imported a load of Dutch elm lumber from Europe. No one knew at that time that the trees contained elm beetles. These beetles carried a deadly fungus. Soon the beetles infested the white elm trees that grow in the United States. The fungus they carried killed the trees. In 1950, some beetle-infested logs were imported to Canada. Before long, the fungus-carrying beetles spread to the elm tree communities here. This disease, called Dutch elm disease, is killing all of Canada's native elm trees (Figure 3.7).

Figure 3.7 *The tree on the left is healthy. The tree on the right has been infested with the elm tree disease.*

Ecological disasters like this have led to limits on the importing of foreign species of plants and animals. Every port of entry to Canada displays pamphlets with the warning shown in Figure 3.8.

don't bring it back!

pests and diseases
brought into Canada
on plant and animal products
cause millions of dollars
of damage to our farms
and forests

if you plan to bring back meat, animals, fruit, vegetables, plants, soil – check with us first!

English/ anglais

Agriculture Canada

Figure 3.8

Using Pesticides

When insects are harmful, people often use pesticides to control the insect populations. A **pesticide** is a chemical used to kill anything considered to be a pest. Mosquitoes and rats are considered pests. Poisons that kill them are called pesticides.

Pesticides are not part of the natural environment. Even though they have beneficial effects, they also can have undesirable side effects. Though intended to kill one type of organism, they can also affect other kinds of organisms in the food web. **DDT** is one pesticide that had both beneficial and harmful effects.

Ideas and Applications

Insects are among the organisms most often thought of as pests. However, very few of the approximately 1 000 000 insect species on earth are pests. Only about 10 000 species eat our crops and cause disease. In fact, many types of insects are beneficial to humans. Insects, such as bees, carry pollen from flower to flower. Pollen is needed for many plants to reproduce. Humans use honey made by honey bees. Humans also use silk made from the fibres of caterpillar cocoons. Insects also help humans by feeding on other insect species, such as aphids and mosquitoes, that we consider to be pests.

The Effects of One Pesticide on the Environment: DDT

DDT was used to stop a typhus epidemic following World War II. People were dusted with the chemical, which killed all the body lice. The lice carried the typhus-causing organisms. DDT was also used to control malaria. It killed the mosquitoes that carried malaria-causing organisms. Besides helping the fight against disease, DDT was used worldwide to kill insects that destroyed food crops. It was a valuable tool used to improve human lives.

However, DDT does not break down and disappear in the environment. It enters the bodies of organisms by way of the food chain.

For example, DDT was used to kill moths that were infecting apple trees. In the autumn, DDT-covered leaves fell to the ground. When organisms such as earthworms decomposed the dead leaves, they took DDT into their bodies. DDT is fat-soluble, so it became stored in the fatty tissue of the worms. Robins that ate the earthworms also took in the DDT, which became stored in the robins' fatty tissues. Other organisms, such as hawks, that ate the robins once again took in the DDT, which became stored in their fatty tissues. See Figure 3.9.

Was the amount of DDT that the robins stored in their bodies the same as the amount of DDT stored in the earthworms' bodies? Activity 3C will help you find out.

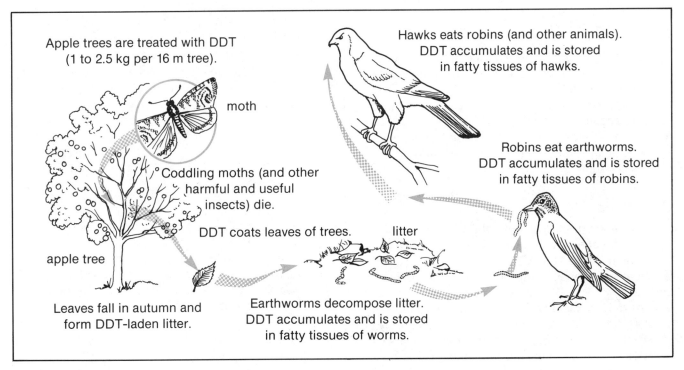

Figure 3.9 *The food chain effects of DDT*

Problem

How does a pesticide such as DDT build up in the bodies of organisms in the food chain?

Materials

Procedure

1. Imagine a pond near a farmer's field that is infested with harmful insects. The farmer sprays the field with DDT. Wind blows some of the pesticide onto the marsh plants. Each plant receives 1 unit of DDT. The DDT stays in the cells of the plant.
2. Using these organisms, draw a food chain to show the flow of energy in this pond ecosystem: marsh plants, minnows, perch, red-tailed hawk.

Observations

1. Suppose that a minnow eats 100 marsh plants in one year. How much DDT builds up in the body of the minnow?
2. A perch eats 50 minnows in one year. How much DDT accumulates in its body?
3. The red-tailed hawk consumes 20 perch in one year. What amount of the pesticide builds up in this consumer?

Questions

1. How much has the amount of DDT increased from the one unit in the marsh plants to the body of the red-tailed hawk?
2. What will happen to the DDT when the hawk dies?
3. The farmer was going to use a new pesticide, AST. It disappears in the environment after only seven days. How would the accumulation of AST have compared to the accumulation of DDT?
4. Why must the use of new pesticides be controlled and monitored very carefully?

Why DDT Was Banned

Even today, small amounts of DDT can be found in every plant and animal on earth. It has even found its way into the fat of arctic whales and antarctic penguins! A major effect of DDT can be seen in the population decline of predator birds such as the osprey, the peregrine falcon, and the bald eagle. Once seen across many northern Canadian forests, these birds are now scarce. They are close to extinction.

Many of these predatory birds died when they consumed prey contaminated with DDT. Another effect on bird populations was that high levels of DDT in the females caused the shells of their eggs to become very thin. In the nest, the eggs cracked and broke, and the developing chicks died.

Since its ban in Canada in 1967, populations of osprey, bald eagle, and peregrine falcon have slowly begun to recover. Should pesticides that produce effects like DDT be banned worldwide? If so, how could the ban be enforced? Questions like these are still unanswered.

Challenge

Form an investigative team to look into the use of pesticides around the school and in the community. Which pesticides are being used? How often are they applied? How long do they last in the environment? What is the effect on the ecology of the area? Is there any group in the community that objects to their use?

Different Kinds of Pesticides

There are as many different kinds of pesticides as there are kinds of pests. Table 3.1 lists several different kinds of pesticides in use today. Pesticides are not only used to kill insects. They are also used to kill algae, birds, bacteria, fungi, and rodents. Each year over 450 000 000 kg of pesticides are produced (Figure 3.10). Improper use, poor control, and inadequate disposal of these pesticides can have harmful effects on the environment. Our government controls today are designed to restrict pesticide use to situations where it appears to be the only effective alternative.

Figure 3.10 *Many pesticides are available for use in and around the home, garden, or farm.*

Table 3.1 *Examples of Pesticides*

PESTICIDE	USE	HOW LONG THEY LAST IN THE ENVIRONMENT
Endrin, Chlordane, Toxaphene	Kills a variety of insects	2 to 20 years
Malathion, Azodrin, Diazon	Kills some insects and plants (weeds)	12 weeks or up to 5 years
Carbyl, Zireb	Kills plants and some insects	2 days to 3 weeks
2,4D and 2,4T	Kills plants	2 days to 4 weeks

Alternatives to Pesticides

The safest method for pest control may not be the easiest or most convenient. However, there are alternatives to using pesticides to control some pests. For example, keeping a garden well watered and soil well turned will help prevent weeds from growing. Before weeds become well rooted, they should be picked from the ground.

Many plants that produce their own poisons against pests can be grown. For example, geraniums produce a poison that repels beetles. Tomatoes and potatoes contain chemicals to guard against some insects and other herbivores. Rhubarb leaves produce a poison that attacks the kidneys and nervous systems of pests that try to eat the leaves.

Safety First

Pesticides are poisons. That's why they kill pests. Because they are poisons, pesticides can also affect you. Figure 3.11 on page 50 gives some safety rules for handling and using pesticides.

Figure 3.11

WARNING

Safety Rules for Using Pesticides

1. Choose the right pesticide.
2. Read labels carefully. Follow directions strictly and never exceed the recommended dosage.
3. Store pesticides safely where children and pets are not likely to find them.
4. Do not mix pesticides in a closed space. Never mix different pesticides together unless you know it is safe to do so.
5. Do not spray on windy days. Be considerate of your neighbours. Respect their feelings about pesticides.
6. Do not spray insecticides until after sunset—a time when bees will have reduced their activities.
7. Wear a mask when spraying to avoid inhaling the pesticide.
8. Wear rubber gloves when using pesticides. Never allow pesticides to touch your bare skin. If your skin does come into contact with pesticides, wash the affected area immediately with water.
9. Do not eat or drink while applying sprays.
10. Do not re-use pesticide containers.
11. Never dump pesticides down the drain. Dispose of empty containers by wrapping them in newspaper and placing them in a sealed garbage bag.
12. To dispose of partly used containers of biocides, call your local authorities or your nearest Pesticide Control Branch.

Self-check

1. Why are there limits on the importing of foreign plant and animal species into Canada?
2. What is a pesticide?
3. (a) How does DDT get into the body of a herbivore?
   (b) How does DDT get into the body of a carnivore?
4. Why was the use of DDT banned in Canada?
5. Besides the use of pesticides, what other alternatives are there for controlling pests?

Science at Work

Scientists have found that insects locate each other and send chemical messages by means of complex chemicals with distinctive odours. These chemicals are called pheromones. Canadian scientists are leading the way in pheromone research. Professor Larry Weiler and his team of researchers at the University of British Columbia have successfully isolated the attracting pheromone of the ambrosia beetle. This beetle destroys millions of dollars worth of lumber each year. By copying this attracting pheromone in the laboratory, scientists can "lure" insects to a central location where they can be destroyed. Not all research has been this successful, however. Pheromones are difficult to reproduce in the laboratory. It may still be many years before all the "bugs" are worked out and pheromone products reach the market.

Pollution and the Environment

When a harmful substance enters the environment, it is called a **pollutant**. Substances such as solid wastes and chemicals are forms of pollutants (Figure 3.12).

As you discovered in Section 3.4, DDT is a type of pesticide that polluted the environment. It produced harmful effects. Let's look at another human interaction that came close to destroying the ecology of the Great Lakes.

A study conducted in 1970 by scientists from Canada and the United States found 500 different chemical pollutants in Lake Ontario. These included DDT, arsenic, lead, and dioxin, probably the world's deadliest pollutant. Also on the list were phosphates.

Figure 3.12 *Aside from being harmful, pollution also creates an eyesore.*

The dumping of wastes into the Great Lakes and other waterways has harmful effects. The wastes can kill populations of organisms, affecting food chains. The results may affect industry, recreation, and sports. So many pollutants were dumped into Lake Erie that it was once called a dead lake. The governments of Canada and the United States began a large clean-up campaign of the Great Lakes.

To understand the effect of certain pollutants, you will conduct an activity. The pollutants are the phosphates from fertilizers and detergents. Phosphates flowed into the Great Lakes for many years. Activity 3D will show you the effect that these phosphates have on the growth of algae.

Challenge

The governments of Canada and the United States have been cleaning up the Great Lakes for many years. Investigate the following aspects of this campaign.
1. What organizations are involved in the clean-up?
2. Who is responsible for the clean-up?
3. What industries are most likely to be involved?
4. What are the health hazards involved?
5. What organisms are most likely to have been affected?

Activity 3D

Problem

What effects do phosphates have on a population of algae?

Materials

3 beakers (250 mL)
1 beaker (100 mL)
graduated cylinder
stirring rod
eye dropper
balance
pond water or aquarium water containing algae
sodium phosphate (2 g)
distilled water

Procedure

1. Label the three 250 mL beakers as 1, 2, and 3. Place 200 mL of pond water into each beaker.
2. (a) Measure 70 mL of distilled water into the 100 mL beaker.
   (b) Carefully measure 2 g of sodium phosphate and add it to the distilled water.
   (c) Mix the solution well until all the chemical is dissolved. Label this beaker "nutrient solution."
3. Add 5 drops of the nutrient solution to beaker 2.
4. Add 10 drops of the nutrient solution to beaker 3.
5. Place the three beakers in an area where they will receive at least 10 h of light every day for 7 d.
6. Repeat steps 3 and 4 once a day for 7 d.
7. Copy Table 3.2 into your notes and keep a record of your results.

Observations

Table 3.2 *Algae Growth*

| DAY | BEAKER | | | CHANGES TO |
| | 1 | 2 | 3 | POND WATER |
	Amount of Nutrient Added			
1	0	5 drops	10 drops	
2				
3				
Etc.				

SAMPLE ONLY

Questions

1. Which beaker was the control? What is the purpose of the control?
2. Which beaker showed the first change? What was this change?
3. If the beakers were models of lakes, what does this show you about the effect of high levels of phosphates in the water?

Ideas and Applications

British Columbia coho salmon have been introduced into the Great Lakes in Ontario. These fish seem to have adapted very well and are now playing an important role in Ontario's fishing industry.

Algal Bloom

When certain pollutants, such as phosphates, enter a lake, some algae will grow very quickly. These phosphates come from the waste water of some industries. A large, green, smelly mass accumulates. This is called an **algal bloom** (Figure 3.13).

Some algae give off poisons that can kill fish. A large bloom that is poisonous can kill all of the fish in a small lake in a matter of days. A large population of algae will also consume the oxygen in the water. The algal population will soon be overcrowded and most of the bloom will die. The dead algae sink to the bottom of the lake.

Figure 3.13 *An algal bloom*

Decomposers begin to consume the dead algae. This activity uses more oxygen from the water. The lower oxygen levels are hard on game fish like trout, pickerel, and bass. These kinds of fish require high levels of oxygen in order to survive. Fish that are able to survive low oxygen levels are carp and perch. Their populations now begin to increase. New food chains become established. Since these fish live on different foods, other populations will increase or decrease. Adding pollutants to the water can upset the balance in an aquatic ecosystem.

Self-check

1. What is a pollutant?
2. Give examples of two different kinds of pollution and how they affect the environment.
3. What is an algal bloom?
4. What effect can an algal bloom have on consumers in a lake?

What Is Your Opinion?

Table 3.3 shows some of the problems that result from human interaction with the environment. They are global (worldwide) problems. But many of them are issues that affect people, plants, and animals in Canada.

Issues involving human impact on the environment often produce strong, emotional debates. Some people feel that governments should take a stronger hand in dealing with environmental issues. Other people feel that governments are already involved more than they should be. Some people feel that forming lobby groups and writing petitions will help. Others feel that more militant (and sometimes violent) action is the only way to be heard. Who is correct? Do you have opinions on any of these issues? Do any of them affect you directly or indirectly?

As a member of society, you will have to make decisions about at least one environmental issue now or in the future. Therefore, you need to practise making informed decisions. In Activity 3E, you will do just that. You will examine one important issue that faces us today. Use the knowledge you possess. You may also have to look further—to the library or to other resources—to find more information.

Table 3.3 *Problems That Result from Human Interaction with the Environment*

NEED	PROBLEMS CAUSED BY INCREASED DEMAND ON THE ENVIRONMENT
More food	• Areas such as tropical rain forests are cleared in order to raise animals such as cattle and chickens. As a result, many species of plants and animals lose their habitats and become extinct. • Soil can't support the amount of food grown in it (soil structure breaks down). • Pesticides alter the chemistry of the soil and affect non-targeted organisms. • Stocks of fish decrease from overfishing by both Canadians and others.
More and better housing	• Only a small percentage of land is suitable for agriculture, but much of this land is also suitable for building houses and apartments.
More raw materials	• Clear-cutting of forests and insufficient reforestation methods reduce the number of trees. • Easily mined mineral ores are being used up. • Easily available resources (coal, natural gas, crude oil) are being used up. • Sites for hydro-electric power are nearly exhausted. • Nuclear energy poses potential dangers. • Air and water pollution result from the processing of most raw materials.
More consumer goods	• Resources and raw materials used to make consumer goods are being exhausted. • Increased industrial production results in more pollution. • Unwanted goods are discarded, resulting not only in pollution, but also in the waste of materials that could be recycled for similar or other uses. • Demand for luxury items, such as furs, results in declining populations of animals.

Activity 3E

Problem

What will be the outcome of your debate?

Materials

stop watch

Procedure

1. Your teacher will provide you with a selection of issues to choose from. You will deal with the chosen issue in the form of a debate. A debate is similar to a court case. Different members of the class present two sides of an argument. The argument is called the resolution. Your teacher will provide you with suggestions for holding a debate.
2. Decide what resources (books, magazines, newspapers, maps, audiovisual tapes, etc.) you will need to help you argue for or against the resolution. Prepare your arguments. Then hold the debate.

Observations

1. Were there any points of view on the issue you debated that weren't considered? If so, name them.
2. Why is it important to examine all sides of an issue before arriving at your conclusion?

Questions

1. Agree or disagree with the following statement: "Issues that affect people far from where I live do not affect me. Therefore, I don't have to be concerned about them." Give reasons for your answer.

How Students Helped Preserve a Salmon Habitat

In October 1979, members of a science class from George Pearkes Junior Secondary School in Port Coquitlam, British Columbia, adopted a nearby stream called Hyde Creek. Hyde Creek is one of over 2000 small streams that drain the coastal area of British Columbia. Populations of salmon come back to these streams near the end of their life cycle to spawn (breed) and die.

The students contacted a Community Advisor with the Federal Department of Fisheries and Oceans. He advised the class how to proceed. He suggested that the students do a detailed study of Hyde Creek and make a proposal for improvement based on their study.

The students set out a detailed action plan. They joined the study teams that interested them most. One student was elected leader for each team. The leaders worked with the classroom teacher. Study teams completed the following challenges.

1. Members of all study teams presented background information to the rest of the class. This included making reports on salmon biology and presenting information about the fishing resource.
2. Plant species were identified, counted, and recorded. Fish traps were used to count live populations of each fish species in the creek. Other animal populations along the creek were also sampled and noted.
3. The entire creek and its tributaries (small branches) were walked and mapped. Salmon spawning areas were marked.
4. Students interviewed long-time residents of the area and members of the city engineering staff. They also collected environmental impact studies that developers had made.
5. Depth, velocity, and discharge of the creek were measured every second day throughout the year. Water samples were sent to government labs for complete analysis.
6. Students prepared newspaper articles, a press conference, a videotape for the community television channel, and a slide demonstration for use in local shopping malls. A salmon awareness questionnaire was developed and the results were analyzed by computer.
7. An incubation box (mini-hatchery) for protecting and hatching salmon eggs was designed.
8. All groups planned and took part in a trip that let them follow the exact route taken by the Hyde Creek salmon to the open sea.

In June 1980, the students completed their report to the Department of Fisheries and Oceans. Permission was granted for the school to begin to enhance the stream in a number of ways, such as cleaning debris and adding fresh gravel. Also, the students' mini-hatchery was built in June in the school's woodwork shop.

In October, students in several classes took part in an "egg take." Under the supervision of the Community Advisor, eggs from several chum salmon females and milt from several males were mixed in a bucket. (Milt is a milky fluid that contains the salmon sperm cells.) Later, about 3000 fertilized eggs were placed in the mini-hatchery. That spring, however, only about 300 eggs hatched. Mud had packed around many of the eggs and suffocated them. A special mud filter was designed and installed for the next year.

In 1981, students placed 5000 eggs in the mini-hatchery. Most of these eggs hatched. Between 1981 and 1983, returning spawners numbered about 300. This means that, of the thousands of eggs that hatched, 300 adult fish survived in the environment to return to spawn. In 1984, the returning spawners numbered 1000—more than triple the number of the previous years!

In 1986, George Pearkes students won an award from the Department of Fisheries and Oceans for their work on Hyde Creek over the years. Students at George Pearkes had made a very real contribution to the environment and to local salmon populations.

Findings and Results from Student Research on Hyde Creek

FINDINGS	RESULTS
1. Lower sections of the stream needed more vegetation along the banks. City workers had trimmed back vegetation to give the creek a groomed look.	A letter was sent to the city. Students were thanked and told that vegetation along the bank would be left to grow.
2. The upper and lower portions of the creek supported healthy populations of trout and salmon.	The class concentrated the second year on improving the salmon habitat in those areas that had a constant water supply.
3. The creek had a history of flooding and drying up. This pattern had become more erratic in recent years. Several farmers have water licences that let them pump water from the creek.	It was decided that chum salmon, whose young leave before the summer drought, were the best salmon species for enhancement.
4. The water flow responded quickly and violently to rainfall. Heavy rains resulted in an immediate flood pattern with rapid drop in water volume when rain ceased.	
5. The creek was seen to be a greatly changing environment.	
6. Most of the creek water was "healthy" and still suitable for salmon. Pollution sources noted included swimming pool discharges, farmers' duck ponds, and mud from construction sites.	Federal fisheries officers were sent to investigate and take action.
7. In the 1950s, an artificial channel had been built for the creek. The channel dried out regularly and killed hundreds of fish. City engineering staff and council were advised that the channel was a danger to the salmon habitat and that a continuous flow of water was needed.	Students received no reply. No action was taken by the authorities. Students did not try to enhance this area.
8. Most people interviewed in the community valued the creek as a recreational resource and supported the school's efforts.	Students realized that the community would be willing to help them in their efforts. Students asked for and got donations of time and equipment.
9. Some members of the community had been dumping garbage into the stream.	The entire school spent an afternoon cleaning up junk. Care was taken not to remove those items that had now become a part of a good fish habitat.
10. Salmon were seen to spawn regularly in certain areas.	These spawning areas were raked clean of mud, and truckloads of fresh gravel were added.
11. The creek was found suitable for salmon enhancement.	An instream incubation box, which had been designed and built earlier, was installed by the students.

Chapter Objectives

NOW THAT YOU HAVE COMPLETED THIS CHAPTER, CAN YOU DO THE FOLLOWING?	FOR REVIEW, TURN TO SECTION
1. Explain the balance in a natural ecosystem.	3.1
2. Explain the effect of too many consumers in a model ecosystem.	3.1
3. Describe the effects of fire on an ecosystem.	3.1
4. Explain how succession affects ecosystems.	3.1 and 3.2
5. Describe the importance of preserving and protecting wildlife habitats.	3.3
6. Explain how the whooping crane has been saved from extinction.	3.3
7. Explain why there are restrictions for bringing foreign plants and animals into the country.	3.4
8. Describe how DDT accumulates in the tissues of organisms.	3.4
9. Give alternatives to pesticides.	3.4
10. Perform an investigation to study the effects of phosphates on algae growth.	3.5
11. Make informed opinions on ecological issues.	3.6

Words to Know

succession
extinct
wildlife sanctuary
pesticide

DDT
pollutant
algal bloom

Tying It Together

1. When is an ecosystem balanced?
2. (a) What effect does the removal of herbivores have on an ecosystem?
   (b) What effect does the removal of carnivores have on an ecosystem?
3. Describe how succession affects an ecosystem.
4. Describe how Dutch elm disease got started in North America.
5. In your own words, describe what an endangered species is.
6. Give three examples of endangered species.
7. Why does DDT accumulate in the tissues of organisms?
8. Describe two effects of DDT on the lives of predatory birds?
9. Draw a food chain to show the flow of DDT through a woodlot ecosystem.
10. If there are alternatives to pesticides, why do you think the alternative methods are not used as often?
11. (a) List five different pollutants found in and around the school.
    (b) How could the number of these pollutants be reduced?
12. How does an algal bloom affect the ecology of the lake in which it occurs?

Applying Your Knowledge

1. DDT has been found in the bodies of arctic whales. Explain how it could have reached this animal.
2. You have been asked to work on a project to design an ecologically efficient housing project near a sandy beach. Draw a plan showing the following:
   (a) where you would locate the development
   (b) the vegetation surrounding the development
   (c) how people would have access to the beach
   (d) how you would landscape the area
   Include any special precautions you feel are necessary to protect the environment, but don't forget that the purpose of the project is to build homes.
3. Imagine that your school building was demolished and the site left vacant. Assume that no humans were allowed on the site. Describe what you think the school grounds would look like after 100 years.

Projects for Investigation

1. Choose two animals that are endangered species and find out what is being done to try to save them from extinction. How might you help? Make a report to the class on your findings.
2. Populations of tent caterpillars have increased greatly in several Canadian provinces. These caterpillars feed on the leaves of maple trees, oak trees, and birch trees. What effect do these insects have on the ecological balance in these communities? How are the populations being controlled?
3. Before a new pesticide is sold, it must pass rigorous testing. What types of tests are performed before pesticides may be sold? What results might make the pesticides unsuitable for regular use?

4. Farming is one of Canada's largest industries. Find out what is being done to make farms more productive. How can areas that are not suited for farming be made to produce crops? How do these methods affect different populations of animals that inhabit the fields?
5. What are organic gardens and organic farms? What methods are used to protect organic gardens and farms from pests? Would you be willing to pay higher prices for organically grown fruits and vegetables?

Unit 1: Community Ecology

MATCH

In your notebook, write the letters (a) to (h). Beside each letter, write the number of the word in the right column that corresponds to each description in the left column.

(a) includes both biotic and abiotic factors

(b) groups of organisms of the same species that live in an area

(c) a population in balance with the environment

(d) a convenient area of measurement, such as 1 m²

(e) a large area that has the same climate and soil plus various types of ecosystems

(f) where all life on earth exists

(g) an organism that uses another living thing as a home and a source of food

(h) a species that has died out

1. parasite
2. ecosystem
3. succession
4. population
5. quadrat
6. steady state
7. biosphere
8. extinct
9. biome
10. pollutant

MULTIPLE CHOICE

In your notebook, write the numbers 1 to 10. Beside each number, write the letter of the best choice.

1. What is the original source of energy in a woodland ecosystem?
   (a) trees
   (b) sun
   (c) animals
   (d) fallen trees

2. Which organisms break down dead material and return the useful nutrients to the soil?
   (a) herbivores
   (b) carnivores
   (c) decomposers
   (d) omnivores

3. Which type of organism is a direct user of the sun's energy?
   (a) consumer
   (b) decomposer
   (c) scavenger
   (d) producer

4. What do the arrows in this food chain represent: lettuce → rabbit → snake
   (a) light energy
   (b) migration
   (c) flow of energy
   (d) death

5. Why do biologists take samples at random?
   (a) This is the easiest method.
   (b) Other scientists can make better judgements based on their results.
   (c) They can avoid choosing a very good or a very bad sample.
   (d) They can make sure they have counted all the organisms.

6. Which term includes the other three?
   (a) community
   (b) biosphere
   (c) ecosystem
   (d) biome

7. Which of the following best represents an ecosystem?
   (a) fish in an aquarium
   (b) all the organisms in an aquarium
   (c) all the organisms in an aquarium plus the light source
   (d) all the organisms in an aquarium plus the light, water, and sand

8. Which term includes the other three?
   (a) food web
   (b) food chain
   (c) consumer
   (d) producer

9. A field has an area of 1000 m². Your quadrat measures 1 m². You counted the numbers of dandelions in three random samples. The results were 5, 10, and 6. What is the probable population of dandelions in this field?
   (a) 5000   (c) 7000
   (b) 6000   (d) 10 000

10. Which of the following is an example of a predator-prey relationship?
    (a) a dog with fleas
    (b) two rabbits chasing each other
    (c) a bear searching the waters for salmon
    (d) a tapeworm in a dog's intestine

TRUE/FALSE

Write the numbers 1 to 10 in your notebook. Beside each number, write T if the statement is true and F if the statement is false. For each false statement, rewrite it as a true statement.

1. A niche is an organism's home in the environment.
2. A pesticide is a chemical used to kill pests.
3. Green plants obtain carbon from carbon dioxide in the soil.
4. A wildlife sanctuary is a good area for hunting animals.
5. Over the last 50 years, humans have taken a greater interest in polluting the environment.
6. Omnivores are consumers that eat only plants.
7. Aquaculture is the cultivation of fish and shellfish in a controlled environment.
8. There is an endless amount of clean water on the earth.
9. Most organisms can live without the help of other organisms.
10. Ecology is a science that explores the relationship of living things to their environment.

FOR DISCUSSION

Read the paragraphs below and answer the questions that follow.

The forest was small. The north face of the forest measured 200 m long, and the east face was 300 m wide. Populations of rabbits, chipmunks, and red-tailed hawks made their homes among the trees. On the ground there were centipedes, snakes, and many kinds of insects such as beetles. The soil on the

forest floor was rich in nutrients produced by the decay of fallen leaves. Sprouting up among the fallen leaves was a fine type of grass called red fescue. This type of grass grows very well where there is little direct sunlight. Two of the types of trees in this forest were sugar maple and oak.

An aerial photograph of the forest taken 55 years ago showed 6 oak trees and 18 sugar maples in a sample area 30 m x 20 m. A more recent picture shows a change in the population of maple and oak trees. Now there are 12 oaks and 8 maples in the same sample area.

1. What is the area covered by this forest?
2. Write as many different food chains as you can from the organisms that live in this forest.
3. What populations inhabit the forest?
4. (a) What is the approximate number of oak trees that lived in the forest 55 years ago?
   (b) How many oak trees are there now in the forest?
   (c) How can you explain this difference in the two populations of trees?
5. Why does the red fescue grass grow so well on the forest floor?
6. What role might the beetles and centipedes play in this forest ecosystem?
7. What differences would there be in the abiotic factors of the forest and those of an open field?

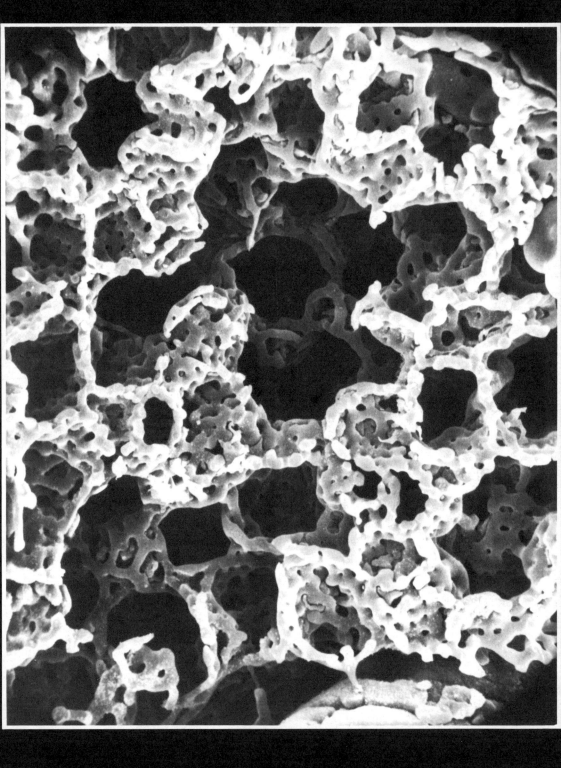

The Functioning Animal

It is certainly difficult to know what the photo on the left is all about. Would it help if you knew that it was taken using a special microscope and magnified 270 times? Even so, it is probably still a mystery!

The photo shows some of the tiny blood vessels that surround the many air sacs in our lungs. So the photo has something to do with breathing. But it also has to do with circulation and some of the blood vessels that carry oxygen and nutrients to all parts of our body. The chapters in this unit are all about life and the fascinating relationships between the systems which permit life to continue.

The Necessities of Life:
Food, Oxygen, and Energy

Key Ideas

- All living things need energy to carry out their activities.
- Energy can take different forms and be changed from one form to another.
- Foods contain energy in the form of chemical energy.
- Different foods contain different amounts of energy.

*I*n these photos, the machines, the fire, and the people all need and use energy in one form or another. The racers need gasoline to propel their dirt bikes. The fire needs fuel—the wood and other materials—to keep it going. The swimmers need "fuel" so they can make it to the finish line. This "fuel," of course, is the food that we eat.

But the subjects in all three photos share another requirement. They all need the gas oxygen. Oxygen must mix with the gasoline to propel the motor bikes. Oxygen must be present to support the fire. Oxygen is breathed in by the people in the pictures. Once inside our bodies, oxygen combines with carbon and hydrogen from digested foods within our cells. These very special processes make available the energy to run, to swim, and to think. This chapter, then, is all about the necessities of life: food, oxygen, and energy.

What Is Energy?

Energy can be defined as the ability to do work. Energy can take different forms, such as light and heat. In Figure 4.1, several different forms of energy are being used. For example, mechanical energy, the energy of motion, is being used to lift the fishing line (and, hopefully, a fish) out of the water. What other forms of energy are being used in this illustration?

Energy can be transformed or changed from one form to another. In Figure 4.1, find an example of one form of energy being changed into another form.

The different forms of energy in Figure 4.1 are causing work to be done. When a force causes an object to move through a distance—for example, the car being moved in the picture—work is being done.

Figure 4.1 *Different forms of energy. How many can you name?*

4.2

Putting Chemical Energy to Work

Figure 4.1 showed some important forms of energy—heat, mechanical energy, and light energy. Our lives depend on them. We also use another form of energy—chemical energy. We all know that gasoline is a chemical. When ignited in a controlled way, it drives our motor bikes and automobiles. This is another example of energy being transformed or changed from one form, chemical, to another form, mechanical.

All living things, including the swimmers in the opening photographs, use chemical energy to enable them to move. Foods, of course, contain chemical energy. Activity 4A will demonstrate some interesting facts about energy. In the experiment, the chemical energy in food will be changed to heat. From the experiment you will also be able to find the amount of heat released by different foods.

The unit used to measure both energy and work is called the **joule (J)**. We now have to watch our joules rather than our calories when dieting. A joule is roughly the amount of energy required to raise two golf balls a height of 1 m. Ten French fries yield about 665 kJ. You would have to work for 30 min to burn off all that energy!

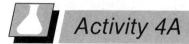
Problem

Which contains the most food energy—bacon, marshmallows, or peanuts?

Materials

1 large juice can cut as in Figure 4.2 (a)
a peanut, small pieces of bacon, a marshmallow
ashes
thermometer
test tube
beaker (100 mL)
matches
graduated cylinder (10 mL)
cork and pin
balance

Procedure

1. Copy Table 4.1 into your notebook. Use it to record your observations.
2. Before doing this activity, make a hypothesis as to which of the foods contains the most energy. Give reasons for your hypothesis.
3. Examine the can shown in Figure 4.2 (a). The opening at the bottom lets you place the food inside, while the centre hole at the top is for holding a test tube of water. The little holes allow air to pass through. Make sure that your test tube fits properly.
4. Measure 10 mL of water into a graduated cylinder as shown in Figure 4.2 (b). Pour the water into the test tube.
5. Place the test tube in the can. Measure the initial temperature of the water with the thermometer. See Figure 4.2 (c). Record the temperature on your observation table. Remove the thermometer.
6. With a balance, measure the mass of the peanut. Record the mass in grams on your observation table.
7. Dip the peanut into the ashes so that it will light more readily. Now place the peanut on the end of a pin stuck into a cork. See Figure 4.2 (d).

8. Light the peanut. Make certain it is burning. Quickly place the cork and the peanut in the bottom of the can, directly under the test tube. See Figure 4.2 (e). There should be a space of about 1 cm between the bottom of the test tube and the peanut.
9. Let the peanut burn completely.
10. Take the final temperature of the water and record this on your observation table.
11. Repeat steps 3–10 for the other foods. Record all of your values.

Questions

1. Which of the three foods produced the largest rise in temperature?
2. Which food produced the greatest temperature increase per gram of food burned? (Clearly distinguish in your mind the difference between this question and question 1.)
3. Are there any energy losses in this experiment? If so, how would they affect the results?
4. Was your original hypothesis correct? Explain.

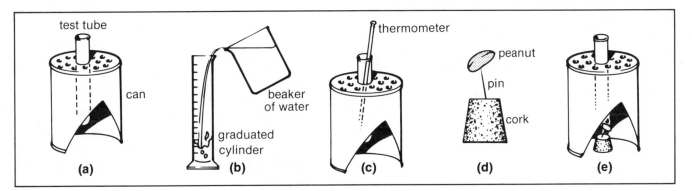

Figure 4.2

Observations

Table 4.1 *The Relative Amounts of Energy in Common Foods*

	PEANUT	BACON	MARSHMALLOW
1. Volume of water used (mL)			
2. Starting temperature of water (°C)			
3. Final temperature of water (°C)			
4. Mass of food (g)			
5. Rise in temperature (°C) (subtract your value for number 2 from number 3)			
6. Rise in temperature per gram of foodstuff = $\dfrac{\text{number 3 - number 2}}{\text{number 4}}$ (°C)/g			

Energy in Food

The three foods used in Activity 4A are examples of three common food chemicals. The peanut is rich in fat, protein, and carbohydrate. The marshmallow contains sugar, which is a carbohydrate. Bacon is rich in fat and contains some protein. Most foods contain more than one of these three groups of chemicals. Activity 4A showed that different foods contain different amounts of chemical energy. During the burning, energy as well as the gas carbon dioxide was released.

Energy is released in your own body when products of digestion are further broken down within your cells. This is called catabolism. **Catabolism** is the release of energy within the cells. Unlike the burning of the food in Activity 4A, the release of energy in your cells is much slower and more controlled.

But where did all this food energy come from? Peanuts grow on plants. Sugar comes from sugar cane, sugar beets, and many types of fruit. Peanut plants and sugar cane store up energy from sunlight. Bacon comes from a pig. But most of the pig's food comes from plants.

You will recall that green plants carry on photosynthesis. The process of photosynthesis requires the energy of light. This light energy is converted into chemical energy in food. One such food produced by photosynthesis is starch. The production and storage of food is called **anabolism**. Thus, photosynthesis is said to be an anabolic process. Anabolism includes all energy-storing processes.

In summary, energy can be stored (anabolism) or released (catabolism). Together, all of the energy-storing and energy-releasing processes are called **metabolism**. These important changes are summarized in Figure 4.3. Note that all of these processes take place in living plant and animal cells.

When energy is released in your body, the process takes place within your cells. This is called **cellular respiration** and is a form of catabolism. Remember that energy-storing activities are very similar to energy-releasing activities.

Figure 4.3 *Important energy relationships in the world around us*

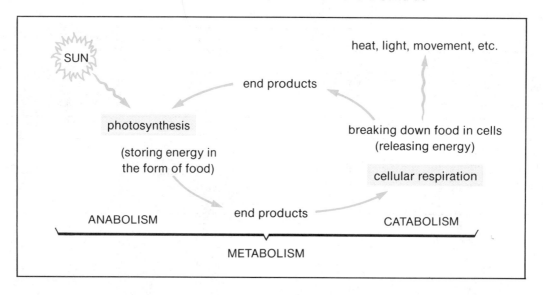

Chapter Objectives

NOW THAT YOU HAVE COMPLETED THIS CHAPTER, CAN YOU DO THE FOLLOWING?	FOR REVIEW, TURN TO SECTION
1. Define the term energy.	4.1
2. Name at least four different forms of energy.	4.1
3. Understand that energy can be transformed from one form to another.	4.1
4. Recognize that energy can be measured.	4.2
5. Measure both energy and work in joules.	4.2
6. Perform an experiment to compare the relative amounts of energy contained in some common foods.	4.2

Words to Know

energy
joule (J)
catabolism
anabolism
metabolism
cellular respiration

Tying It Together

1. Define the word energy.
2. Name two pieces of evidence that suggest a runner is using energy.
3. What unit is used to measure energy?
4. List five characteristics of energy.
5. In scientific terms, how do you know when work is done?
6. Define the biological term cell.
7. (a) What is catabolism?
   (b) What is anabolism?
   Give an example of each.
8. Describe in simple terms the process of metabolism.

Applying Your Knowledge

1. Both Mario and Susan are going on a diet.
   (a) What type of food should they cut down on during their diet? Explain.
   (b) What additional information should they have regarding foods and dieting before they begin?
2. While working in a hospital lab, you find a food that releases the same amount of heat per gram as did the bacon in Activity 4A.
   (a) What can you conclude about the type of food it is?
   (b) What additional tests would you like to be able to make on this food to be sure of your conclusion?

Projects for Investigation

1. You are about to run a 2 km race. You decide that munching on a few cubes of table sugar might give you extra energy for the race. Is this a wise decision? Do research to find out about the possible danger(s) associated with sugar consumption. Does sugar provide any benefits? What foods contain large quantities of sugar? Do a survey among your friends to determine their sugar-eating habits.

Breathing and Gas Exchange

Key Ideas

- The air we inhale differs from the air we exhale.
- Some simpler forms of life do not need a system for bringing oxygen into the organism, while more complex organisms need some kind of respiratory system.
- In the human respiratory system, the exchange of oxygen and carbon dioxide takes place in the alveoli in the lungs.
- Smoking interferes with the proper functioning of the respiratory system.

The face mask and snorkel shown here are common at most beaches. Notice that the masks completely cover the nostrils of the swimmers. Why is this usually the case? While swimming, the mouthpiece end of the snorkel is held in the mouth while the other end extends above the surface of the water. Again, why is this arrangement necessary?

Regardless of where we are, we have to keep breathing. But what is so special about the air we breathe? How does the air that we breathe in (**inhale**) differ from the air that we breathe out (**exhale**)? Let's begin by examining this last question.

Activity 5A

Problem

How do the contents of inhaled air differ from the contents of exhaled air?

Materials

2 Erlenmeyer flasks (250 mL)
2 glass tubes (10 cm)
2 glass tubes (15 cm)
2 rubber stoppers (2-holed)
clean drinking straw
ethanol
Y-tube
limewater, freshly prepared (300 mL)
wooden splint and match
glass jar

CAUTION Safety goggles should be worn when testing for gas with a burning splint. Y-tubes must be sterilized before and after a person uses them unless a fresh, clean drinking straw is used by each student.

Procedure

1. Copy Table 5.1 into your notebook. Use it to record your observations.
2. Before beginning this activity, suggest ways in which you think inhaled air might differ from exhaled air.

3. Assemble the apparatus as shown in Figure 5.1. Insert a fresh clean drinking straw into the end of the rubber tubing or else rinse the free end in ethanol to disinfect it.
4. While pinching the rubber tubing shown on the right side of Figure 5.1, inhale deeply through the stem of the Y-tube.
5. Release your hold on the right-hand tubing and pinch the tubing shown on the left side of the Figure 5.1. Now exhale.
6. Repeat steps 4 and 5 a number of times until there is a marked change in the appearance of one or both of the flasks.
7. Record all of your observations in your table.
8. Light a wooden splint. Now place the burning splint into the glass jar. Hold it in the jar until the flame goes out. Add a few millilitres of limewater to the jar and shake. Record your observations.

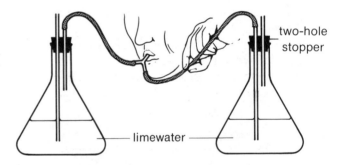

Figure 5.1 *Apparatus for performing Activity 5A. Why is limewater placed in the two flasks?*

Table 5.1 *The Difference between Inhaled and Exhaled Air*

	APPEARANCE OF LIMEWATER BEFORE BREATHING THROUGH FLASKS	APPEARANCE OF LIMEWATER AFTER BREATHING THROUGH FLASKS
Left flask		
Right flask		
	APPEARANCE OF LIMEWATER BEFORE ADDING IT TO THE JAR WITH THE BURNING SPLINT	APPEARANCE OF LIMEWATER AFTER ADDING IT TO THE JAR WITH THE BURNING SPLINT
Jar with burning splint		

Observations

(see Table 5.1)

1. What was the appearance of the limewater before you started breathing into the flasks?
2. Describe clearly any observations that you made while performing step 4. Try to explain these observations.
3. Describe what happened to the limewater when you performed step 5.
4. What happened to the limewater when you performed step 8?
5. (a) In which of the two flasks was the final appearance of the limewater like that in step 8?
   (b) What is the name of the gas that has reacted with the limewater?

Questions

1. What difference is there between inhaled and exhaled air?
2. Which kind of air contains the same gas that the burning wood produced?
3. What kind of gas produced the change in the limewater?

Ideas and Applications

The importance of oxygen to living cells cannot be overemphasized. A human could live for three or four weeks without food and for nearly a week without water. Without oxygen an average person's brain would be dead in about eight *minutes*.

Inhaled and Exhaled Air

Activity 5A shows that inhaled air does differ from exhaled air. This difference is important in terms of what breathing is all about. Note how the results of the exhaled air compared with the product of burning. You will recall that when food is burned, one of the main products is carbon dioxide. For review see Activity 4A.

You inhale air that is rich in oxygen. The gas oxygen is also required for most forms of burning. You exhale air that is rich in carbon dioxide. This gas is a product of burning. Of course, the food you eat is not really "burned" in the usual sense of the term. It is broken down chemically. This occurs first by enzymes in your digestive tract and then by more enzymes in your individual cells. The breathing system, therefore, serves to exchange gases you need and those which you must get rid of.

Self-check

1. Define the terms inhalation and exhalation.
2. How does inhaled air differ from exhaled air?
3. During Activity 5A, air bubbles appeared in one of the flasks even though you were inhaling. Account for this fact.

Breathing Systems in Different Organisms

All animals share the common need to take in oxygen. Similarly, these organisms must get rid of the body's waste gases. How do different organisms meet this need?

Single-celled Organisms

Single-celled organisms such as the amoeba and paramecium have little need for a breathing system because of their small size. Every part of the inside of the organism is very close to the surface of the cell where the exchange of gases takes place. This exchange is shown in Figure 5.2. You can see that the concentration of oxygen is higher outside the membrane than inside. The carbon dioxide concentration is higher on the inside of the membrane. In general, gases will *diffuse* (move) from an area of higher concentration to one of lower concentration. Although nitrogen gas appears on both sides of the membrane, it is not actually involved in the breathing process. It is included to remind you that nitrogen is a major component of air.

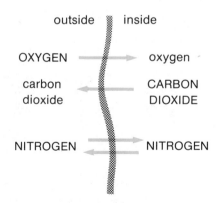

Figure 5.2 *The exchange of gases across a membrane. What conditions must be met if oxygen gas is to pass from the outside to the inside?*

Earthworms

The common earthworm, like the amoeba, does not have an organized breathing system. It does, however, take in oxygen. The oxygen must dissolve in the thin film of moisture on the skin before it can diffuse inward. Nutrients, too, must be dissolved in water before they can be absorbed through the walls of the digestive tract.

You have probably seen what happens to an earthworm when it is forced out of an underground burrow during a heavy rain. If the worm ends up on the sidewalk when the sun comes out again, it often dies. This occurs because it cannot keep its skin moist. When this happens, it cannot dissolve oxygen from the air. In part, this explains why many simpler organisms stay in cool, damp places.

Insects

Insects do possess a breathing system. It consists of a series of tiny openings (*spiracles*), connected to a series of tubes and air sacs (Figure 5.3).

The next time you have a chance to do so, examine a living insect with a hand lens. You will see the bottom of the abdomen—the back end of the body—move in and out. This is rather like your own rib cage. Farmers can make use of the breathing systems of insects to control them.

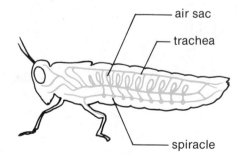

Figure 5.3 *The breathing system of a grasshopper. How does a knowledge of this system help a farmer control grasshoppers?*

Some insecticides (chemicals used to kill insects) contain poisons. The insects breathe in the insecticides and die. Other insecticides are dusts that clog up the breathing pores. This also kills the insects.

Frogs

Frogs belong to that group of animals called *amphibians*. These animals live a part of their lives in water and a part on land. To be able to do this, frogs must have a breathing system that enables them to breathe under water. They must also have a system that allows them to breathe on land.

THE LIFE CYCLE OF A FROG

To understand gas exchange in a frog, you need to know a little about the life cycle of a frog. There are many different kinds of frogs. We will discuss the common leopard frog. It has this name because it has skin marking like a leopard.

As you can see in Figure 5.4, a frog begins life as a fertilized egg. The eggs of the female frog and the sperm of the male frog are passed into the water. It is here that fertilization takes place. The fertilized eggs cluster together in a speckled black and white jelly-like mass. These "blobs" appear along the shores of lakes and ponds in the spring of the year.

Most fertilized eggs eventually become tadpoles. Tadpoles are water creatures. They breathe by means of gills. Gradually, the gills on the outside of the tadpole are replaced by gills on the inside. Like a fish, the tadpole now takes in water through its mouth. This water is then passed over the gills and out through slits on the sides of the head. Gas exchange occurs on the surface of the gills.

The body of the tadpole continues to change and begins to look more like a frog. It takes about nine to eleven weeks for a fertilized egg to become an adult frog.

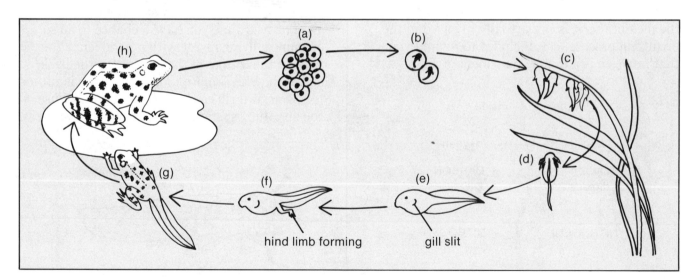

Figure 5.4 *The life cycle of a frog. At different times in the life of a frog, it can breathe in air and/or in water.*

An adult frog has three ways of breathing. It can breathe through its skin, through the lining of its mouth, or through two well-developed internal lungs.

For the skin to act as an organ of gas exchange, it must be kept moist at all times. A moist skin is a feature of all frogs. Frogs breathe through the skin during the cold months of the year. At this time, they burrow into the mud on the lake bottom and spend the winter there. Gas exchange through the skin is sufficient to keep the frog alive since it is not active at this time.

The second place where gas exchange takes place is through the lining of the mouth. If you watch a frog sitting on a lily pad, you will see a rapid lowering and raising of the floor of the mouth. These movements take place while the lungs are closed off by the glottis (Figure 5.5). The glottis is found at the back of the throat of the frog. As with the surface of the skin, oxygen enters the lining of the mouth and carbon dioxide leaves.

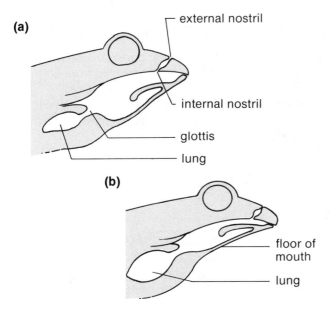

(a)

— external nostril

— internal nostril

— glottis

— lung

(b)

— floor of mouth

— lung

Figure 5.5 *Mouth and lung breathing in an adult frog*

The third method of breathing takes place through the two lungs. It occurs on most occasions when the frog is out of water. To make it easier to follow, the steps involved are numbered below.

1. Air first enters the mouth through the nostrils.
2. To increase the volume of air that enters, the frog lowers the floor of its mouth.
3. Once the air is inside, the frog closes the valves of the nostrils.
4. Next, it raises the floor of the mouth and opens the glottis. This forces air into the lungs.
5. The many branches of each lung end in tiny sacs called *alveoli*. The alveoli, in turn are surrounded by tiny blood vessels called *capillaries*. The gas exchange occurs through the thin walls of the alveoli. Oxygen enters the capillaries for transport to all parts of the body. Carbon dioxide leaves the blood vessels and passes into the alveoli.
6. Once the exchange of gases has taken place, the frog breathes out. The frog does this by contracting the muscles of the body wall near the lungs. At the same time, the glottis and the valves of the nostrils are opened. The mouth remains closed while both mouth and lung breathing is taking place.

Birds

How can birds fly incredible distances without stopping? Imagine trying to run for 100 km or more without once stopping to catch your breath! In many ways, birds are suited for flying. One of the most important of these is the breathing system.

The breathing system of a bird consists of a pair of internal lungs, a series of connected tubes, and some air sacs (Figure 5.6). When the bird raises its wings during flight, the rib cage drops or moves out and air enters the bird. An exchange of gases then takes place in the lungs. Oxygen enters and carbon dioxide leaves. When the bird lowers its wings and exhales air, a *second* rush of air passes through the lungs. This is all made possible by a special arrangement of air tubes and sacs, as well as by the lungs themselves. As a result, the bird is actually obtaining a new supply of oxygen both during inhaling *and* exhaling. This process is summarized in Figure 5.7.

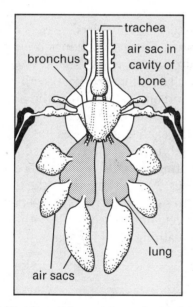

Figure 5.6 *The breathing system of a bird. What function do the air sacs play?*

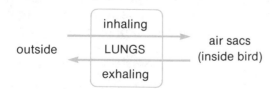

Figure 5.7 *How birds obtain "fresh" air during both inhaling and exhaling*

Self-check

1. Why doesn't an amoeba require a special breathing system?
2. In terms of gas exchange, what is perhaps the most serious problem facing organisms that live on the land?
3. Like most organisms, an earthworm is made up of many cells. Although most of these cells are inside the body, the earthworm does not have a true breathing system. How is this possible?
4. Name the three most important parts of the breathing system of a grasshopper, which is a typical insect.
5. (a) At what three sites in the body does the exchange of gases occur in a frog?
   (b) Choose one of these sites and explain how gas exchange occurs.
6. Describe the features of a frog's head which enable it to live in the water.
7. Explain how a bird is able to fly long distances without stopping to rest.

Ideas and Applications

People who fish know that during the heat of the summer, game fish such as lake trout are found in the deepest parts of a lake. Cold water, which is found at the bottom of a lake in summer, contains a higher concentration of oxygen than warmer water.

The Human Breathing System

Like other more complex animals, you possess a special breathing system. This is shown in Figure 5.8. Air first enters the breathing system, usually through your **nostrils**. From here, the air passes into the **nasal passages**. These passages serve to warm the air and to moisten it with fluid called mucus. **Mucus** is secreted by the cells lining the walls of the nasal passages. In addition, the lower surface of the passages possesses tiny hair-like structures, called **cilia**. These wave back and forth and trap particles of dust. When you blow your nose, your body gets rid of the dust as well as some mucus.

After the air leaves the nasal passages, it passes down the back of the mouth through an area called the **pharynx**. Next, the air enters the **trachea** or windpipe. This section of the system is reinforced by a series of pieces of flexible **cartilage**. Each piece of cartilage is in the shape of a half-ring (Figure 5.8). If you apply gentle pressure with your fingers to the front of your throat you will be able to feel the cartilage "give"

a little. Because of its flexibility, this cartilage prevents the throat from becoming blocked if, for example, you are struck by an object.

On the way to the lungs, the air passes through the voice box or **larynx**. It is located in the upper portion of the trachea. Each of your two **vocal cords** are rather like a thick violin string. They are stretched across the larynx. As air is forced across these cords, they produce different sounds. The sounds depend on the length and the degree to which the cords are tightened.

The air leaves the trachea and enters the lungs by way of the two **bronchi** (singular: **bronchus**). One bronchus enters each lung. Once inside the lungs proper, the bronchi branch again and again, like branches on a tree. The lesser branches of this network are called **bronchioles**. The bronchioles only have small pieces of randomly placed cartilage for support. Finally, the air ends up in tiny grape-like sacs called **alveoli** (singular: **alveolus**). There are more than one million alveoli in each lung (Figure 5.9).

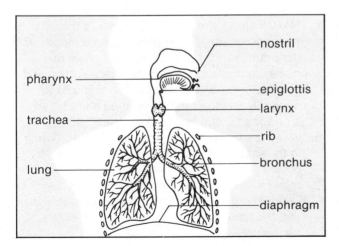

Figure 5.8 *The human breathing system. What conditions must be met so oxygen can move from the alveoli into the blood stream?*

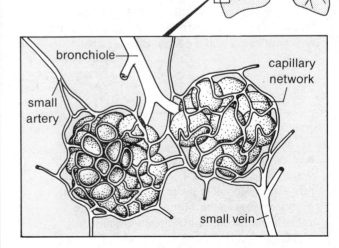

Figure 5.9 *The air sacs (alveoli) and blood vessels in a human lung*

As you know, gases must be dissolved in order to be exchanged. The alveoli are lined with a thin film of moisture that permits this exchange. Also, the walls of the alveoli are only one-cell thick and are lined with many capillaries. **Capillaries** are the smallest of the blood vessels of the body. Oxygen from the air diffuses through the film of moisture and the membranes of the alveoli into blood in the capillaries. As was the case with the other organisms studied so far, oxygen diffuses into your blood while carbon dioxide diffuses outward from your blood to the air in your lungs (Figure 5.9).

In Activity 5B, you will look at how you get air into and out of your lungs. You will also find out how much your lungs will hold. This is called your **vital capacity**.

Ideas and Applications

Males usually have a more prominent larynx. It can be seen in front of the throat. You probably know it as the "Adam's apple." The average male has a deeper voice than the average female. This is because the male's vocal cords are longer and make deeper bass sounds.

Challenge

Not all of the air that enters the lungs actually makes it to the surface of the alveoli where the gas exchange takes place. Suggest imaginary modifications to the human gas exchange system that would make the system more efficient.

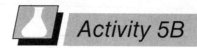

Activity 5B

Problem

What is the vital capacity of your lungs?

Materials

large bottle (6–8 L)
rubber tubing (1 m)
clean drinking straw
ethanol
small glass plate
large, shallow container with an overflow spout

> **CAUTION** The rubber tubing must be sterilized before and after being used by a student unless a fresh, clean drinking straw is used for each student.

Procedure

1. Copy Table 5.2 into your notebook.
2. Pour water into the shallow container up to a depth of about 5–8 cm.
3. Pour 500 mL of water into the bottle. Make sure the bottle is level. Using a waterproof marking pen, mark a line on the bottle at the water level.
4. Repeat step 3, adding water and marking lines at 1000 mL, 1500 mL, etc., until the bottle is filled.
5. Next, fill the large bottle with water to the very top. Place a small glass plate over the mouth of the bottle. While holding the glass cover in place, *carefully* turn the bottle upside down and place it in the container of water. If you have done this successfully, there should not be any air trapped in the bottle. See Figure 5.10.
6. When the mouth of the bottle is under the water in the shallow container, remove the glass cover.
7. Insert the rubber tubing into the neck of the bottle and push it up to the top. Make certain that the tubing is not pinched where it enters the bottle.

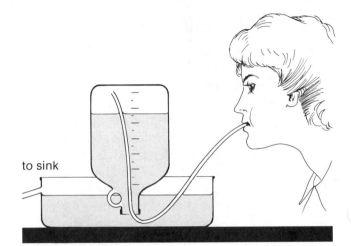

to sink

Figure 5.10 *Set-up for Activity 5B. Be sure that the overflow spout is aimed into a sink.*

8. Insert a fresh, clean drinking straw into the end of the rubber tubing or else rinse the free end of the rubber tubing in ethanol to sterilize it. Rinse the tube again in water.
9. Inhale as deeply as you can. Then, with your mouth over the end of the rubber tubing, exhale as much of your breath as you possibly can. Have your partner note what happens to the water in the bottle.
10. Once you have exhaled as much as you can, quickly seal off the open end of the tube with your finger. Now remove the tubing from the bottle. Make certain that the neck of the bottle remains under water at all times.
11. Record the amount of air that is now contained in the bottle.
12. Your teacher may have you repeat the activity using some or all of the following variables. In these cases, the student pairs should be about the same age and mass.
   (a) an athletic versus a non-athletic person
   (b) a person who plays a wind instrument versus one who does not
   (c) other variables of your own choosing

Observations

Table 5.2 *Determining the Vital Capacity of Human Lungs*

1. The vital capacity of the first student was _____ L.
2. Circle or fill in the word that describes the student:
   The student was male/female, is athletic/non-athletic, played/did not play a wind instrument, and has a mass of about _____ kg.
3. Vital Capacities

VARIABLE	VITAL CAPACITIES	MEASURED IN LITRES (L)
Sex	Male	Female
	_____ L	_____ L
Athlete	Athlete	Non-athlete
	_____ L	_____ L
Musician	Plays a wind instrument	Does not play a wind instrument
	_____ L	_____ L
Others (state)		

Questions

1. Do you think that the vital capacity values which you obtained in this activity represent the absolute capacity of your lungs? Explain.
2. What bearing, if any, does the sex of a person have on the vital capacity?
3. What appeared to be the most important variable which led to differences in vital capacity?
4. How do you think the vital lung capacity of a person could be increased?

The Control of Breathing

Breathing is one body activity that you do not have to think about. The rate at which you inhale and exhale varies with body activity. You do, however, have to breathe 24 h each and every day of your life. A slight interruption of even a few minutes usually leads to death.

How is this breathing system controlled? Surprising as it might seem, the body checks the concentration of carbon dioxide rather than the concentration of oxygen in your blood. The control centre is located at the base of your brain (Figure 5.11). You have probably seen a TV show or a movie in which someone receives a severe blow on the back of the head. This can knock the person unconscious. It can also put the control centre out of action. The person may stop breathing and death may result. Perhaps you have also heard about infant crib deaths in which parents find their otherwise healthy baby dead in its crib. Some doctors suggest that this is because of the failure of the control centre to send signals to the lungs to carry on breathing. Normally, of course, you carry on breathing, even during sleep.

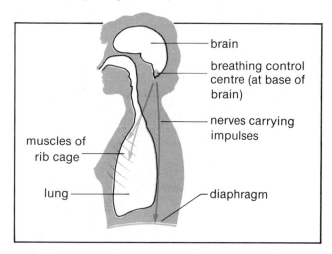

Figure 5.11 *A side view of the head and lungs. The centre controlling breathing movements is located at the base of the brain.*

The Act of Breathing

In addition to the control centre at the base of the brain, the body makes use of the muscles of the chest and diaphragm to help you to breathe. The **diaphragm** (see Figure 5.8) is a thin sheet of muscle located just above the stomach. It separates the chest region from the abdomen.

When the diaphragm is relaxed, it resembles the model in Figure 5.12 (a). When the diaphragm contracts, it tightens like the head of a drum. Figure 5.12 (b) shows that this produces a greater volume in the chest region surrounding the lungs. This *reduces* the air pressure surrounding the lungs. As is the case with balloons, if the air pressure surrounding the lungs is reduced, the elastic nature of the lungs enables them to expand. If the air pressure in the surrounding air exceeds the air pressure surrounding the lungs, air will enter the lungs. This takes place until the pressure becomes equal inside and outside. This is the act of inhaling. When the diaphragm relaxes, the volume of the chest cavity is decreased. The increased pressure on the lungs expels the air. This is the act of exhaling.

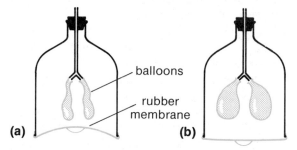

Figure 5.12 *A model to show how air enters and leaves the lungs. The rubber membrane at the bottom of the jar represents the diaphragm, and the balloons represent the lungs. Why do the balloons (lungs) fill with air when the rubber membrane (diaphragm) contracts?*

Muscles of the rib cage are also involved in the act of breathing. At the same time that the diaphragm muscle contracts, the muscles of the rib cage also contract. The result is that the rib cage is lifted up and away from the body. Again, this increases the volume of the chest cavity and assists in bringing air into the lungs.

Challenge

To check the action of the diaphragm and the rib cage muscles, you might want to perform the following simple activities.

1. While sitting on a chair, bend forward at the waist as far as you can do so comfortably. Now take a deep breath. How successful were you in doing this? The pressure that you felt would be in the area of the diaphragm.

2. While sitting upright, place your hand on your chest. Again take a deep breath and see what happens to your rib cage. Now exhale. What was the final position of your rib cage?

Artificial Respiration—A Matter of Life and Death

It's always easy to look back after something happens and say, "Next time, I'll do things differently." Usually, you do get a second chance. If, however, someone is drowning and no one on the scene knows how to perform **artificial respiration**, the victim does *not* get a second chance. Take time *now* to learn how to perform artificial respiration correctly. At the earliest opportunity take a first aid course offered by such organizations as the St. John Ambulance Association or the Canadian Red Cross.

The St. John Ambulance people refer to the *vital needs* of the body as follows. It's as simple as A, B, C:

Airway—ensure that the air has a clear passage to the lungs.

Breathing—should be adequate to allow enough oxygen to enter the lungs and pass into the blood.

Circulation—must be sufficient to carry the oxygen-containing blood to all of the living cells of the body.

Several points are worth stressing. First, a person can be unconscious but still breathing. If breathing is going on more or less normally, check to see that the airway is clear. The tongue sometimes becomes lodged in the back of the throat, causing asphyxiation. In the case of severe electrical shock or drowning, unconsciousness can be accompanied by a stoppage of breathing. Such a situation requires *immediate* action—every second counts. The most effective method of artificial respiration is the mouth-to-mouth (or mouth-to-nose) method. If the victim is suffering from severe electrical shock, shut off the power *before* beginning artificial respiration. Here, then, is the mouth-to-mouth method.

MOUTH-TO-MOUTH ARTIFICIAL RESPIRATION

1. If you come upon a victim who is unconscious and not breathing, check to see that the airway is clear. Do this *before* beginning artificial respiration. To do so, lift the victim's neck and press the forehead so that the head is tilted backwards (Figure 5.13). The chin should now be pointing upwards.

2. It is probably easiest to perform mouth-to-mouth respiration with the victim lying on a flat surface on his or her back. However, in the case of a swimming accident, you can begin the process while the victim is still in the water.

3. Hold the victim as indicated in Figure 5.14. In this position you will prevent the tongue from slipping back into the throat and blocking the air passage.

4. Now pinch the victim's nose, and, with the same hand, apply pressure to the forehead. This holds the head in the correct position (Figure 5.15).

5. Take a deep breath, open your mouth wide, and place it over the victim's mouth. It is important that you make a tight seal. Now blow a full breath of your air into the victim. This is done in a single puffing action (Figure 5.16). Out of the corner of your eye, watch to see that the victim's chest rises.

Figure 5.13 *Checking to see that the airway is clear.*

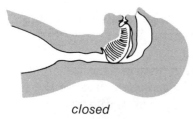

closed

(a) *If the head is not tilted back, the airway is sometimes blocked.*

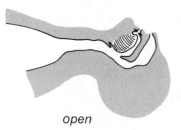

open

(b) *When the head is tilted back and the neck raised slightly, the airway is clear. Air may now pass to the lungs.*

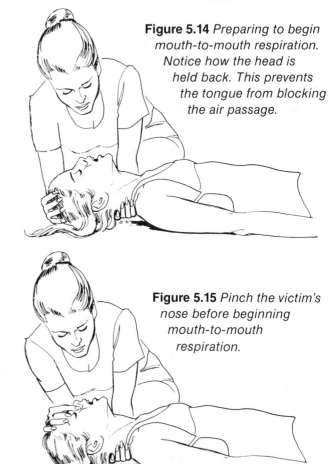

Figure 5.14 *Preparing to begin mouth-to-mouth respiration. Notice how the head is held back. This prevents the tongue from blocking the air passage.*

Figure 5.15 *Pinch the victim's nose before beginning mouth-to-mouth respiration.*

6. Remove your mouth from the victim's and turn your head to observe the victim's chest cavity fall (Figure 5.17). This procedure should be repeated every 5 s or about 12 to 15 times per minute. Don't worry too much about the rate. It can be measured by your own breathing rate.

7. The first four breaths should be as rapid as possible. You are trying to get as much oxygen into the blood as quickly as you can. Often this is all that is needed to get the person breathing again.

8. Up to this point, no mention has been made of seeking medical help. *The first person on the scene should always begin artificial respiration immediately.* The second person should call a doctor as soon as possible.

This procedure can be used under most circumstances. However, if someone has been involved in a car accident and the face has been badly injured, it might not be possible to perform mouth-to-mouth artificial respiration. It might be necessary to use the Sylvester Method or some other approach. These methods are not described here. You should, however, take time to find out more about them.

MOUTH-TO-NOSE ARTIFICIAL RESPIRATION

The mouth-to-nose method is used in a situation where there is damage to the mouth but not to the nose area. When the victim is a young child, use a method where you make a seal over both the mouth *and* the nose of the child. Then proceed with the mouth-to-mouth method. Note that a child breathes much more rapidly than an adult. When working on a very young child, you should breathe in short, shallow, fairly rapid breaths.

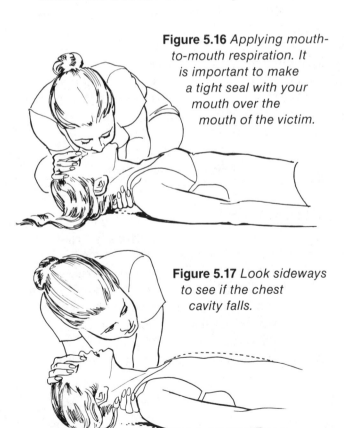

Figure 5.16 *Applying mouth-to-mouth respiration. It is important to make a tight seal with your mouth over the mouth of the victim.*

Figure 5.17 *Look sideways to see if the chest cavity falls.*

Self-check

1. Starting with the nostrils, list the structures through which air will pass on its way to the alveoli in the lungs.
2. Describe an alveolus.
3. What function do the cilia in the nasal passage perform in breathing?
4. Describe the role played by (a) the diaphragm and (b) the muscles of the rib cage in the act of breathing.
5. If you come upon a person who is lying on the ground and is not breathing, what is the first thing that you should do?
6. What are the three vital needs of the body as set out by the St. John Ambulance Association?

Diseases That Attack the Breathing System

The Common Cold

You wake up in the morning with an achy feeling in your head. Your eyes are watery and your nose is runny. Even though you just got out of bed, you feel exhausted. Chances are, you have a common cold. The cold is but one example of the many diseases which attack the breathing system of the body.

Why is a cold called a cold? Long ago, people thought that colds were caused by cold weather, but this is not true. More colds *do* take place during the colder months of the year. This is probably because we spend more time inside during the cold weather, close to other people. The viruses that cause colds are transmitted from one person to another when someone coughs or sneezes (Figure 5.18).

Figure 5.18 *Coughing is one way that the common cold virus is spread. That is why you should cover your mouth when you cough.*

If you have a cold, be sure to get lots of rest and drink plenty of fluids. There are also many products on the market designed to make you feel better. But there is presently nothing which can cure your cold.

Laryngitis

Occasionally, a common cold is accompanied by a case of **laryngitis**. This is a condition where the mucus membranes lining the larynx (voice box) become inflamed. As well, the vocal cords become swollen with fluid. This usually results in hoarseness or a loss of the voice. But laryngitis is not only caused by the cold virus. It can occur as a result of inhaling irritating fumes, including tobacco smoke. Heavy smokers often develop rather hoarse, scratchy voices. Laryngitis can also be caused by simply talking too much!

Although laryngitis is generally not too serious in an adult, it can be very serious in a young child. This is because the swollen vocal cords can severely reduce the size of the opening in the larynx. All of the air that we breathe in and out must pass through the larynx. A vaporizer containing mild chemicals is often suggested by a doctor to relieve the discomfort of laryngitis.

Bronchitis

As the name suggests, **bronchitis** is a disease that affects the region of the bronchioles. Because of its location, it is a more serious condition than a common cold or laryngitis. Like the common cold, it is often caused by one or more types of viruses. The condition is characterized by a buildup of fluids in the trachea and the bronchi which lead into the lungs.

Bronchitis is frequently also caused by cigarette smoking and the inhaling of other vapours that irritate the lining of the breathing system. Once the irritant is removed, the bronchitis usually clears up very quickly.

Pneumonia

The term **pneumonia** is a general one which applies to a very serious infection of the lungs. It can be caused by viruses, bacteria, or even fungi. In most cases, however, it is caused by one of the *pneumonococcus* bacteria. Like most of the diseases that strike the breathing system, it can be passed on to another person by coughing or sneezing.

The symptoms of the disease include sudden chills, followed by fever. There are usually also chest pains as well as a very deep, hoarse cough. It also becomes extremely difficult to breathe. As the disease progresses, there is a buildup of fluids, including some blood, in the lungs. The blood results from the breakdown of some of the membranes of the alveoli.

Pneumonia most often attacks people who are not very well to begin with. Once established, it takes constant medical attention to control it. It is a common cause of death in the elderly.

People with pneumonia are almost always hospitalized. A person with a severe case of the disease is often placed in a plastic "tent" erected over the bed (Figure 5.19). The medical staff then control the air in the tent, making it more humid as well as increasing the concentration of oxygen. Plastic tubes are sometimes passed through the larynx, the trachea, the bronchi and bronchioles to suck out the fluids that have collected there.

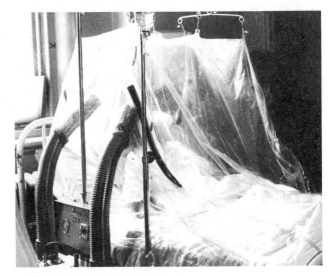

Figure 5.19 *An oxygen tent in a hospital. Why is smoking prohibited in a room where oxygen is being used?*

Ideas and Applications

There are many different strains of the cold virus, probably as many as 60. This is why it is so difficult for the body to defend against all of these "foreign invaders." Tests show that vitamin C is particularly effective in killing many kinds of viruses. This has led some researchers —most notably the two-time Nobel prize winner, Linus Pauling—to suggest that a daily intake of large doses of vitamin C (5000 mg or more) can help prevent colds. This treatment of the common cold is still controversial and should be used only if specifically prescribed by a doctor. There is a danger to the body when you suddenly stop taking very large doses of vitamin C.

Asthma

At some point in your life, you will probably meet a person who suffers from **asthma**. You may already have met such a person. *Asthmatics* (people with the condition) undergo bouts of coughing and wheezing. They have great difficulty breathing. An attack can be brought on by inhaling pollutants in the air. These could include such things as pollen, animal hair, cigarette smoke, and even household dust. It can also begin after exercise or even if the person is under some kind of stress. The condition is very complex. As many as 75% of children with asthma have a family history of the disorder, but other factors are also involved.

Self-check

1. List the signs and symptoms of laryngitis.
2. (a) Describe bronchitis.
   (b) Name two causes of bronchitis.
3. What are three things that can cause pneumonia?
4. What are four things that can start an asthmatic attack?
5. In general, what can you do to reduce the likelihood of becoming ill with any of the diseases of the breathing system?

Smoking and Our Breathing System

Emphysema is a disease of the lungs. The walls of the cells of the air sacs (the alveoli) are stretched to the point where they lose their elasticity. The changes in these cells also prevent the exchange of gases from taking place. Sometimes the alveoli rupture and blood enters the lungs.

Emphysema is associated with a number of diseases such as pneumonia and asthma, as well as **chronic bronchitis**. Bronchitis is a condition where the trachea and bronchi are irritated. Chronic emphysema usually accompanies chronic bronchitis. A major cause of both chronic bronchitis and emphysema is smoking. Emphysema can also be caused by prolonged exposure to coal dust, asbestos, or other chemicals present in the air.

You have probably heard quite a lot about smoking and health. But who do you believe when it comes to information about smoking? Every person has a choice to either smoke or not smoke. If the person who talks to you about smoking is a smoker, this might colour the way that information is presented. The same holds true for a non-smoker. But you are studying science. And in a science class you try to gather as much information as you can *before* arriving at any conclusions.

Challenge

Do research to answer the questions below. Useful sources of information include the library, Canadian Heart and Stroke Foundation, the Canadian Cancer Society, the Canadian Lung Association, the Addiction Research Foundation, and companies that manufacture cigarettes. You can organize your findings in the form of an oral or written report or a poster.

1. Are death rates higher for women smokers than for men smokers?
2. What are mainstream smoke and sidestream smoke? How do these affect both smokers and non-smokers?
3. What diseases are commonly associated with cigarette smoking? How do they affect the breathing system?
4. What substances are found in cigarette smoke? Do cigarette manufacturers add other substances to tobacco in the manufacturing process?
5. Are "light" cigarettes safer than regular or unfiltered cigarettes?
6. How do insurance rates compare for smokers and non-smokers?
7. In what ways is cigarette smoking addictive?
8. Even when smokers know the risks of smoking, why do they continue to smoke?
9. Some municipalities are banning smoking in public places, including schools. Is this an effective way of stopping people from smoking? Has it improved the air in the workplace?
10. What programs are available for people who wish to stop smoking?

Chapter Objectives

NOW THAT YOU HAVE COMPLETED THIS CHAPTER, CAN YOU DO THE FOLLOWING?	FOR REVIEW, TURN TO SECTION
1. Distinguish between the gases present in inhaled and exhaled air.	5.1
2. State why a single-celled organism does not need a breathing system.	5.2
3. Describe how an earthworm, a typical insect, and a bird take in oxygen and exhale carbon dioxide.	5.2
4. State the function played by air sacs in a bird's breathing system.	5.2
5. Explain the function of the nasal passages, cilia, pharynx, trachea, epiglottis, bronchi, and bronchioles.	5.3
6. Describe in detail the structure and function of the alveoli of the human lung.	5.3
7. Determine the vital capacity of human lungs.	5.3
8. Describe the role played by the diaphragm and the muscles of the rib cage in breathing.	5.3
9. Describe in the correct order the steps involved in performing mouth-to-mouth artificial respiration.	5.3
10. Describe how a cold, laryngitis, asthma, and pneumonia affect the breathing system.	5.4
11. Evaluate the risks associated with smoking.	5.5

Words to Know

inhale
exhale
nostril
nasal passage
mucus
cilia
pharynx
trachea
cartilage
larynx
vocal cord
bronchi (singular: bronchus)
bronchiole
alveoli (singular: alveolus)
capillary

vital capacity
diaphragm
artificial respiration
laryngitis
bronchitis
pneumonia
asthma
emphysema
chronic bronchitis

Tying It Together

1. How does inhaled air differ from exhaled air?
2. (a) For a positive test for carbon dioxide, what solution do you add to the carbon dioxide?
   (b) What colour should the added solution turn to indicate the presence of carbon dioxide?
3. How does oxygen enter and carbon dioxide leave an amoeba?
4. An arctic tern flies over 16 000 km from its summer home in the Arctic to its winter home in the Antarctic. Much of this is done over open water. Describe how the tern's breathing system allows it to fly long distances without stopping for a rest.
5. In as much detail as possible, describe an alveolus.
6. In a short paragraph, describe mouth-to-mouth respiration.
7. Under what conditions would you use mouth-to-mouth respiration?
8. Distinguish clearly among the following three diseases of the breathing system:
   (a) laryngitis
   (b) pneumonia
   (c) common cold

9. What is emphysema?
10. A smoker has what is often called a "smoker's cough." In an advanced state, it is a form of chronic bronchitis. What happens to the breathing system of a person with bronchitis?

Applying Your Knowledge

1. You are caught in a burning building. Knowing what you do about the products of burning and about the need for oxygen to breathe, how would you attempt to make your way to an exit? Explain your answer.
2. Two candles are placed in a jar and lit. One candle is very short, the other is taller. A lid is placed on the jar. Which candle will go out first, the short one or the tall one? The answer to this question has a definite link to question 1.
3. You know that oxygen gas must be dissolved before it enters the cells of the body. The lining of the alveoli in your lungs is moist. Why, then, is it not possible to breathe under water without drowning?
4. Answer *either* the (a) part *or* the (b) part of the following question.
   (a) You are a smoker but your best friend does not smoke. In a paragraph, give your friend reasons why you think smoking is an acceptable thing to do.
   (b) You do not smoke but your best friend does. Give your friend sound reasons why he or she should quit smoking.

Projects for Investigation

1. Find out why face masks and snorkels are not usually permitted in public swimming pools.
2. With your teacher's permission, obtain cow or pig lungs from a local butcher or meat packer. Try to identify the trachea, bronchi, and alveoli. Cut into the lung tissue and examine the clusters of alveoli and blood vessels closely. Make a sketch, including notes about colour and texture.

Digestion: Breaking It Down

Key Ideas

- All organisms require nutrients to carry out their normal activities.
- There are two types of digestion: mechanical digestion and chemical digestion.
- Enzymes break down food so it may be absorbed through the lining of the stomach and intestines.
- Many diseases can affect the digestive system.

What has the following properties?
- It is longer than the longest snake.
- It contains chemicals strong enough to blister paint. Even so, it does not destroy itself.
- Sometimes, it is quite acidic, while other times it is basic.

The answer is your own digestive tract. This chapter is all about what happens to food once it enters an organism. Different organisms have different ways of treating food. All organisms require food to make bodily activities possible.

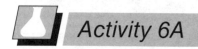

Let's start at the beginning—where food enters the body. What happens to food when it enters the mouth? Back in Chapter 4, you saw that food contains energy. But the body must do some things to this food before it can be used for energy. In this activity, you will investigate what happens in the body to a common food substance—starch. Starchy foods include crackers, bread, and flour.

Problem

What happens to a soda cracker before you swallow it?

Materials

plain, unsalted soda cracker
white bread (a piece about 0.5 cm²)
spatula
watch glass or glass plate
iodine solution in a dropping bottle
starch (flour)
sugar
disposable cup

> **CAUTION** Iodine is a corrosive liquid that will stain the skin, clothing, desk tops, and floors. Take care to avoid spilling. Quickly wipe up any accidental spills, and rinse with water.

Procedure

1. Copy Table 6.1 into your notebook. Use it to record your observations.
2. Place a small quantity of starch on a glass plate or watch glass. Now add one or two drops of iodine solution to the starch. Record any colour change on your table. This change in colour is said to be a positive test for starch.
3. Rinse the glass plate and repeat step 2. This time, use sugar instead of starch. Record the result with sugar in your table. Is starch present?

4. Again, rinse the plate and repeat step 2, first with the white bread and then with a soda cracker. Record the results in your observation table. Is starch present in these foods?
5. Using a disposable cup, rinse out your mouth thoroughly with water. Now generate a small quantity of saliva. (It helps to think of food you like to eat!) Place the saliva on a clean glass plate. Test the saliva for starch.

> **CAUTION** Dispose of your cup when you finish using it.

6. Place a small portion of soda cracker in your mouth and chew it for 5 min. Do *not* swallow it. Put the remains of the cracker and the saliva from your mouth in a clean watch glass. Test with iodine solution for the presence of starch. Record your findings in your table.

Table 6.1 *Establishing a Test for Starch and Discovering What Happens to a Soda Cracker Before it is Swallowed*

SUBSTANCE TESTED	OBSERVATIONS COLOUR OF SUBSTANCE TESTED	
	BEFORE ADDING IODINE SOLUTION	AFTER ADDING IODINE SOLUTION
Starch		
Sugar		
White bread		
Saliva		
Soda cracker (before chewing)		
Soda cracker (after chewing)		

Observations

1. (a) Which of the foods contained starch?
   (b) Which foods did not contain starch?
2. How did you know the foods *did* contain starch?

Questions

1. Using observations from your activity, how would you describe a positive test for starch?
2. What do you think happened to the starch in the soda cracker after it had been chewed for 5 min?
3. What happens chemically to a soda cracker after it has been chewed for 5 min?
4. What does this activity tell us about the nature of chemical digestion as it begins in your mouth?

Challenge

Starch is stored in the seeds, roots, and stems of plants. As a nutrient, it is common in grains, beans, peas, potatoes, and their products. Prepare some specimens to examine under the microscope and use iodine solution to identify the location of starch deposits in foods that you think contain starch. Prepare a report on your findings, and attach labelled drawings of your observations.

The Role of Saliva in Digestion

You know the food you eat is changed once it enters the body. Activity 6A shows that **saliva** plays some part in this change. Quite apart from anything else it might do, saliva serves to wet our food. It actually makes it quite slippery. This makes food easier to swallow.

Saliva also chemically breaks down starch into smaller molecules. In the case of starch, the smaller molecules are sugar. This is one of the most important facts about digestion. The process of digestion serves to break down foods so the products can enter the body cells more easily.

Self-check

1. Describe a positive test for starch.
2. State two functions performed by saliva.
3. Briefly, what is the purpose of digestion?

Getting the Food "In"

All living organisms must take in nutrients. These are contained within the food that organisms eat. Nutrients are used to build new cells and to supply the energy that enables organisms to move. These are only two of the many functions served by nutrients. Nutrients include proteins, carbohydrates, and fats (Table 6.2). Remember that every living cell must have these important substances.

The cell must either obtain nutrients or produce them itself. If it fails to do so, the cell will die. The digestive tract is the pathway taken by the food as it passes through the organism. In most animals, the tract begins at the mouth and ends at the anus.

Single-celled Organisms

The amoeba is a microscopic organism that lives in water. The entire organism consists of a single cell. Because of its small size, there is no need for a special *system* for taking food to all parts of the organism. Some of the necessary nutrients are taken in across the cell membrane. Much of the food, however, is engulfed by the amoeba and "swallowed" whole. A food vacuole is then formed. Digestion takes place inside the vacuole.

Earthworms

Although *much* larger than an amoeba, the common earthworm is still relatively small. Unlike the amoeba, an earthworm is made up of thousands of individual cells. You will recall that each and every living cell must have nutrients to live. It would be impossible for all of the cells to be in contact with food from the outside. To solve the problem, the food enters the worm by means of a digestive tube (Figure 6.1). This tube passes from the front of the worm to the back. Once the food has been broken down, it is absorbed through the walls of the digestive tract and enters the blood vessels. It is then carried by the blood to all the cells of the body. Lobsters, insects, and spiders have digestive tracts similar to, but slightly more complex, than that of the earthworm.

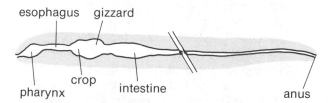

esophagus   gizzard

pharynx   crop   intestine   anus

Figure 6.1 *The digestive tube (tract) of a common earthworm. Where does the food go once it is digested?*

Table 6.2 *Nutrients of the Human Body*

NUTRIENT	POSSIBLE FOOD SOURCE	WHAT ARE THEY USED FOR IN THE BODY?
Carbohydrates	Baked goods, fruit	Source of energy
Proteins	Meat, eggs, dairy products	Source of chemicals used to build muscles and other tissues
Fats	Dairy products, meats	Source of energy; used to build parts of cells; stored in the body
Minerals	Milk, fruit, and vegetables	Used to build bones, teeth, and blood
Vitamins	Fruit and vegetables	Used in many chemical reactions in the body
Water		Used in virtually all life processes; a major part of blood

Frogs

Adult frogs have a digestive system very much like that of humans. Like humans, frogs are omnivores. That is, they eat a variety of foods, both plant and animal. In the tadpole stage, the frog is a herbivore. It only eats plant matter. The length of the **digestive tract**—the tube through which the food passes—is longer in a tadpole than in an adult frog (Figure 6.2). This helps it to do the more difficult job of digesting plants.

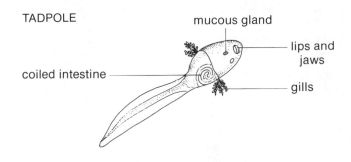

TADPOLE

mucous gland

lips and jaws

coiled intestine

gills

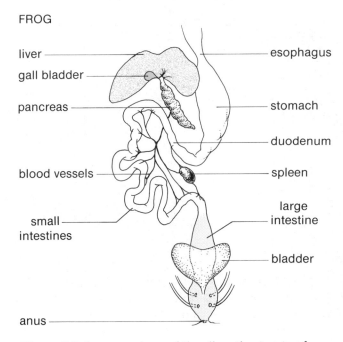

FROG

liver

esophagus

gall bladder

pancreas

stomach

duodenum

blood vessels

spleen

large intestine

small intestines

bladder

anus

Figure 6.2 *A comparison of the digestive tracts of a tadpole and a frog*

Birds

The digestive tract of a typical bird is, in some ways, similar to the earthworm in that both have a crop and a gizzard (Figure 6.3). In most animals, the food passes directly to the digestive tube as soon as it is eaten. Birds have an extra part called the crop. The **crop** is a bag-like swelling in the bird's food passage. It allows the bird to gulp a lot of food quickly without waiting to chew it. Undigested food is stored and moistened in the crop until it can be digested. The food is then passed to the stomach, which has two parts. The first part secretes digestive enzymes. The second part—a muscular sac called the **gizzard**—is a grinding stomach. Birds swallow small, sharp stones that act as teeth. When the muscles of the gizzard contract and relax, the stones help to grind up the food. This action is part of the process of *mechanical digestion*. You will find out more about mechanical digestion in Section 6.3 of this chapter.

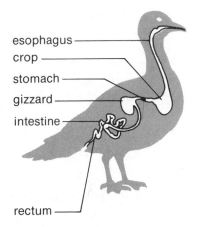

esophagus

crop

stomach

gizzard

intestine

rectum

Figure 6.3 *The digestive tract of a bird. What part or parts of the tract are not found in humans?*

Humans

The digestive tract of the human is similar to the tracts of other complex animals. It is described in detail in Figure 6.4. Organs such as the salivary glands, the liver, the gall bladder, and the pancreas help in digestion. The **digestive system** consists of the digestive tract *plus* the related organs. The functions of these organs will be discussed in Section 6.3.

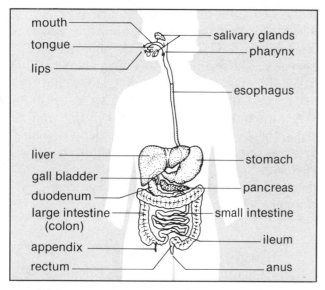

Figure 6.4 *The human digestive system. Which part of the system sometimes becomes infected and has to be removed?*

Self-check

1. What are the two functions served by nutrients taken into the body?
2. Name six nutrients required by humans, and indicate a good source of each one.
3. Why does the amoeba not require a digestive tract?
4. Why is the digestive tract of a tadpole longer than the digestive tract in an adult frog?
5. How is a bird able to survive, even though there are sometimes long intervals between meals?

Breaking Down the Food

Before examining the stages of digestion, consider the following simple example. It shows *why* digestion is necessary. Suppose you try to pass a large object through a small opening. Chances are, it won't fit. It might be necessary to take the object apart in order to get it inside (Figure 6.5). Once through the opening, you might decide to rearrange the parts to make something completely new. You could also use parts already inside to add to your new creation.

Digestion is very much like this example. You must break down the food that you eat. This takes place in the digestive tract. This would be the "outside" in Figure 6.5 (a) and (b), since the food has not yet reached the body cells.

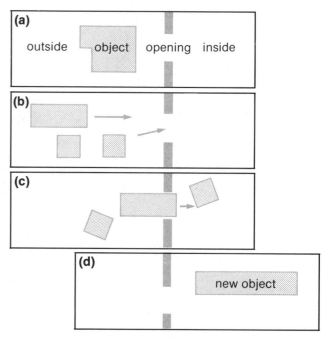

Figure 6.5 *Moving an object from outside to inside through a small opening. This example is similar to what happens when food is digested.*

The broken down food then passes through the lining of the digestive tract and actually enters the blood stream and body cells. See Figure 6.5 (c). The end products of digestion are now really "inside." Here, the products can be rearranged or reassembled to form one of many different chemical compounds found inside the body. See Figure 6.5 (d).

The act of taking food into the mouth is called **ingestion**. At this point, the process of digestion begins. Consider digestion as a two-stage process involving (a) **mechanical digestion**, and (b) **chemical digestion**.

Mechanical Digestion

Mechanical digestion is the *physical* breaking down of food. The process begins in the mouth where the food is first chewed by the teeth and mixed with saliva. A normal tooth is covered by a hard enamel (Figure 6.6). A tooth is very much alive, as you probably know from visits to your dentist! While you chew your food, the **salivary glands** secrete a fluid called saliva. The salivary glands are located under the tongue and in the back corners of the lower jaw. As mentioned earlier, saliva serves to lubricate the food, to make it easier to swallow, and to begin chemical digestion. It also helps to clean your teeth.

Figure 6.6

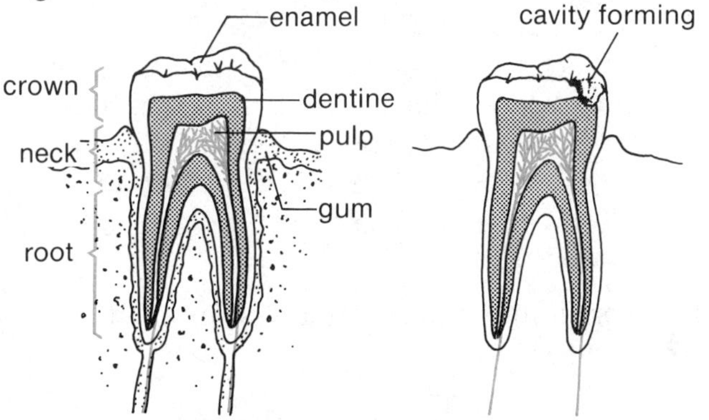

(a) A normal, healthy tooth   (b) An unhealthy tooth

Your tongue plays an important role in moving food around in the mouth for proper chewing. It also helps you swallow. The **epiglottis**, a flap of tissue deep in the throat, also assists in the act of swallowing (Figure 6.7).

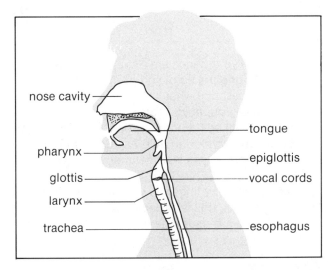

Figure 6.7 *A side view of the mouth and throat, showing the epiglottis. What function does the epiglottis play?*

Challenge

Examine a dentist's model of adult teeth, or look at those of a friend. Prepare a chart to show the number, shape, and possible function of each kind of tooth you observe. Do the shape and function of each kind of tooth suggest a certain kitchen utensil to you? If so, name the utensil on your chart.

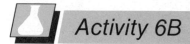

Activity 6B

Problem

What are the functions of the tongue and epiglottis in mechanical digestion?

Materials

Procedure

1. Make sure your hands are clean. Use your fingers to grip the tip of your tongue. Now swallow. Describe what happened.
2. Now locate your epiglottis and larynx. Your epiglottis will be found in the back of your throat above your larynx (Figure 6.7). Looking from the outside, your larynx is sometimes called your Adam's apple (Figure 6.8).
3. Place your index finger on your Adam's apple (your larynx). This is easier to locate if you are a male, since it is usually larger in a male than in a female. Again swallow.

Figure 6.8 *A student with his finger on his "Adam's apple." What exactly is this structure? What does it do?*

Observations

1. Describe the sensation of swallowing while holding the end of your tongue. Was it easy or difficult to swallow?
2. What happened to your Adam's apple as you swallowed?

Questions

1. What is the function of the tongue?
2. What is the role of the epiglottis in swallowing?

What Causes Choking?

You might still be puzzled as to the part played by your epiglottis in the act of swallowing. Look carefully at Figure 6.7. As you can see, the epiglottis covers the top end of the windpipe (**trachea**). As you swallow, the larynx moves up and meets the epiglottis. This closes off the opening to the windpipe as the food passes down your esophagus (food tube). If food did enter your windpipe you would start to cough and possibly choke.

Sometimes when you laugh and try to swallow at the same time, you do choke. This happens because some air is forced from your lungs as you laugh. The escaping air prevents the epiglottis from covering the opening to the windpipe. As a result, some food particles can enter the windpipe causing you to choke.

HELPING A VICTIM OF CHOKING

A person can choke to death if a piece of food goes down "the wrong way." If a person appears to be choking, ask him or her to speak. If the person simply clutches at his or her throat or changes colour, he or she probably *is* choking. *Send someone for help immediately* and then quickly go to work on the victim.

1. Stand behind and wrap your arms around the victim's waist (Figure 6.9).
2. Put your fist against the abdomen, above the navel and below the ribs.
3. Press into the abdomen with a *sudden* strong upward jerk. This forces the air from the lungs and should free the air passage. Repeat several times, if necessary. *Do not hit the patient on the back. This may make things worse.*

For more information, take a good first aid course.

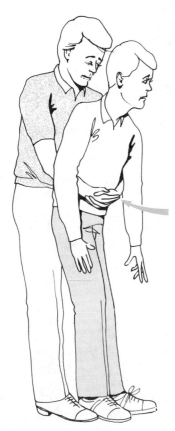

Figure 6.9 *Assisting a choking victim. Send for help before starting the steps used to dislodge something stuck in a person's throat.*

Ideas and Applications

Occasionally, some food and digestive juices are squeezed back up the esophagus. When this occurs, you experience heartburn. It has nothing to do with the heart, but since you often feel the pain near the heart, it is called heartburn. The digestive juices contain acids which produce the burning sensation.

The Role of the Stomach and Intestines

Once the food reaches the stomach, it is mixed with digestive juices released by the cells lining the stomach. This mixing is assisted by the strong muscular walls of the stomach. Food remains in the stomach from one to nine hours, depending on what was eaten (Figure 6.10).

The food is now in a semiliquid state. It is prevented from leaving the stomach by two valves. Each valve is basically a ring of muscle. When the muscular valve (*pyloric sphincter*) at the lower end of the stomach relaxes, and the muscles in the walls of the stomach contract, the food is forced into the small intestine. The **small intestine** is made up of three parts, the duodenum, the jejunum, and the ileum. See Figure 6.4. More will be said about the action of the chemicals (enzymes) added to the food in Section 6.4.

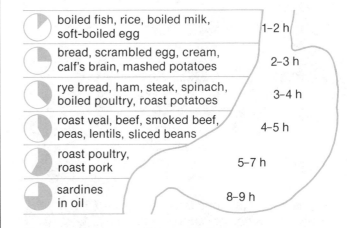

boiled fish, rice, boiled milk, soft-boiled egg	1–2 h	
bread, scrambled egg, cream, calf's brain, mashed potatoes	2–3 h	
rye bread, ham, steak, spinach, boiled poultry, roast potatoes	3–4 h	
roast veal, beef, smoked beef, peas, lentils, sliced beans	4–5 h	
roast poultry, roast pork	5–7 h	
sardines in oil	8–9 h	

Figure 6.10 *Not all kinds of foods are digested in the same length of time. What type of food appears to take the longest to be digested?*

The food is moved along the length of the digestive tract by the action of muscles. Sometimes the food is moved forward. Sometimes it is simply moved back and forth. In the latter case, the food is being mixed further. The two methods of moving and mixing food are shown in Figure 6.11. The act of moving food forward—called **peristalsis**—requires the co-ordinated use of two bands of muscle, circular and longitudinal. When a circular muscle contracts, it squeezes the food and moves it backward or forward. At the same time, the longitudinal muscles relax. This allows the squeezed part to become *longer*. Think of what happens when you squeeze a lump of putty. It becomes longer and thinner. When a longitudinal muscle contracts, it makes the intestine *shorter*.

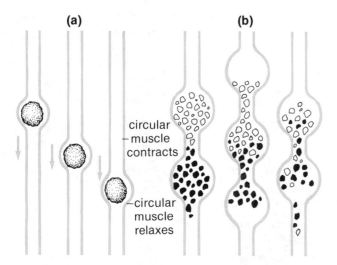

(a)   **(b)**

circular muscle contracts

circular muscle relaxes

Figure 6.11 *In* **(a)***, food is moved forward in the digestive tract by peristalsis. In* **(b)***, the food is simply moved back and forth. The moving and mixing is aided by the muscles of the intestine.*

Here are the steps involved in moving food along the intestinal tract by peristalsis. The main muscle band used for this is the circular muscle.

Step 1. A section of circular muscle along the tract relaxes.

Step 2. Immediately behind it, a section of circular muscle contracts.

Step 3. As a result, the food in the tract moves in the direction of the relaxed muscle. That is, it moves forward.

Step 4. These first three steps are repeated many times along the digestive tract. The movement looks rather like waves on the surface of water.

Self-check

1. What is mechanical digestion?
2. What function does the tongue play in the swallowing of food?
3. (a) What causes choking?
   (b) How can you help a victim of choking?
4. In your own words, describe the process of peristalsis.

Ideas and Applications

Vomiting is peristalsis in reverse. An irritation somewhere in your digestive system can cause an intense series of muscle contractions, moving materials back to your mouth. Your air passages close, and the powerful muscles of your stomach wall and your lower abdomen then force out the irritating substances.

Chemical Digestion

Let's begin the study of chemical digestion with a lab activity. In Activity 6C you will make an "artificial intestine," and place starch in it. The "artificial intestine" will be made from dialysis tubing. See Figure 6.12. You may recall from your Grade 9 study of osmosis that this tubing allows some substances to diffuse through it, but not others. You will recall from Activity 6A that iodine solution can be used to test for starch.

Challenge

Many large meals are preceded by an appetizer. Appetizers serve to "excite" the digestive system, getting it ready for the meal to follow. The stomach muscles are stimulated to contract, mixing the stomach fluid. Find out the ingredients of several appetizers. Which ingredients do they have in common? What is the significance of the digestive system's response to such compounds?

Activity 6C

Problem

Can starch pass through an artificial intestine?

Materials

starch solution
iodine solution in a dropping bottle
dialysis tubing
beaker (400 mL)

Procedure

1. Copy Table 6.3 into your notebook and use it to record your observations.

> **CAUTION** Iodine is a corrosive liquid that will stain the skin, clothing, desk tops, and floors. Take care to avoid spilling. Quickly wipe up any accidental spills, and rinse with water.

2. Soak the dialysis tubing in lukewarm water for several minutes.
3. Once the membrane is soft, tie a knot in one end of the tubing. Be careful not to rip the tubing.
4. With the knot firmly in place, place a quantity of starch solution into the open end of the tubing. It is much easier if a partner can assist you.
5. Hold the tubing upright so as not to spill the starch. Then tie a knot in the open end of the tubing (Figure 6.12). Try to avoid trapping air bubbles in the sac. You should now have a small "sausage," knotted at both ends, containing the starch solution.
6. Rinse the "artificial intestine" under a tap.
7. Place the tube in the beaker and fill the beaker with lukewarm tap water until it covers the tube.
8. Add enough drops of iodine solution to the water in the beaker to give it a light brown colour.

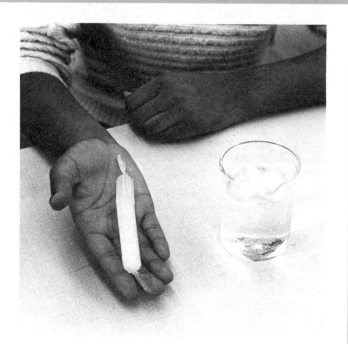

Figure 6.12 *How is this sausagelike tube similar to the digestive tract in your body?*

Observations

(see Table 6.3)

1. Make sure to record any observations right after adding the iodine solution to the water.
2. After 20 min, note any changes that have taken place in the colours of the solutions both inside and outside of the tube.
3. If possible, record any observations made the following day.

Questions

1. If the membrane used had been made of a different material, would you expect the results to be the same? Explain.
2. Describe a simple activity to see if sugar will pass through the kind of membrane used in Activity 6C. What result would you expect?
3. How might this activity be related to a human digestive tract?
4. What conclusions can you draw about the movement of starch across an artificial intestine?

Table 6.3 *Does Starch Pass Through an Artificial Intestine?*

	INITIAL COLOUR	COLOUR AFTER 20 MIN	COLOUR THE FOLLOWING DAY	OTHER CHANGES
Starch solution inside the tubing				
Iodine solution outside the tubing				

The Action of Enzymes

You will recall that starch is broken down into smaller parts by the action of saliva. In addition to lubricating your food, saliva contains a special substance called an enzyme. It is this enzyme, called *amylase*, that breaks down the starch. As shown in Activity 6C, food breakdown is necessary. Without it, food could not pass through the walls of the intestine and into the blood stream.

An **enzyme**, then, is a complex chemical that breaks down a large chemical molecule (for example, starch) into smaller molecules (for example, sugars). The enzyme itself is not used up in the reaction. How do these special proteins called enzymes work? An explanation is shown in Figure 6.13.

Enzymes are very specific in their action. A fat-digesting enzyme, for example, can only work on a fat. A protein-digesting enzyme can only break down proteins.

Enzymes are also special in that they can only work under very specific conditions. For example, if the body temperature rises much above the normal body temperature, enzymes do not work very well. If an enzyme becomes overheated, it changes its shape. Then it can no longer fit the molecule it used to break down.

If you eat too much "rich food" you sometimes end up with an excess of stomach acid. This is commonly called *acid indigestion*. There are many products on the market that work to neutralize the extra stomach acids. Each enzyme can only function in an acid of a very specific concentration.

Figure 6.13 *A model of an enzyme. The two shapes fit together like a lock and key. In a similar way, an enzyme fits a molecule of food and helps to break it apart.*

Table 6.4 *The Action of Some Digestive Enzymes*

WHERE THE ENZYME WORKS	NAME OF THE ENZYME	WHAT THE ENZYME WORKS ON	PRODUCTS	pH RANGE
Mouth	Amylase	Starch	A type of sugar	5.6-7.6
Stomach	Pepsin	Protein	Parts of proteins	1.5-8.5
Stomach	Lipase	Fats (lipids)	An alcohol and fatty acids	
Small intestine	Amylase	Starch	A type of sugar	5.8-8.5
Small intestine	Lipase	Fats (lipids)	An alcohol and fatty acids	
Small intestine	Trypsin	Protein	Simpler protein parts	
Small intestine	Erepsin	Protein parts	Amino acids	
Small intestine	Maltase	Maltose	Simple sugars	
Small intestine	Lactase	Lactose	Simple sugars	

The concentration of acid is measured on a scale from 0 to 14. The number 0 represents the *highest* concentration of acid. The number 7 is the neutral point. Above number 7, the solutions are basic or alkaline. The scale is called the pH scale. You will learn more about the pH scale in Chapter 18. Table 6.4 shows some of the range of enzyme actions in the digestive tract. It also shows the pH of that part of the digestive tract.

The Action of Bile

Bile is a green-coloured liquid produced in the liver. Bile is *not* an enzyme. It is stored in a sac called the gall bladder (Figure 6.4). When bile is required, it passes down a tube called the **bile duct** and enters the small intestine. Here the bile serves to separate clusters of fat molecules. It works rather like dishwashing detergent loosening and removing fat from a greasy frying pan. Once the clumps of fat molecules have been separated from one another by the bile, a fat enzyme goes to work. The molecules are broken down further into the chemicals that make up the fat molecules.

Self-check

1. Why does food have to be digested?
2. In your own words, describe how an enzyme works.
3. What happens to an enzyme when it is heated to a high temperature?
4. How is the artificial intestine in Activity 6C like a real intestine?
5. (a) What is meant by the term pH?
   (b) How is this term related to digestion?
6. Use Table 6.4 to answer the following questions.
   (a) What are the two products of the action of the enzyme lipase in the small intestine?
   (b) What enzyme in the small intestine acts on protein to produce amino acids? Amino acids are the chemical parts that go together to make proteins.

The Absorption of Nutrients

Food has been broken down by enzymes. Now the end products are ready to be absorbed into the blood stream. Compared with the original nutrients—fats, carbohydrates, and proteins— the products of digestion are simpler and smaller molecules. At this point, before being absorbed, these chemicals are in a *dissolved* form. **Absorption** is the act of taking these products of digestion and transporting them across the membranes of the cells that line the small intestine. Most, but not all, of the absorption of digested nutrients takes place in the small intestine. On the other side of the membranes, the nutrients pass into the blood vessels which carry them to all of the living cells of the body.

The intestines are well equipped to absorb nutrients. They are very long. The small intestine of an adult human is about 6.5 m long! This means that there will be a large surface area through which the nutrients can be absorbed. The walls of the intestine are folded or wrinkled (Figure 6.14). This further increases the surface area available for absorption. The surface of the intestine is lined with millions of tiny finger-like projections called **villi** (singular: **villus**). A single villus is shown in Figure 6.15.

Figure 6.14 *Cross sections of a tube and the digestive tract. Notice how much more surface area there is in the digestive tract.*

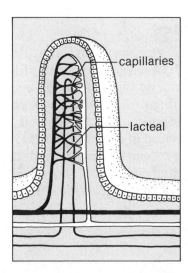

Figure 6.15 *A simple villus. The many blood vessels will help carry the digested food to all parts of the body.*

The villi increase the surface area for absorption still further. The intestines are lined with many blood vessels. These blood vessels will carry the nutrients to the cells. Intestines also have many fat-collecting vessels called *lacteals*. Some quite large molecules can enter the lacteal vessels. These vessels eventually lead into the larger blood vessels near the heart.

While digestion is taking place, water serves as a good fluid for mixing the enzymes with the food. But once digestion has occurred, much of the water is absorbed and retained by the body for future use. Most of the absorption of water takes place in the **large intestine**. It is here that the waste end products of digestion—often things that the body can't digest, such as fibre— are made more solid. The waste is then passed from the body as **feces**. With all of the steps and chemical processes taking place, it's just as well that you don't have to think about digestion while food is taking its fascinating journey through the body!

Challenge

You have learned that digestion can take several hours depending upon the food eaten. But it is common knowledge that a person who drinks a quantity of alcohol can become drunk in a matter of minutes. How can this be explained?

Self-check

1. Where in the digestive tract does most of the absorption of nutrients take place?
2. It has been said that not all nutrients are completely broken down before entering the blood stream. If these molecules are not completely broken down, where do they enter the blood stream and where do they end up?
3. List three features of the intestine that make it an ideal structure for absorbing nutrients.

Diseases That Attack the Digestive System

There are many disorders or diseases that effect all parts of the digestive system. Remember that the digestive system includes organs such as the liver and pancreas in addition to the organs of the digestive tract.

Ulcers

You have probably heard the expression, "It's enough to give you an ulcer." The speaker is usually referring to some irritating, stressful situation. For all that we hear about ulcers, they are still poorly understood. In the simplest terms, an **ulcer** is a crater-like depression in the skin or lining of the digestive tract. It results from the death of cells caused by a variety of factors.

Ulcers of the digestive tract are often called *peptic ulcers*. Many of the digestive juices secreted by cells associated with the digestive system are very acidic. If this acid accumulates, it can, in some cases, eat away the cells lining the tract. This produces the ulcers. The troublesome part is that doctors do not always know what causes the ulcers. In some cases they are related to diet, while in other cases they are brought on by stress. Heredity may also play some part in whether or not a person is prone to develop ulcers. Ulcers are often very painful. A victim of ulcers can gain some relief from the pain by taking antacids and eating very bland foods. But the underlying cause must be dealt with by doctors.

Gallstones

As the name suggests, **gallstones** are associated with the gall bladder. The **gall bladder** acts as a holding tank for bile salts which are produced in the liver (Figure 6.16). Over a period of time, a stone consisting of bile pigments and calcium salts can develop in the gall bladder (Figure 6.17). If this stone becomes stuck in the neck of the bladder, it can prevent the bile from passing down the duct to the small intestine.

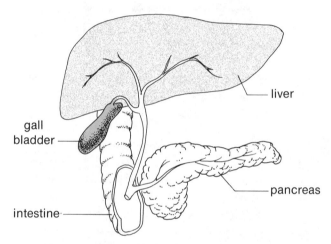

Figure 6.16 *The relationship between the liver and the gall bladder. The gall bladder stores bile salts produced in the liver.*

Figure 6.17 *Gallstones, sometimes found in the gall bladder, develop over a long period of time.*

If the stone is small enough, it can be carried along with the bile to the small intestine and out of the body. However, if the stone becomes stuck and does not move, an operation is often needed. A doctor will inject a chemical into the veins to help pinpoint the specific location of the stone. Once the stone is located, an operation is performed to remove it.

Cirrhosis of the Liver

The liver is the largest gland in the body. It carries out many chemical functions. The liver is one of our essential organs. **Cirrhosis**, a serious liver condition, is most commonly caused by the consumption of large quantities of alcohol over a long period of time. It can also be caused by poor diet or by an infection leading to hepatitis (see below).

The symptoms are the same regardless of the cause. They include nausea, weight loss, general weakness, and abdominal pain. Since all of the symptoms can also be caused by other diseases, doctors carry out a number of tests to determine whether the person actually has cirrhosis. These tests include X rays, blood tests, a general physical examination, and a minor operation called a biopsy. During a liver biopsy, a surgeon will remove small sections of liver tissue for further examination.

Treatment for cirrhosis includes maintaining a well-balanced diet which is rich in vitamins and protein, plenty of rest, and no alcohol. Given the chance, the liver can repair itself naturally. But the process takes a long time.

Hepatitis

Hepatitis is another disease of the liver caused by a number of agents. Some of the major causes of the condition are bacteria or viruses, parasites, alcohol, and drugs. Symptoms of the disease include an inflammation of the liver itself, considerable pain in the abdominal region, and jaundice. The skin of a person suffering from jaundice has a pale yellow colour. This is caused by higher than normal levels of certain fatty chemicals in the blood.

Depending upon the cause and severity of the disease, the treatment for hepatitis varies. Most patients recover completely. But in severe cases, hepatitis can lead to cirrhosis of the liver.

Challenge

Prepare a table of substances and activities that affect your respiratory and digestive systems. The substances and activities should include the following: diet (select specific foods), smoking, playing a wind instrument, exercise, type of job. For each substance and activity, state the negative or positive effect it would have on the respiratory and digestive systems.

Self-check

1. With a dictionary, find the meaning of the terms *symptom, diagnosis,* and *treatment*. These terms are often used when discussing diseases.
2. A person has a flushed appearance with several prominent blood vessels clearly visible on the face. This is one of the symptoms of cirrhosis of the liver.
   (a) What are three other symptoms of the disease?
   (b) What three tests might a doctor perform to determine for certain that this individual has cirrhosis?
3. What treatment might a doctor prescribe for a peptic ulcer?

Chapter Objectives

Words to Know

saliva
digestive tract
crop
gizzard
digestive system
ingestion
mechanical digestion
chemical digestion
salivary gland
epiglottis
trachea
small intestine
peristalsis
enzyme

bile
bile duct
absorption
villi (singular: villus)
large intestine
feces
ulcer
gallstone
gall bladder
cirrhosis
hepatitis

Tying It Together

1. What happens to the starch molecules in a soda cracker that has been chewed in the mouth for several minutes?
2. In a positive test for starch, what colour should the iodine solution turn?
3. Name two good sources of protein in the diet.
4. Name two good sources of carbohydrates in the diet.
5. The amoeba does not have a need for a special system for taking in food. Explain why.
6. Birds have an extra part in the digestive tract that is not found in humans. Name this part and explain its function.
7. What is the role of the tongue in digestion?

8. What name is given to the process that moves food forward in the digestive tract?
9. Why is the action of an enzyme similar to the action of a lock and key?
10. State the end products of digestion for each of the following:
    (a) a carbohydrate (such as starch)
    (b) a protein (such as cheese)
    (c) a fat (such as bacon fat)
11. (a) Name four diseases that attack the digestive system.
    (b) Choose one disease and explain how it affects the digestive system.

Applying Your Knowledge

1. Saliva is a basic substance. Why does saliva stop digesting starch once the starchy food is swallowed and reaches the stomach?
2. Ulcers are crater-like depressions that develop into open sores. They are sometimes found in the stomach. Since the digestive juices contain acids, find out why more sores do not develop on the lining of the stomach.
3. Using your knowledge of digestion, solve the following mystery:

Case #1745—More Than a Bad Case of Indigestion
Inspector I. Gotcha of the Everytown Police Department arrived at the scene of the crime at 23:00. The victim, a woman approximately twenty-eight years old had been killed by a single shot from a .45 calibre revolver. None of the neighbours reported hearing a loud sound. An autopsy was performed on Ms. X at approximately midnight. Although dishes in Ms. X's apartment contained the remains of a roast pork meal, there was no evidence of any remains of pork in Ms. X's stomach.

Early the following morning, a male friend of the victim, a Mr. Y, was brought in for questioning. He admitted that he had been with Ms. X the day before, but that, following dinner at Ms. X's apartment, he had returned home and had spent the rest of the evening reading. Unfortunately, he did not have a good alibi since he had not spoken to anyone since he left Ms. X's place.

Further questioning revealed that they had eaten dinner together at 20:00 and that he had left her apartment at 21:00 sharp.

The above was one line of questioning that Inspector Gotcha pursued. Based on this, however, would you judge Mr. X's story to be true or false? Use the biology you have learned in this chapter to attempt to solve the crime.

Projects for Investigation

1. Find out what causes the following diseases of the digestive system: diabetes, appendicitis, and diarrhea.
2. Doctors often speak of the need to have enough fibre in your diet. Much of this fibre is undigestible cellulose, a substance found in plant cells. What does this fibre do and why is it important? Since it cannot be digested, what happens to it?
3. On June 6, 1822, at a trading post near the junction of Lake Huron and Lake Michigan, a young Canadian fur trader named Alexis St. Martin was accidentally shot in the side. Dr. William Beaumont, the surgeon at a nearby American fort, was summoned to help St. Martin. St. Martin survived, but the wound left a permanent opening 5 cm wide leading through the skin and layers of muscle into his stomach. Find out how this accident was responsible for much of what we now know about the workings of the human stomach.

Circulation

Key Ideas

- The transport system of organisms serves many important functions.
- The circulatory system consists of the heart, blood vessels, and blood.
- Blood pressure is dependent on a number of factors.
- The kidneys are part of the excretory system.
- All body systems are essential for the proper functioning of an organism.

C hances are, the ambulance in the opening photo is taking a heart attack victim to a hospital. Every minute counts. Heart attack plays no favourites. It's the number one cause of death in Canada. More Canadians die from heart attack than they do from traffic accidents. Why is the heart so necessary to life? What do the heart and circulation do for you? What can go wrong? This chapter will provide the answers to these and other questions. Let's consider first why organisms (including humans) need some kind of internal transport system.

Why Are Transport Systems Needed?

All living organisms require energy to live, to move, and to breathe. The *transport systems* of organisms help to provide this energy. But the transport system does other things as well. Some of the functions are as follows:

1. Every organism needs water for chemical reactions to occur inside the body. The transport system moves this water to the places where it is needed. Our blood is made up mainly of water.
2. The transport system serves to move the nutrients from digested food to all of the living cells of the body.
3. The transport system carries oxygen to the cells where it combines with chemicals such as glucose. The result is the release of energy for all body activities.
4. The transport system carries waste products to sites where they are removed from the organism. The wastes include such things as carbon dioxide and urine.
5. In some organisms, the transport system carries **hormones**. Hormones are the "chemical organizers" of the body. An example of a hormone is epinephrine, which is often called adrenalin. This chemical lets you respond very quickly when you find yourself in a dangerous situation.
6. Included in most transport systems are cells or chemicals that protect the body from infection. In humans, for example, the transport system contains white blood cells. These cells engulf invading bacteria. They also produce antibodies, which are chemicals that neutralize bacteria. Finally, some white blood cells produce antitoxins that react with poison products produced by bacteria to make them harmless.

7. Blood also contains a protein that assists in the making of blood clots. Blood clots speed up the healing of wounds.

A transport system in an organism usually consists of three parts. The first part is a fluid in which the transport takes place. This fluid is the blood. The second part is a set of vessels that contain the fluid. These vessels are the blood vessels. The third part of the system consists of one or more pumps that move the fluid around the body. These pumps are the hearts. Let's first examine the fluid component, blood.

Ideas and Applications

The body protects itself in several ways. For example, antibodies, produced by the body's immune system, kill invading microbes such as bacteria and viruses. Sometimes the antibodies coat the surfaces of these organisms and make them easier for the white blood cells to identify and destroy. If the body's immune system is attacked by the AIDS virus, the body is no longer able to protect itself against many life-threatening diseases. The AIDS virus itself does not kill. It does, however, make it easier for other bacteria and viruses to kill.

Blood: A Very Special Fluid

The composition of **blood** will vary from organism to organism. The features of blood that follow are those of human blood.

Blood consists of both liquids and solids. To the unaided eye, blood appears to be completely liquid. But with the aid of a compound microscope, you can see solid parts. These solid parts are the cells.

Blood plasma is the straw-coloured liquid portion of the blood. It is over 90% water. The remaining 10% of the liquid is made up mainly of three parts. The blood proteins make up the first part. These proteins enable the blood to form clots. The serum proteins make up the second part. These serum proteins fight infections. Ions (charged particles) of chemical elements such as calcium, magnesium, and chlorine make up the third part. These chemicals serve very specific roles in the body. Calcium, for example, is used to build bones and teeth. Blood plasma also serves to transport carbon dioxide, oxygen, food, and body wastes.

The solid part of our blood consists of red and white cells and platelets (Figure 7.1). The **red blood cells** contain the protein, **hemoglobin**. When someone is pale and tired, it

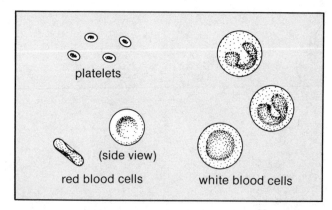

Figure 7.1 *Types of human blood*

could be due to a lack of iron in the blood. Iron makes up a small but very important part of each hemoglobin molecule. The iron is situated in the molecule of hemoglobin like a hub in the centre of a wheel (Figure 7.2). Oxygen from the lining of the lungs becomes attached to the hemoglobin. In this way, oxygen is carried in the blood vessels to all parts of the body.

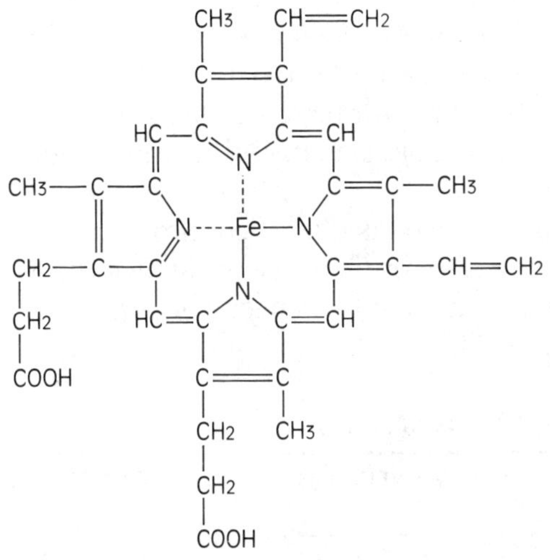

Figure 7.2 *A part of a hemoglobin molecule. Notice the presence of iron (Fe) in the middle of the group.*

The **white blood cells** are larger than the red and vary in size, shape, and function. There are several types of white blood cells. These include the disease-fighting *leucocytes* and *lymphocytes*.

The smallest cells found in the blood are the **platelets**. They are so named because they look like tiny plates. Chemicals are released by the platelets when the skin is cut and the platelets rupture. These chemicals help to form blood clots. A blood clot on the surface of the skin helps to stem the flow of blood and thus reduce blood loss.

Blood normally travels in vessels inside the body. But like pipes in a plumbing system, the vessels leak. There is a purpose for this leaking. Leucocytes, for example, squeeze out between the cells lining the walls of some of the tiny blood vessels. Red blood cells cannot do this. In the body cavity, leucocytes engulf (swallow) bacteria. But leucocytes also protect you when you cut yourself. You have undoubtedly seen pus form near such a cut. This pus contains leucocytes that died while "battling" an infection. Table 7.1 gives a comparison of the properties of types of blood cells.

Table 7.1 *Properties and Functions of Types of Blood Cells*

| PROPERTY | RED BLOOD CELLS | WHITE BLOOD CELLS | | PLATELETS |
		LEUCOCYTES	LYMPHOCYTES	
Where they are produced	In marrow of long bones	In marrow of long bones	In spleen and lymph glands	In marrow of long bones
Cells in 1 mL of blood	5×10^{12}	6×10^9	2×10^9	2.5×10^{11}
Relative size	Small	Largest	Large	Smallest
Function	Carrying oxygen to all living cells	Engulfing bacteria, etc.	Making antibodies to fight germs	Helping in blood clotting
Presence of cell nucleus	Absent	Present	Present	Absent

Problem

What does human blood look like under a microscope?

Materials

prepared blood slides
compound microscope

Procedure

1. Examine a prepared slide of human blood under a microscope. Look at it first under low power. Then turn to medium or high power.

Observations

1. Describe, using diagrams, the cells you see with the aid of a microscope.
2. Compare the cells with those in Figure 7.1.
3. Which type of cell appears to be the most numerous?
4. Which part of the cell appeared to be stained? The stain used to prepare these slides is called Wright's blood stain.

Questions

1. Based on your observations, what types of cells are present in human blood?

Types of Human Blood

When someone requires blood after a serious accident, a doctor cannot give the victim just any type of blood. The victim must receive a type of blood that the body will accept. This situation is similar in organ transplant operations. Sometimes the patient will reject a donated organ if the blood and tissue types are not matched exactly.

If an unacceptable type of blood is given, this leads to a massive clotting of the blood. This can result in the death of the patient. Although hospitals today will test your blood before any kind of operation, it is useful to know your own blood type.

Human blood is classified into four kinds or *types*: A, B, AB, or O. Table 7.2 shows the type of blood you can give to someone or receive from someone. This depends on your blood type.

Table 7.2 *Types of Human Blood*

BLOOD TYPE	CAN RECEIVE BLOOD FROM	CAN DONATE BLOOD TO
Type O	Type O only	Types O, A, B, and AB
Type A	Types O and A	Types A and AB
Type B	Types O and B	Types B and AB
Type AB	Types O, A, B, and AB	Type AB

Self-check

1. What are four important functions performed by blood?
2. Distinguish clearly between a red blood cell and a platelet.
3. List three things contained in blood plasma.
4. Use Table 7.2 to answer the following questions.
   (a) Why is Type O blood often called the **universal donor**?
   (b) Why is Type AB blood often called the **universal receptor**?

Every year, over 700 000 Canadians donate blood at over 8000 clinics across Canada. Hospitals across Canada receive over 6000 units per day of this donated blood. The organization that makes all this possible is the Canadian Red Cross Society. The Red Cross collects, tests, and stores blood and blood products. All the blood comes from voluntary donations. It is processed by the Red Cross into more than 20 specialized blood products. Before being processed, the blood is screened for type, as well as for viruses such as AIDS and Hepatitis B, and bacteria such as those that cause syphilis.

The Canadian Red Cross Society gets about 80% of its funding from provincial governments and about 20% from the federal government. But without people—the blood donors themselves and thousands of volunteers—this organization could not continue to help save lives and support medical research.

Ideas and Applications

An average human male adult contains about 5 L of blood. An average female adult contains about 3.3 L.

Blood Vessels

Blood is carried around the body by means of blood vessels. All of these vessels together make up the **circulatory system**. A simplified diagram of the entire system appears in Figure 7.3. The vessels carrying blood *away* from the heart are called **arteries**. Those carrying blood *toward* the heart are called **veins**. Smaller arteries are called *arterioles*, while smaller veins are called *venules*.

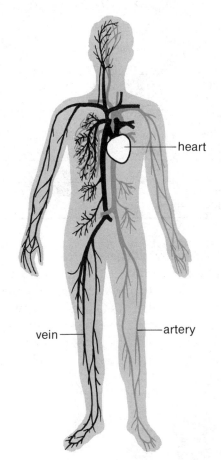

Figure 7.3 *The human circulatory system. Arteries carry blood away from the heart, and veins return blood to the heart.*

Table 7.3 *A Comparison of Blood Vessels*

POINT OF COMPARISON	ARTERY	VEIN	CAPILLARY
Diagram (cross section)	artery	vein	capillary
Flexibility	Very elastic	Not as elastic as the arteries	Not very elastic
Direction of blood flow	Away from the heart	Toward the heart	From a small artery to a small vein
Valves	Not present	Present	Not present
Thickness of walls of vessels	Quite thick	Thinner than in the arteries	Only one cell thick

In terms of what they do, the tiny **capillaries** are probably the most important vessels (Figure 7.4). The exchange of gases and the transfer of nutrients take place between the network of capillaries and the surrounding body cells. The features of the three major types of blood vessels are summarized in Table 7.3.

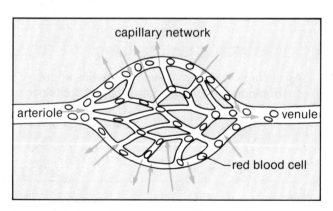

Figure 7.4 *A capillary network. This is where nutrients and gases are exchanged.*

What Happens When You Are Cut?

Usually, when you are cut, the blood oozes out of the wound. This means that you have cut a vein. If, however, the blood comes out in spurts, then you have cut an artery. Think about this for a moment. The blood flowing *away* from the heart is under pressure. Thus, it is not surprising that the blood spurts out each time the heart contracts. Fortunately for us, the arteries are rarely close to the surface of the skin and tend to be cut only in serious accidents. The blood in the veins, on the other hand, is making its way back to the heart. It is under less pressure. As a result, the blood simply oozes out when you cut a vein.

The blood in the veins flows back to the heart so slowly that there is a danger of the blood flowing *backward*, away from the heart. To prevent this, there are **valves** present in the veins (Figure 7.5). The valves are like pockets lining the veins. As long as the blood flows toward the heart, the pockets remain collapsed. But when the blood flows backward, the pockets swell with blood and prevent the backflow.

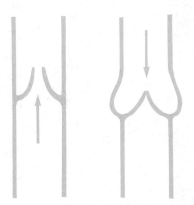

Figure 7.5 *Valves in the veins. They prevent blood from flowing in the wrong direction.*

Self-check

1. Distinguish between an artery and a vein with respect to both structure and function.
2. Why are capillaries often said to be the most important blood vessels in the body?
3. (a) Which of the three types of blood vessels have valves in them?
   (b) Why does this type of blood vessel have valves?
4. What should you do if you find someone with a cut on their arm? What additional information would you like to have in order to answer this question?

The Heart: The Body's Pumping Station

The Heart of a Fish

Not all organisms have a heart like that of a human. Not all organisms require such a complicated heart to live where they live. In animals such as freshwater fish, the blood flows through the heart once and then on through the gills. In passing through the gills, the blood is forced through a number of tiny blood vessels. It is at this point that the exchange of gases takes place. Much of the pressure developed by the contraction of the heart is lost as the blood passes through the gills. Finally, the blood flows, rather slowly, to all parts of the body (Figure 7.6).

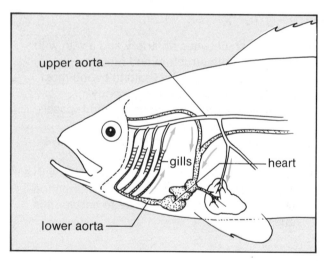

Figure 7.6 *The heart of a fish. How does it differ from a human heart?*

The Human Heart and Circulatory System

The human circulatory system requires a more elaborate pumping system for a variety of reasons. First of all, within rather narrow limits, the human body temperature is kept constant (about 37°C). We are said to be warm-blooded creatures. The important point, however, is that the body temperature does not change very much. Our bodies have to work hard to maintain this constant temperature. This requires moving blood around the body to assist in cooling in hot weather or to help keep us warm in winter. We also need a good pumping system to maintain normal blood pressure. This pressure is necessary to filter the blood through our kidneys and exchange gases in the lungs. For these and other reasons, the human heart must be very efficient.

The human heart is really a double pump (Figure 7.7). The first pump—the right side of the heart—pumps blood through the lungs where oxygen and carbon dioxide are exchanged.

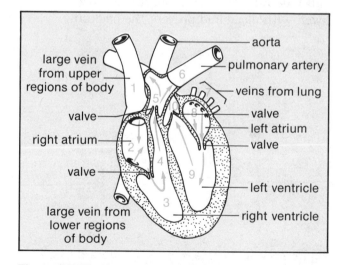

Figure 7.7 *The human heart. Trace the path of blood through the heart. Why do the ventricles have to be much larger than the atria?*

The second pump—the left side of the heart—pumps the freshly oxygenated blood (from the lungs) to all parts of the body. If we only had one pump, the pressure of the blood would simply be too low after the blood passed through the lungs. The second pump is needed to force the blood through all of the body organs. Humans are not the only organisms with a heart that is a double pump. The same heart structure is found in all mammals such as dogs, cats, and elephants. Birds also have the same kind of heart.

Now look again at Figure 7.7. The parts of the heart and the adjoining blood vessels are numbered. The numbers refer to the path taken by the blood as it passes through the heart. Note the presence of valves at four key points in the heart. Although these valves differ in structure, they all serve the same function. They prevent the blood from flowing back into the chamber it just left. Trace the blood flow through the heart and the lungs. The **pulmonary artery** carries blood that is low in oxygen. This makes the pulmonary artery unlike all other arteries in the body. All other arteries carry blood that is rich with oxygen. Like all other arteries, however, the pulmonary artery does carry blood away from the heart.

As you can see from Figure 7.7 and 7.8, the blood makes *two* trips through the heart for every *one* complete trip around the body.

Figure 7.8 is a simplified diagram of circulation in a human being. The exchange of gases and digested foods, etc., takes place in a capillary network. Here, the walls of the capillaries are only one cell thick.

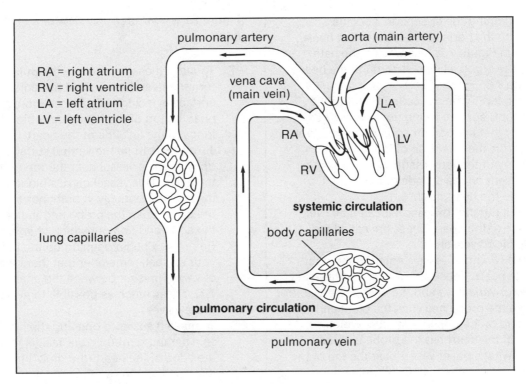

Figure 7.8 *Simplified diagram of human circulation*

Problem

How is the heart of a mammal designed to enable it to pump blood to all parts of the body?

Materials

fresh mammalian heart (for example, sheep, pig, or calf)

dissecting instruments (scalpel, scissors, probes, and forceps)

dissecting tray (with wax coating)

CAUTION When using dissecting instruments, always make cuts away from your body. The scalpel is very sharp.

Procedure

1. Before beginning the dissection, become familiar with the parts of the mammalian heart as shown in Figure 7.7. Also, review the path taken by the blood as it flows through the heart. See Figure 7.8.
2. Place the heart in the dissecting tray with the ventral (front) surface facing you (Figure 7.9). Remember that the part on your *left* as you look at the heart is the *right* side of the heart.
3. Remove any of the fatty tissue (white in colour) that is present on the outside of the heart. Do not cut into the heart itself.
4. There are a number of vessels located all over the surface of the heart. These are called the **coronary blood vessels**.
5. Locate the two main vessels entering the right side of the heart. These are two very large veins, the *superior vena cava* and the *inferior vena cava*. Take the probe and stick the blunt end into the end of the uppermost tube. Which chamber of the heart has the probe entered?
6. The somewhat smaller vessel near the top of the ventral surface of the heart is the **pulmonary artery**. This branches off and carries blood to the lungs.

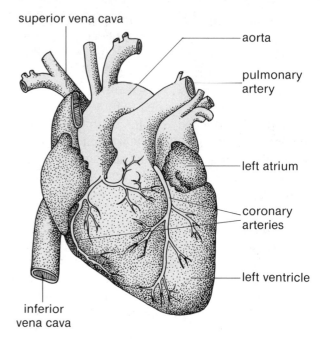

Figure 7.9 *A ventral (front) view of a mammalian heart*

superior vena cava

aorta

pulmonary artery

left atrium

coronary arteries

left ventricle

inferior vena cava

7. To make it easier to locate the **pulmonary veins**, turn the heart over so that the dorsal (back) surface is facing you. The pulmonary veins, near the top of the heart, carry blood from the lungs to the left side of the heart.
8. Turn the heart so the ventral surface is facing up. The large vessel near the top of the heart is the **aorta**. This vessel carries blood away from the heart. Eventually, it branches to all parts of the body. Push the probe into the open end of the aorta and find out which chamber it enters.
9. Before you begin opening up the heart with your scalpel, remember that there are a number of valves present between the chambers (Figure 7.7). Try as much as possible to *avoid* cutting these valves.
10. To make it easier to open up the heart, think of it as a hamburger bun. Your task is to cut around the edge of the heart (the "bun") in such a way that you can remove the top (ventral) walls of the four chambers of the heart. If you do this you will expose the insides of all four chambers.

11. Now compare your dissection with Figure 7.7. Compare also the relative thickness of the walls of the atria with those of the ventricles.
12. Note the number of flaps of tissue making up the valve between the right atrium and ventricle. Compare this with the valve between the left atrium and ventricle. Examine the other valves present in the heart.

Observations

1. How does the thickness of the walls of the atria compare with that of the ventricles? Suggest a reason why there is such a difference.
2. Compare the thickness of the muscular walls of the two ventricles. If there is a difference, suggest a reason why this is so.

Questions

1. Suggest a possible function for the coronary blood vessels.
2. In general, what functions do the valves perform in the heart?
3. Suggest a function for the several fibrelike structures that are attached to the valves separating the atria and the ventricles.
4. How is the heart designed to enable it to pump blood to all parts of the body?

Self-check

1. Why does a human require a more elaborate pumping system than a fish?
2. Why is the human heart really a double pump?
3. After the blood passes through the heart of a yellow perch, it passes directly through the gills and on to the remainder of the body. Comment on the effect that this has on the blood pressure of a fish.
4. Describe the valves present in a mammalian heart with respect to both structure and function.

The Heart at Work

You know your heart "beats" and pumps blood throughout your body. But a heartbeat is really made up of more than one sound. The first, the longest and loudest, is called the "lub." It is caused by valves snapping shut while other valves open. As the ventricles (the two main pumping chambers of the heart) begin to contract, the valves between the atria (the smaller upper chambers of the heart) and the ventricles snap shut. At the same time, the valves to the arteries are forced open.

The second sound, a "dub" sound, is both shorter and quieter. It marks the beginning of the relaxing of the ventricles. Again, the sound heard is the closing of valves. This time, it is the sound of the valves closing between the ventricles and the arteries leaving the heart.

If for any reason a valve does not close properly, blood can leak back into a chamber. When this happens the person has an extra heart sound called a **murmur**. Some heart murmurs result from a childhood disease called rheumatic fever. In Activity 7C you will listen with a **stethoscope** to the sounds of your heart. Then, in Activity 7D you will examine factors that affect your **pulse rate**.

Challenge

A heart murmur is only one condition caused by childhood diseases. Find out what other heart conditions are caused at birth (congenital) or in early childhood. Your family doctor or the local branch of an organization such as the Heart and Stroke Foundation will be able to assist you.

Activity 7C

Problem

What sounds does the heart make?

Materials

a stethoscope (bell or diaphragm type)

Procedure

1. To locate the heart, first examine Figure 7.10. Now count your ribs starting from the top down. The sound of the heart can be heard between the fifth and sixth ribs, slightly to the left of the breast bone. The breast bone is the large bone in the centre of your chest.
2. Place the end of the stethoscope at the spot described in step 1.
3. Listen carefully for the "lub-dub, lub-dub" sounds of the heart.
4. After removing the stethoscope, run on the spot for 10 s. Again locate the heart sounds with your stethoscope.

Observations

1. Describe how the heart sounds in step 3 differed from those in step 4.

Questions

1. If the heart sounds are irregular, what would this suggest to a doctor?
2. Would the heart sounds change when you are asleep? If so, how?

Figure 7.10
The relationship between the heart and the ribs

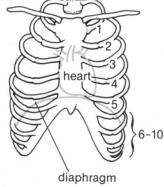
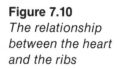

Activity 7D

Problem

What effect do brief periods of exercise and drinking coffee have on your pulse rate?

Materials

watch with sweep second hand
coffee or caffeinated drink

Procedure

1. Copy Table 7.4 into your notebook and use it to record your observations.
2. To take your pulse, you must first locate one of your radial arteries. A radial artery can be found on the inside of your wrist in line with your thumb (Figure 7.11).

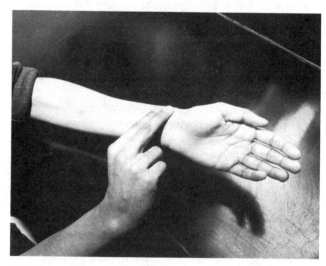

Figure 7.11 *Locating a radial artery in an arm*

3. Take your pulse at rest. Do *not* use your thumb since it also has a pulse. Count the number of beats in 15 s and multiply by 4 to obtain the pulse beats per minute. Record your results in your observation table in your notebook.
4. Now do 5 deep knee bends. To do this, stand upright and bend at the knees while keeping the body straight (Figure 7.12).

5. Record your new pulse rate as in step 3.
6. Time permitting, repeat steps 3 and 4 several more times and record your results. You can rest for 1 min between each set of 5 knee bends.
7. On a piece of graph paper, plot your pulse rate in beats per minute on the *y*-axis against time in minutes after completing the final knee bends on the *x*-axis.

Figure 7.12 *Doing deep knee bends. The back must be kept straight.*

Observations

(*see Table 7.4*)

1. What was your pulse rate at rest?
2. At what point during this activity did your pulse rate reach its maximum?
3. Following the deep knee bends, how long did it take your pulse rate to return to normal?

Table 7.4 *The Effects of Different Factors on Pulse Rate*

The pulse rate is measured in beats per minute. Use the formula in step (a) below to determine all of the other pulse rates.

(a) Normal pulse rate at rest =
$$\frac{\text{number of beats}}{15\text{ s}} \times 4 \qquad = \underline{\hspace{1cm}}$$
(b) Pulse rate after 5 deep knee bends ..... = _____
(c) Pulse rate after 5 more deep knee bends .... = _____
(d) Pulse rate after another 5 more knee bends .... = _____
(e) Pulse rate 1 min after final 5 knee bends .... = _____
(f) Pulse rate 2 min after final 5 knee bends .... = _____
(g) Pulse rate 3 min after final 5 knee bends .... = _____
(h) Pulse rate 4 min after final 5 knee bends .... = _____

Continue recording at 1 min intervals until the pulse returns to "at rest" level. Make more spaces in your table if necessary.

(i) Pulse rate before drinking a cup of coffee .... = _____
(j) Pulse rate after drinking a cup of coffee .... = _____

Questions

1. What is considered a "normal" pulse rate for a person aged 15, 16, or 17 years old?
2. What factors would influence pulse rate other than the ones considered during this activity?
3. Suggest a possible substance in coffee that would alter the pulse rate. Is this substance present in all coffees? Explain.
4. What conclusion(s) can you draw about the effects of exercise and coffee drinking on the human pulse rate?

The Heart and Blood Pressure

The rate at which the heart beats is related to blood pressure. They are not, however, the same thing. **Blood pressure** is dependent upon a strong heart beat. But other factors are also involved in determining blood pressure.

Pressure can be defined as a force acting on a unit of area. If you think of the heart as supplying the force, then the blood vessels can supply the area or space on which the force acts. Expressed in another way, the diameter of the blood vessels plays an important part in establishing blood pressure. If blood is forced to travel through a small vessel, the pressure in the vessel will be *high* (Figure 7.13 (b)). If the same volume of blood passes through a *larger* vessel, the pressure will be *lower* (Figure 7.13 (a)).

Some chemicals in the body can cause a change in the size of blood vessels. This change in size can increase or decrease blood pressure. The chemicals that can do this are called hormones. They are produced by some of the glands in the body and are passed into the blood stream.

Older people sometimes suffer from a buildup of deposits of fatty substances along the walls of blood vessels. One such substance is *cholesterol.* In time, the reduced diameter of the vessels leads to an increase in blood pressure.

In addition to the size of the vessels, blood pressure depends upon the amount of blood passing through the vessels. Blood pressure increases, for example, when the ventricles of the heart contract. This forces more blood through the nearby arteries. The highest blood pressure, created when the ventricles contract, is called **systolic pressure**. The ventricles then relax and the blood pressure goes down. The point of lowest blood pressure, called **diastolic pressure**, occurs just before the ventricles contract again.

When a doctor measures your blood pressure, both your systolic and diastolic pressures are measured. The pressure is usually measured in a major artery on the inside of the arm (Figure 7.11). Perhaps you have seen blood pressure recorded on a chart as 120/80. The first figure is the systolic pressure. The second figure is the

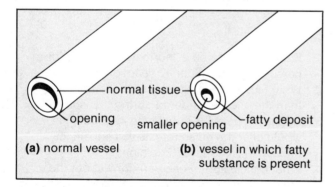

Figure 7.13 *The effects of fatty substances in blood vessels. In* **(a)**, *the blood has a larger opening to flow through. In* **(b)**, *the opening is smaller. Since the same amount of blood must flow through the clogged vessel, the blood pressure increases.*

Figure 7.14 *An instrument for measuring blood pressure*

diastolic pressure. In a doctor's office, blood pressure is usually measured in millimetres of mercury. However, scientists measure pressure in kilopascals, and it is possible that doctors might soon do the same.

The instrument for measuring blood pressure is shown in Figure 7.14. Although such instruments do differ a little, each usually consists of a gauge for measuring pressure, a fabric cuff which can be inflated, and a bulb for pumping up the cuff. A stethoscope is also used.

The principle involved in determining blood pressure is as follows. The cuff of the measuring instrument is wrapped around the upper arm and inflated. The stethoscope is clipped under the cuff as shown in Figure 7.15. The cuff is pumped up until a pulse beat can no longer be heard in the artery of the arm. At this point, the pressure in the cuff is greater than the pressure in the artery. The air is then gradually let out of the cuff. As this is happening, the doctor listens on the stethoscope. At the same time, the doctor watches the pressure gauge (Figure 7.15).

The pressure at which the doctor first hears the blood pulsing through the artery is the systolic pressure. At this point, the pressure in the artery of the arm just exceeds that of the cuff. More air is allowed to escape from the cuff. The pressure in the gauge continues to fall. The diastolic pressure is recorded at the point when the doctor hears a soft, muffled sound which soon disappears altogether. Sometimes the doctor will repeat the procedure several times and average the results.

Self-check

1. In your own words, describe a heart murmur.
2. You have discovered that exercise increases your pulse rate. Using your knowledge of how the body functions, explain *why* the pulse rate is faster.
3. Find out what effect, if any, smoking has on pulse rate.
4. What factors can result in increases in blood pressure?

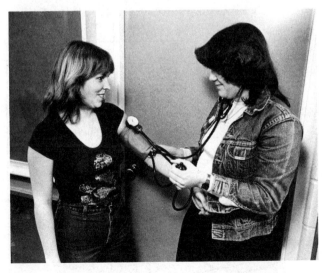

Figure 7.15 *Measuring blood pressure. Notice that the stethoscope is placed under the cuff on the upper arm.*

The Role of the Kidneys

In general terms, you already know that the kidneys have a part to play in getting rid of fluid waste from the body. The fluid is called *urine*. But the kidneys have a much more important function to perform. They play a major part in regulating the amount of water in the body at any given time.

A person can last for a long time without food but only for a very short period without water. Water is used in all parts of the body, both inside and out. Water is lost from the body in a number of ways. Examine Table 7.5. Most water loss takes place through making urine in the kidneys. Water is also lost through the lungs as gas exchange is taking place. To show the loss of water through the lungs, breathe on a mirror held in front of your face. The mirror will fog up because of the water vapour in your breath. Some of the water given off by the body results from the "burning" of foods within the cells of the body. We also lose body water and some body salts as we sweat. Finally, to a much lesser extent, water is lost through the feces.

Table 7.5 *Daily Water Gain and Loss by a Human*

WATER INTAKE		WATER OUTPUT	
Liquids	1200 mL	Urine	1500 mL
Food	1000 mL	Feces	150 mL
Oxidation of food	300 mL	Lungs	300 mL
		Skin (sweating)	550 mL
Total	2500 mL	Total	2500 mL

All this water must be replaced by the daily intake of liquids and foods. Perhaps surprisingly, much of the water we need is contained in the food we eat.

The two **kidneys** (Figure 7.16) are the main organs of the body responsible for changing the concentration of water and chemicals in the blood. Each kidney contains many tiny filtering units called *nephrons*. But a nephron is much more than a simple filter. Under the control of certain body glands, each nephron filters the blood passing through it, adds or removes chemicals, and produces urine. If the body loses water quickly—for example, by sweating at the

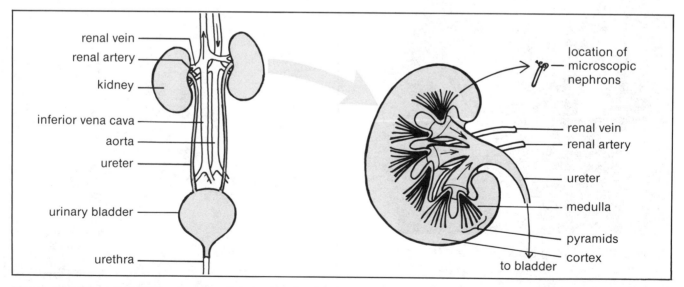

Figure 7.16 *The two kidneys, responsible for much of the "fine tuning" of the fluids present in the body*

surface of the skin while running on a hot day— less urine will be produced and passed from the body. That is, the kidneys reabsorb more water and return it to the blood vessels that pass through the kidneys. The kidneys can be looked on as the organs of the body that do the "fine tuning" necessary to maintain a healthy body.

Self-check

1. The kidneys produce urine from body waste. What other very important function do the kidneys perform?
2. What are the three main sources of water in the body?
3. Why is it so important that the amount of water taken into the body each day is equal to the amount of water that is lost?
4. What is a simple test for showing that your breath contains water vapour?
5. In addition to playing a part in controlling the amount of urine formed, what other functions do the nephrons of the kidney play?

Challenge

The action of tiny tubes (called nephrons) within the kidneys regulates which substances stay in the body and which are excreted. Use a reference book to obtain information about the ability of the nephrons to reabsorb, as well as filter, substances from the blood.

How the Organ Systems Fit Together

The body of most organisms consists of a number of organ systems. Here are the ten organ systems that are found in the human body:

- the digestive system
- the circulatory system
- the respiratory system
- the excretory system
- the muscular system
- the nervous system
- the skeletal system
- the reproductive system
- the integumentary (skin) system
- the endocrine (gland) system

Take a moment and try to imagine what would happen if the body lacked one of these systems. For example, if you did not have a skin, the body would quickly lose the water necessary for life. If you did not have a skeletal system, the body could not be supported in the normal manner. Without a muscular system, the skeletal system would not be very effective. To function properly, the bones must have points of attachment (such as muscles and ligaments) to other nearby bones.

Not one of these systems could exist independently of the others. Also, each system usually performs more than one role, so each system maintains a relationship with more than one other system. Together they make a healthy, functioning organism.

In Activity 7E, you will dissect a frog. When you do so, you will see how the respiratory, digestive, circulatory, and excretory systems are physically related to one another.

Activity 7E

Problem

Where are the respiratory, digestive, excretory, and circulatory systems located in a frog?

Materials

frog
dissecting tray
T pins
dissecting instruments (forceps, scissors, scalpel, probe)

CAUTION When using dissecting instruments, always make cuts away from the body. Scalpels are very sharp. Handle them with extreme care.

Procedure

1. Place the frog on its back (dorsal surface) in the dissecting tray.
2. Spread out the limbs. Now, with the T pins, fasten the frog to the wax in the tray. Do so by passing the pins through the webbing between digits ("fingers" and "toes") of the limbs of the frog. The pins should slant away from the body to make it easier to do the dissection.
3. With forceps, gently lift the loose skin away from the body. Using scissors, make a small cut in the middle of the abdomen. See Figure 7.17.
4. Now, with scissors, carefully cut along the midline of the abdomen, from the point where the legs meet to the tip of the lower jaw. Again, look at Figure 7.17.
5. Make cuts towards each of the four limbs as shown in Figure 7.17. Next, using forceps and scalpel, pull the skin away from the muscle layer beneath it (Figure 7.18). The frog definitely has a true, outer skin. Pin the skin down out of the way to make your next cuts easier.
6. Repeat steps 4 and 5, this time cutting the muscle tissue of the abdomen and chest region. Again, pin the tissue back out of the way. You can now see many of the internal organs of the frog.

7. In order to see the heart, using strong scissors or bone cutters, cut through the pectoral girdle (the large bones in the shoulder region) as shown in Figure 7.19. The heart lies at about the midpoint in the shoulder region.
8. With the internal organs now fully exposed, compare your frog with Figure 7.20. Figure 7.20 is a labelled diagram showing many of the internal organs. Note the use of the letters R, D, C, and E to represent the four systems respiratory, digestive, circulatory, and excretory.
9. By carefully moving the larger organs to one side, as in Figure 7.21, you will be able to see the kidneys, the major organs of excretion.
10. It is difficult to locate all of the many blood vessels present in a frog. You can, however, find the heart. It is located at the midpoint in the shoulder region. If you are careful, you should be able to remove the thin sac that surrounds and protects the heart.

Observations

1. Locate the liver using Figure 7.20 as a guide. What is the function of the liver in digestion?
2. Locate the small, green gall bladder among the lobes of the liver. What is the function of this organ? The answer to this question and question 1 are related but not the same.
3. Describe the appearance of the lungs using Figure 7.20. Why are they so small?
4. Locate the stomach using Figure 7.20. It will be found under the liver. Notice the point where the stomach stops and the small intestine begins. What prevents the food from trickling at all times from the stomach into the small intestine?
5. Gently pull the small intestine aside to locate the thin, clear, plastic-like substance called the *mesentery*. The mesentery holds the parts of the digestive tract in place. What function do the blood vessels in this area serve?

Questions

1. In your own words, describe the *functional* relationships among the four systems studied in this activity.

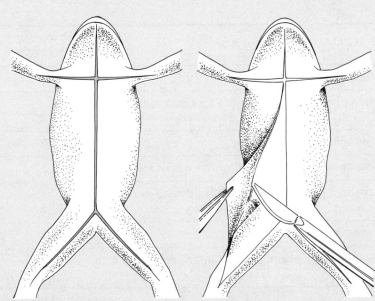

Figure 7.17 *Initial cuts for the frog dissection*

Figure 7.18 *Cutting back the outer skin of the frog*

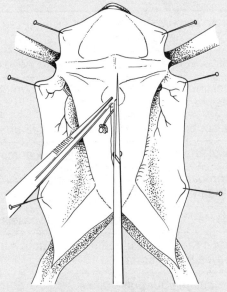

Figure 7.19 *Cutting the bones in the shoulder region to expose the heart*

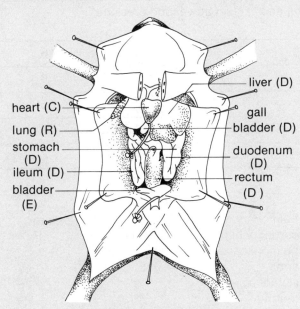

heart (C)
lung (R)
stomach (D)
ileum (D)
bladder (E)

liver (D)
gall bladder (D)
duodenum (D)
rectum (D)

Figure 7.20 *The internal organs of a frog*

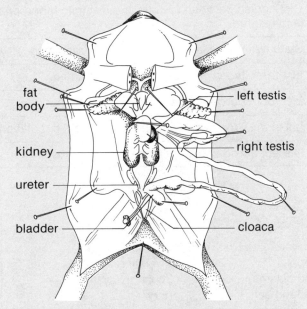

fat body
kidney
ureter
bladder

left testis
right testis
cloaca

Figure 7.21 *By moving the digestive organs aside, you can locate the two kidneys. This is a male frog. A female would probably have a large number of eggs in the abdomen.*

Chapter Objectives

NOW THAT YOU HAVE COMPLETED THIS CHAPTER,
CAN YOU DO THE FOLLOWING?

FOR REVIEW,
TURN TO SECTION

	FOR REVIEW, TURN TO SECTION
1. List seven reasons why organisms need transport systems.	7.1
2. Describe both the liquid and solid components of blood, and state the function of blood plasma.	7.2
3. Describe and state the functions of human blood cells.	7.2
4. Explain why some blood types are compatible and/or incompatible with other blood types.	7.2
5. Compare an artery, vein, and capillary with respect to structure, flexibility, direction of blood flow, and the presence or absence of valves.	7.3
6. Identify the major chambers and vessels of the heart.	7.3
7. Trace the flow of blood from the time it enters the right atrium of the human heart until it leaves by the aorta.	7.4
8. Calculate your pulse rate.	7.5
9. List three factors that increase blood pressure.	7.5
10. Distinguish between systolic and diastolic blood pressure, and explain how blood pressure is measured.	7.5
11. State two roles played by kidneys in organisms.	7.6
12. List three types of water intake for a human.	7.6
13. List four sources of water loss for a human.	7.6
14. Label the organs of respiration, digestion, circulation, and excretion on a diagram of a frog.	7.7
15. Dissect a frog and identify the organs of respiration, digestion, circulation, and excretion.	7.7

Words to Know

hormone
blood
blood plasma
red blood cell
hemoglobin
white blood cell
platelet

universal donor
universal receptor
circulatory system
artery
vein
capillary
valve

pulmonary artery
coronary blood vessel
pulmonary vein
aorta
stethoscope
murmur
pulse rate
blood pressure
systolic pressure

diastolic pressure
kidney

Tying It Together

1. State six functions of a transport system.
2. What is the solid part of blood made up of?
3. (a) The straw-coloured liquid part of blood is over 90% water. What is it called?
   (b) What is the remaining 10% made up of?
4. Compare red and white blood cells with respect to the following:
   (a) where they are produced
   (b) their functions
   (c) whether or not a nucleus is present
5. Compare an artery and a vein with respect to the following:
   (a) the flexibility of the vessels
   (b) the presence or absence of valves
6. Which type blood is called the universal donor? Explain why.
7. (a) What is the largest blood vessel in the human body?
   (b) What is the smallest blood vessel in the human body?
8. What direction does blood flow in the arteries: toward the heart or away from the heart?
9. What direction does blood flow in the veins: toward the heart or away from the heart?
10. What function is served by the heart valves?
11. (a) How many chambers does a fish heart contain?
    (b) How many chambers does a human heart contain?
12. List three things that can raise blood pressure.
13. What is a heart murmur?
14. What two functions are served by the kidneys?

Applying Your Knowledge

1. Use your knowledge of biology to solve the following problem:

   The soldier was badly wounded when the shell exploded near him. He had already lost a lot of blood when the medic arrived. There wasn't enough time to rush him to a hospital. They would have to give him blood on the spot. Three soldiers nearby had Type O, Type B, and Type AB blood.

   Which of the three soldiers could donate blood to their comrade? Explain why.
2. A baby is born with a small opening between the left and right ventricle. Assuming that the baby lived, what effect would this have on the movement of the blood through the heart? What effect would this have on the general health of the baby? Hint: Use what you know about what happens to blood when it moves through the heart and the lungs.
3. Leucocytes are able to destroy bacteria that invade the body. Knowing that these blood cells feed in the same way as amoeba, describe how a leucocyte would kill a bacterial cell.

Projects for Investigation

1. Find out why a blood clot that forms inside a blood vessel in the body—perhaps as a result of a bruise—can lead to a very serious health situation.
2. People who work in occupations where they must remain still for long periods of time often suffer from painful varicose veins. What is the cause and treatment for this condition?
3. The English scientist William Harvey was the first scientist to discover how blood circulates. He made this discovery over 300 years ago, before microscopes had even been invented! Find out how Harvey made his discoveries.

Nutrition:
A Real Balancing Act

Key Ideas

- The body needs varying amounts of six main nutrients each day.
- Eating from the four food groups can help ensure a balanced diet.
- Exercise is needed in addition to a proper diet to ensure that the body functions properly.

We are all familiar with going into a store and buying groceries. Many of the products we buy are advertised on TV or in the local paper. We buy things for different reasons. Sometimes we are looking for something sweet. At other times, we might want some fruit or vegetables or a breakfast cereal. But how often do we examine the label to find out exactly what is in the package we are buying?

What's on a Label?

Table 8.1 lists the contents of three common food products. In Canada, the ingredients of packaged foods must be listed in order from the largest to the smallest amount present. What are the three products, (a), (b), and (c), in Table 8.1? The answer appears at the end of this chapter. Try to figure it out before looking.

Table 8.1 *The Labels of Three Common Packaged Foods*

(a) Cheese (milk ingredients, bacteria culture, salt, rennet, and/or pepsin and/or microbial enzyme, calcium chloride, lipase), modified milk ingredients, water, sodium phosphate, salt, flavourings, spices, colour, sorbic acid.
(b) Wheat bran, glucose-fructose or liquid invert sugar, liquid sugar, malt syrup, salt, fresh prune concentrate, reduced iron, thiamine mononitrate, folic acid, and B.H.T.
(c) Sugar (may also contain dextrose), modified cornstarch, cocoa, mono- and diglycerides, sodium phosphate, artificial flavour, food colour (contains tartrazine)

The label quiz points out that there are many different things in the food we eat. What do these things do? Why are they there?

Challenge

What are your five favourite packaged foods? Obtain the labels from these products. Make a list on separate pages of the substances in each food. Have your friends in class guess what each product is. What substances do you think are nutrients? Which substances do you think are food additives? Do you think you are eating the "right" foods?

Nutrition and Health

Nutrition is defined as the science of food and nutrients and their relation to health. **Nutrients** are the components of food the body needs to maintain good health. Nutrients include carbohydrates, fats, proteins, minerals, vitamins, and water. However, the food we eat includes more than nutrients. Some of the items in Table 8.1, like the chemical sorbic acid, preserve food until it is eaten. Such chemicals, when added to a food, are called **food additives**. Vitamins and minerals are added to food in order to "enrich" it, but they are considered to be nutrients and not additives. You will find out more about additives later in this chapter.

Nutrition plays a real role in the life you lead. The food you eat can affect the way you look, feel, and act. Basically, food serves your body in the following three ways:

1. It provides you with the energy to move and live a normal life.
2. It provides you with the raw materials that are rearranged and used to make new cells and to repair old ones.
3. It provides you with the materials to make substances to control important body functions. These substances include hormones such as insulin and adrenalin.

Good nutrition is much more than simply developing good eating habits. If you are eating an acceptable mix of foods, your body is more able to resist disease. Someone who is "run down," that is, someone who is not eating or sleeping properly, is far more likely to catch a cold than someone who is eating properly. In Activity 8A you will examine some of the main nutrients and establish some tests to identify them.

Problem

How can we test for the presence of sugars, fats and oils, and proteins in our food?

Materials

glucose
fat or vegetable oil
gelatin (or any other protein)
several pieces of different foods, such as apple, nuts,
    bread, etc.
Bunsen burner
lighter
brown paper bag
spot plate
Benedict's reagent
Biuret reagent
test tube holder
test tube rack
4 Pyrex test tubes
safety goggles

Procedure

1. Copy Table 8.2 into your notebook. Use the table to record all of your observations. Now carry out the following tests.

CAUTION While heating chemicals over a Bunsen burner be sure to wear safety goggles. Take care also not to point a test tube you are heating at anyone.

A. TEST FOR A SIMPLE SUGAR

1. Add a very small amount of glucose, a simple sugar, to a Pyrex test tube containing 5 mL of Benedict's reagent.
2. Heat the solution to boiling over a Bunsen burner flame (Figure 8.1). After it reaches a boil, continue heating for 2–3 min.
3. Record your observations in your table.

Positive test: If Benedict's reagent turns orange to brick red, a simple sugar is present. If it turns a light green colour, there is little or no sugar present.

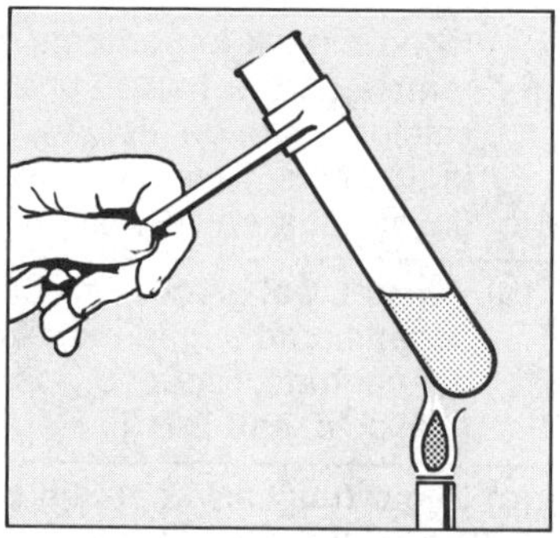

Figure 8.1 *Testing for a simple sugar. Hold the test tube at an angle. Do not aim it at anyone.*

B. TESTING FOR A FAT OR OIL

1. Place one or two drops of an oil or a small amount of fat onto a piece of a brown paper bag. Rub the spot with the tip of your fingers for a few seconds.

Positive test: If a fat is present, the paper will appear translucent. Translucent means that light can pass through the fat spot on the paper very easily.

Table 8.2 *Testing for Sugar, Fats and Oils, and Proteins*

NUTRIENT	REAGENT OR TEST USED	INITIAL COLOUR	FINAL (POSITIVE) RESULT
A. Simple sugar (glucose)			
B. Fat or oil			
C. Protein (gelatin or egg white)			

C. TESTING FOR A PROTEIN

There are many tests for proteins. Each one tests for a particular chemical, usually an amino acid. An amino acid is one of the "building blocks" or units of a protein (Figure 8.2).

1. Pour a mixture of gelatin powder and water into a test tube. About 5 mL of water will be enough.
2. Add an equal amount of Biuret reagent to the test tube.

Positive test: If protein is present, Biuret reagent will, in most cases, turn a pale violet or pink colour. The Biuret test will not work for all proteins but it will work for most.

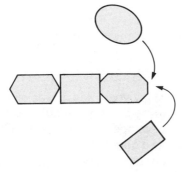

Figure 8.2 *Model to show amino acids being linked together to form a part of a protein*

D. TESTING UNKNOWNS

1. Apply each of the three tests to a variety of common foods. Your teacher may wish to give you the names of the foods or simply identify them as Food A, Food B, etc.

Observations

(see Table 8.2)

Questions

1. Which nutrients—carbohydrates, fats, and proteins—were present in each of the foods tested in part D?

Other Nutrients

Carbohydrates, **fats**, and **proteins** are the building blocks from which the cells of the body are constructed. Vitamins, minerals, and water also also vital nutrients. **Vitamins** and **minerals** are required in smaller quantities than other nutrients. But they must be present for many of the chemical reactions that keep us functioning normally.

VITAMINS

It has taken a long time to find out that vitamins are a necessary part of our diet. This is mainly because only very small amounts are required each day. They are necessary because our bodies cannot make them and must add them from foods we eat. Up until the end of the last century, doctors recognized that there was some relationship between deficiencies in diet and particular diseases. For example, it was known over 200 years ago that limes and lemons prevented the disease scurvy. People with scurvy would feel very weak. They would suffer from swollen gums, ulcers, and have tough, scaly skin. The deficiency was from a lack of vitamin C. Most vitamins were identified in the early part of the twentieth century.

Ideas and Applications

Back in 1535, Jacques Cartier didn't know about vitamin C. While exploring the coast of Newfoundland, 100 of his 110 men came down with scurvy. Fortunately the Indians helped by giving his men a drink made from spruce needles. Spruce needles are rich in vitamin C.

Problem

How can we test for the presence of vitamin C?

Materials

lemon juice
other fruit juices
indophenol
dropper
test tube

Procedure

1. Pour about 5 mL of indophenol into a test tube. The indophenol should be blue in colour at this point.
2. With a dropper, add 5 drops of lemon juice (Figure 8.3). After each drop, shake the test tube. Note any colour changes that take place.

Positive Test: If any vitamin C is present in the lemon juice, the blue colour of the indophenol will turn colourless.

3. Test several other juices for the presence of vitamin C.

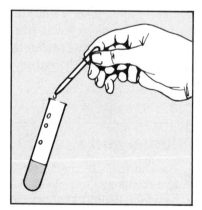

Figure 8.3 *Adding lemon juice to indophenol*

Observations

1. In your notebook, include all observations you made with (a) the lemon juice and (b) other juices tested.

Questions

1. Design a simple test to compare the *concentration* of vitamin C present in the different juices tested.
2. Which juice tested had the highest concentration of vitamin C?

Ideas and Applications

You might be throwing valuable vitamins away at mealtime. Many vitamins dissolve in water. If you cook vegetables in water and throw out the water, you are also throwing out the vitamins. You can save and eat the vitamins by using the water to make gravy and soups or to mash the potatoes.

Ideas and Applications

Many years ago, it was observed that people living in mountainous, inland areas often developed a large swelling in their neck known as a goiter. These people were not getting enough iodine in their diet. Iodine is found in most seafood, which was lacking in the diet of these people. To overcome this problem, iodine was added to table salt and the problem was solved. Even today, if you read the label on a box of salt, you will see that it has been "iodized" to make sure that everyone obtains enough iodine to prevent goiter.

MINERALS

The body requires small amounts of vitamins. It also requires small amounts of a number of different minerals. The mineral group includes calcium (used in making bones and hard teeth) and iron (necessary in the making of hemoglobin, the red pigment of the blood). Unlike carbohydrates, fats and oils, and proteins, neither vitamins nor minerals need to be digested. Both can pass directly into the blood stream through the lining of the digestive tract.

As is the case with water soluble vitamins, you lose some minerals when you cook your food. Some of the minerals end up in the water used for cooking. That's why you shouldn't throw away water used for cooking many foods.

WATER

Water is also classed as a nutrient. It is required to maintain your good health. Water serves as a solvent to carry many substances around the body in the blood stream. These substances include dissolved oxygen, waste materials, hormones, vitamins, and minerals, among others.

Water also acts as a lubricant to reduce friction at the joints where two bones meet. Water plays a role in helping to regulate body temperature. When you perspire (sweat), the evaporation of water on the surface of the skin serves to cool the body.

Fibre: Not a Nutrient, But Still Important

Dietary **fibre** is a term used to describe various substances that are made up of a mixture of cellulose and other large, complex carbohydrates. Different types of fibre can be found in whole-grain flours, bread and baked goods, cereals, fruits, and vegetables (Figure 8.4).

Your body lacks the enzymes necessary to break down the molecules in fibre. Thus, you cannot digest it. It simply remains in the body and moves through the digestive tract until it is eliminated. In some ways, fibre increases the efficiency of the elimination process. Some types of fibre retain water. These fibres keep the feces moist and ease their passage through the intestines. This prevents or relieves constipation.

Fibre also seems to play a role in reducing cholesterol levels in the blood. The reason for this is unclear, however. Thus, some scientists have suggested that fibre in the diet may help to reduce heart disease. The low-fibre diets characteristic of North Americans have also been linked to a high incidence of intestinal cancer. Such cancers are much less common in parts of Africa, for example, where the traditional diet is high in fibre.

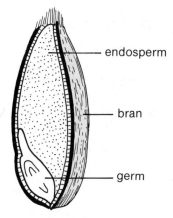

Figure 8.4 *The parts of a kernel of grain. The major portion, called the endosperm, is composed primarily of starch. The germ also contains some starch. The bran is composed mostly of cellulose. Thus, it is a good source of fibre. The bran is removed during the making of white bread, but it is at least partially retained in whole wheat and bran breads.*

Self-check

1. Why is it that, in Canada, sugar is not called a food additive even though it is added to many packaged cereals?
2. List three ways in which food serves the body.
3. Describe a chemical test for the following:
   (a) a simple sugar
   (b) a fat
   (c) a protein
   (d) a starch (recall the test you used in Chapter 6)
4. Why should you cook vegetables in as little water as possible?
5. Describe a positive test for vitamin C.
6. What role does the mineral calcium play in your body?
7. What role does fibre play in your body?

Ideas and Applications

One of the main items in the diet of the Masai tribe in East Africa is a drink consisting of milk and blood. The blood is drawn from a large vein in the neck of a living cattle beast. When this drink is combined with some fruit and vegetables, it makes for a very nutritious balanced diet.

The Four Food Groups

So far we have discussed the six nutrients necessary for a healthy body. When you go shopping, it would be very difficult if you had to check each product for its nutrients. In fact, unless the product is packaged, this information would not be available. A quick check of the sources of the various nutrients reveals that they are found in a range of different foods. So perhaps the easiest thing to do is to eat a variety of foods. In this way you would get enough of each nutrient. With this in mind, Health and Welfare Canada has produced a handbook entitled *Canada's Food Guide*.

In the *Food Guide*, all foods are divided into four food groups:

1. milk and milk products
2. bread and cereals
3. fruits and vegetables
4. meat and meat alternatives

Table 8.3 *Comparison of Foods from the Four Food Groups*

1. **Milk and Milk Products** Yogurt, ice cream, milk puddings, milkshakes, buttermilk, cheddar cheese
2. **Bread and Cereals** Instant rolled oats, most ready-to-eat cereals, many kinds of crackers, most cooked cereals, spaghetti, macaroni, noodles, white or brown rice, whole wheat or enriched bread
3. **Fruits and Vegetables** Avocados, cans of fruit, peas, rutabaga, onions, potatoes, bananas, cabbage, carrots, apples, frozen orange juice, strawberries, mushrooms
4. **Meats and Meat Alternatives** Frozen fish fillets, corned beef, cornish game hen, lamb chops, pork tenderloin, round roast, shrimp, T-bone steak, canned tuna or mackerel, eggs, dried peas, beans or lentils, peanut butter, pork liver, turkey, hamburger, chicken

The secret to using the *Food Guide* is to select, each day, a balanced diet made up from all four food groups. The guide is not intended to be rigid and inflexible. However, you cannot select a food from one group and exchange it with a food from another group. This is because the foods in the other groups lack specific nutrients present in the first group. For example, by substituting a cereal for a dairy product, you will be denying yourself the calcium which is found chiefly in milk products. Figure 8.5 depicts the various food groups. Table 8.3 shows how the four food groups form the basis for a nutritious diet.

milk and milk products

meat and meat alternatives, 2 servings

bread and cereals, 3–5 servings

fruits and vegetables, 4–5 servings

Figure 8.5 *The four major food groups*

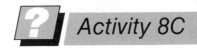
Problem

What categories do some common foods fall into according to *Canada's Food Guide?*

Materials

a bag containing labels, diagrams, or empty cartons from a variety of common foods

Procedure

1. Design a table to record your observations.
2. Working with a partner, remove the labels, diagrams or cartons from the bag one at a time. With your partner, decide to which of the four food groups the article belongs.

Observations

1. Record your decisions in your table.

Questions

1. What difficulties did you experience classifying the foods represented by the labels in the bag?
2. Suggest recommendations that could be made to food producers to make the classifying easier.
3. Which foods, if any, were almost impossible to classify?
4. Based on this activity, what specific conclusion(s) can you draw with respect to the labelling of food products in Canada?

Self-check

1. What are the four major food groups in *Canada's Food Guide*?
2. Why should you not exchange a food from one group with a food from another group if you are trying to have a balanced diet?
3. For breakfast you decide to have orange juice and a poached egg on a plain piece of whole-wheat toast.
   (a) Which of the four food groups is not represented in this meal?
   (b) What could you add to this meal so that all four food groups are represented?
4. What would happen to you if you rarely ever ate anything from one of the food groups?

Challenge

Study the graph below. Why is the heart rate of the cross-country runner lower than that of the students who do not engage in any long-distance running? What effect does eight weeks of training seem to have on the average heart rate of the student group? Why might this change occur?

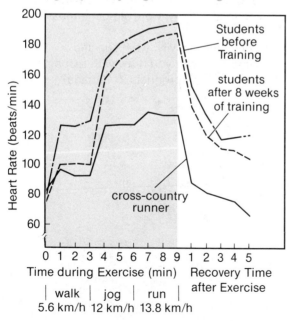

Exercise and Health

It is particularly important during the teen years to get enough exercise. This is because during this period new fat cells are being laid down in the body tissue. If no attempt is made to work these off, they will, in time, become permanent. It is much more difficult to reduce body mass once you are out of your teens. There is much more to body mass gain or loss than simple exercise but there are a number of activities that you can do to work off the energy obtained by eating different foods. Table 8.4 lists four of these activities.

Table 8.4 demonstrates that there is a great deal of energy in many different foods. A "quarter pounder" hamburger, just counting the bun and the meat, would yield about 2000 kJ. To burn off this amount of energy, you would have to walk for over an hour and a half!

Ideas and Applications

In studies with teenagers, Dr. Jean Mayer, a world famous nutritionist, made a surprising discovery. He found that students with high body mass, on average, ate *less* than their slim classmates. However, they exercised less than their slimmer friends.

138

Table 8.4 *The Relationship between the Energy Content of Food and Exercise*

FOOD	PORTION	ENERGY PER PORTION (kJ)	EXERCISE TIME REQUIRED TO BURN OFF THE ENERGY FROM THE FOOD EATEN (min)			
			WALKING	BICYCLING	SWIMMING	RUNNING
Apple	1 average	392	15	9	7	4
Beef, ground	113 g	1369	63	40	29	17
Bread, white	1 slice	336	15	10	7	4
Bread, whole grain	1 slice	302	14	9	6	4
Candy bar	1 average	1134	52	33	24	14
Chocolate chip cookies	2	420	19	12	9	5
Coffee, black	250 mL	0	0	0	0	0
French fries	10	655	30	19	14	8
Honey	45 mL	260	12	8	6	3
Oatmeal	188 mL	420	19	12	9	5
Raisins	125 mL	680	31	20	14	8
Rice, brown	125 mL	441	20	13	9	5

Self-check

1. There are several factors which lead to a gain in body mass in a person. What are two such factors?
2. Suggest two sensible ways in which you can control your body mass.
3. Make use of the information in Table 8.4 to answer this question. Assume that you have just eaten an order of French fries.

   (a) On average, how many kilojoules would this portion contain?
   (b) How long would you have to walk to burn off the kilojoules from your French fries?
   (c) If you wanted to burn off one-half of the energy by walking and one-half by swimming, how long would you have to swim?

Teenagers and Nutritional Problems

Some of Canada's largest hospitals have clinics that specialize in helping teenagers who have nutritional problems. Why do these clinics exist? What special nutritional problems do some teenagers have? An interview with a dietician at such a clinic recently gave us the answers to these questions.

Q. What is the most common problem that you encounter among teenagers?

A. About half of the teenage patients that I see have a problem with obesity; that is, their body mass is 25% or more over what it should be. These patients are referred to the hospital by their family physician or school health service.

Q. What do you do when you meet with them?

A. First, I find out about them. I ask about other members of their family, about what exercise they get, and about how long they have been overweight. I am also interested in when they eat, and what else they are doing while they are eating.

Q. What are the usual answers?

A. Many of the teenagers have had a weight problem since they were very young, and many have family members who are also overweight. The great majority of them, perhaps 90%, get no exercise at all.

Q. Why are you interested in what else they are doing while they eat?

A. Many people eat while their minds are elsewhere, for example, while watching television, so they are not aware of how much they are actually taking in.

Q. What can you do to help them?

A. I have them keep a record of what they eat for a day, then discuss this with them, showing them the *Canada Food Guide*, which describes the different food groups and how much of each is required each day. I advise them to cut down on foods which are high in fats and carbohydrates. We work together to set up a meal plan, listing what sorts of food and how much to eat at meals and snacks. How they eat is also important. I advise them to sit with their family or friends at meals, think about their food, and enjoy it. Most obese people don't like doing strenuous exercise, so I first just try to get them to walk more: about thirty minutes a day. Even walking briskly to and from school every day would be a big improvement for these teenagers.

Q. What foods are the worst offenders?

A. The real junk foods are soft drinks and candy. Sometimes the whole problem of obesity can be solved by cutting out just a few items. Drinking too many healthful drinks can also be a problem. For example, milk and fruit juices contain many nutrients but also many kilojoules. Cutting down, even on these healthful

snacks, will make a big difference in body mass over a period of time. Of course, they will then need to make sure they drink plenty of water so their bodies get enough of this important nutrient.

Q. What is the success rate for the people you counsel? How many of them are able to lower their mass to a more normal level?

A. The short-term success rate is fairly good. Most patients can lower their mass during the time that they are being counselled. The long-term success rate is not so encouraging. There has to be a real desire on the part of the patients to take charge of themselves and modify their lifestyles. For those who have the determination, success is certainly possible.

Q. Do any of your patients have vitamin deficiencies?

A. Vitamins are added to many foods, so deficiencies severe enough to cause symptoms are very rare among teenagers who eat.

Q. What do you mean by "teenagers who eat"?

A. About a quarter of the patients whom I counsel are suffering from *anorexia nervosa*, a disorder in which patients eat little or nothing. These teenagers may be very hungry, but they have become so concerned with being thin that they stop eating. They develop vitamin deficiencies and become emaciated, and may make themselves so weak that they collapse.

Q. Is it only teenagers who develop this disorder?

A. It usually begins in the teen years or slightly earlier, but also may continue for many years after. It is primarily a disorder of girls. Ninety percent of anorexic patients are female.

Q. What causes this disorder?

A. It usually starts when a teenager is trying to exert control over her own life, and trying to establish her own identity. The eating disorder is a collection of symptoms which reflect her inner mental turmoil.

Q. What can you, as a dietician, do to help a person who is anorexic?

A. Since it is thought that the disorder is caused by the patient's feelings about herself, she usually has discussions with a psychiatrist as well as a dietician. We explain the importance of good nutrition, and try to make her feel more relaxed about herself so that she can eat more normally.

Q. What is the success rate in dealing with anorexic patients?

A. Many recover enough to lead normal lives. But there are some who starve to death.

Q. Are there any other nutritional disorders that are common?

A. The other problem that I encounter is *bulimia nervosa*, which is similar to anorexia in some ways. Bulimic patients are also mainly teenage girls who are concerned about their bodies, and

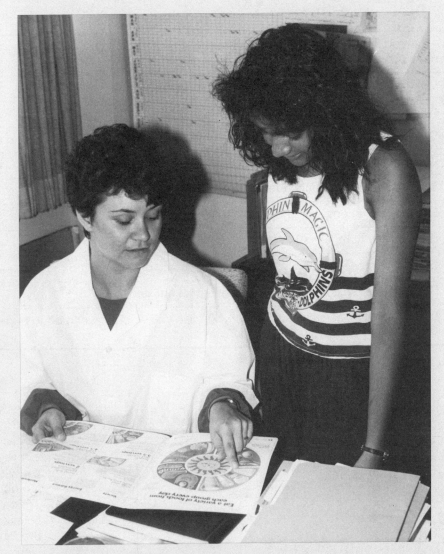

about growing up. They eat in binges, and then make themselves vomit or purge themselves with laxative. Their mass may be normal, so they may not appear to be ill. However, doing this several times a week can seriously damage their health.

Q. What can be done to help them?

A. Here again, counselling by a dietician and a psychiatrist may help. The younger the patients are when we get to see them, the greater is our success rate.

Chapter Objectives

NOW THAT YOU HAVE COMPLETED THIS CHAPTER, CAN YOU DO THE FOLLOWING?	FOR REVIEW, TURN TO SECTION
1. List the six nutrients necessary for good health.	8.2
2. State three ways that food serves the body.	8.2
3. Describe and conduct a chemical test to identify a carbohydrate, a fat, and a protein.	8.2
4. Describe and conduct a chemical test to identify the presence of vitamin C in a food.	8.2
5. State the source and function for the minerals calcium and iron.	8.2
6. List three functions served by water in the body.	8.2
7. Explain why fibre, although not a nutrient, is essential for good health.	8.2
8. Given a number of different foods, identify which of the four food groups each belongs to.	8.3
9. Describe the relationship between diet and exercise.	8.4
10. Using Table 8.4, calculate how much exercise you would have to do to burn off the energy gained when you eat specific foods.	8.4

Words to Know

nutrition
nutrient
food additive
carbohydrate
fat

protein
vitamin
mineral
fibre

Tying It Together

1. What is a food additive?
2. (a) What is a nutrient?
   (b) Name the six major nutrients, and describe at least one function performed by each type.
3. List at least three food sources of each of the six major nutrients.
4. Which of the six types of nutrients are important as energy sources for the body?
5. Why did it take a long time to find out that vitamins are a necessary part of our diet?

6. (a) What are two minerals that the human body requires?
   (b) Why is each mineral important?
7. List three reasons why water is essential to life.
8. Are there any substances which are not considered nutrients but which are still useful to the body? Explain.
9. Give three examples of foods contained within each of the four major food groups.
10. Why is exercise important for good health?

Applying Your Knowledge

1. In addition to diet and exercise, what other factors do you think would have an effect on a person's body mass?
2. Your friends suggest you join them for a chips 'n gravy and cola lunch. Having just completed a unit on nutrition, outline the arguments you would use to convince them to try something else.

3. During the 1880s, a Dutch doctor named Christian Eijkman was working in a lab on an island north of Australia. In his lab were some domestic fowl that were very weak and lacked co-ordination. Dr. Eijkman had been feeding them cooked, polished, white rice. When he ran out of the white rice he started feeding them cheaper brown rice. This rice was still in the husks and not "polished." To the doctor's surprise, the birds got better.

(a) What can you conclude from this type of data?

(b) What type of experiment or experiments would you like to carry out to confirm your suspicions? Briefly describe them.

4. You have just eaten an average chocolate bar, followed by a cup of black coffee.

(a) How long would you have to swim to burn off the energy from the chocolate bar?

(b) How long would you have to run if you only drank the coffee but did not eat the chocolate bar? Explain your answer.

(c) Do you think that this food combination represents a suitable intake of nutrients? Explain.

5. Study Figure 8.6.

(a) What does it tell you about the relationship between heart rate and activity level?

(b) What effect did an exercise program have on the heart rate of one of the age groups shown in the figure?

(c) Explain why exercise might have produced this result.

(d) Does the figure reveal any relationship between age and heart rate? Explain.

(e) Why might the relationship exist?

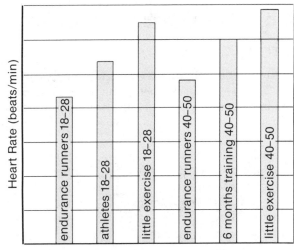

Figure 8.6 *Comparison of the average resting heart rates of young and middle-aged men of various fitness levels.*

Projects for Investigation

1. Fungi are usually the first type of micro-organism to invade bread to use it as a food source. They prefer damp, warm environments and low light. Design an experiment to determine the effectiveness of the preservative in various types of breads. You may wish to include home-baked bread and bakery bread, along with brands from a grocery store. Remember to include a control in your experiment. When you have prepared your procedure, show it to your teacher for approval. Then carry out your experiment.

The answers to the puzzle in Table 8.1, Section 8.1, are

(a) Kraft Cheez Whiz
(b) Nabisco 100% Bran
(c) Jello Pudding and Pie Filling.

Unit 2: The Functioning Animal

MATCH

In your notebook, write the letters (a) to (i). Beside each letter, write the number of the word in the right column that corresponds to each description in the left column.

(a) smallest blood vessels	1. maximum capacity
(b) ability to do work	2. alveoli
(c) site of gas exchange	3. kidneys
(d) amount of air the lungs can hold	4. peristalsis
(e) moves food through the digestive system	5. hemoglobin
(f) involved in chemical digestion	6. carbohydrates
(g) carries oxygen in the blood	7. capillaries
(h) site of urine production	8. liver
(i) a nutrient	9. energy
	10. cholesterol
	11. vital capacity
	12. enzymes

MULTIPLE CHOICE

In your notebook, write the numbers 1 to 10. Beside each number, write the letter of the best choice.

1. Which of the following processes is *not* involved in the obtaining and use of energy by your body?
   (a) metabolism
   (b) photosynthesis
   (c) combustion
   (d) cellular respiration
2. The path air takes into your lungs is
   (a) nasal passage, larynx, pharynx, trachea, bronchi, bronchioles, alveoli
   (b) nasal passage, pharynx, trachea, larynx, bronchi, bronchioles, alveoli
   (c) nasal passage, trachea, larynx, bronchi, bronchioles, alveoli
   (d) nasal passage, pharynx, trachea, larynx, bronchioles, bronchi, alveoli.

3. What conditions are required for any organism to remove its waste carbon dioxide and obtain oxygen from its environment?
   (a) a layer of moisture in which the gases may dissolve
   (b) carbon dioxide in a higher concentration outside the cell
   (c) oxygen in a higher concentration inside the cell
   (d) all of the above
4. Where does mechanical digestion take place?
   (a) mouth, esophagus, and stomach
   (b) mouth, stomach, and small intestine
   (c) mouth and stomach
   (d) mouth only
5. Which of the following is a characteristic of enzymes?
   (a) Enzymes act on specific substances.
   (b) Different enzymes work best under different conditions.
   (c) Enzymes are not used up in chemical reactions.
   (d) All of the above are characteristics of enzymes.
6. Which of the following would decrease the blood pressure measured in a particular blood vessel?
   (a) a large amount of cholesterol present in the blood vessel
   (b) a hormone in the blood that shrinks the diameter of the vessel
   (c) a hormone in the blood that widens the vessel
   (d) a large amount of blood moving through the vessel
7. The human heart acts like two pumps rather than one. This is important because
   (a) blood needs an extra boost in order to reach the brain during stressful exercise
   (b) otherwise blood would lose its pressure after passing through the lungs
   (c) one pump sends blood down to the lower body, the other to the head and arms
   (d) after a heart attack, the second pump can take over.

8. A universal donor has which type of blood?
   (a) Type A
   (b) Type B
   (c) Type AB
   (d) Type O
9. Why is fibre an important part of a healthy diet?
   (a) It is rich in vitamins.
   (b) By digesting fibre, humans obtain valuable energy.
   (c) Fibre increases the efficiency of the elimination process and may help prevent diseases such as heart disease and some cancer.
   (d) all of the above
10. Water is a nutrient required for good health. Which of the following properties of water are important to your body?
    (a) Water makes things slippery.
    (b) When water evaporates, heat is removed from its surroundings.
    (c) Water dissolves many other substances.
    (d) all of the above

TRUE/FALSE

Write the numbers 1 to 10 in your notebook. Beside each number, write T if the statement is true and F if the statement is false. For each false statement, rewrite it as a true statement.

1. The joule is the unit used to measure both energy and work.
2. Pollutants in the air such as animal hair or cigarette smoke do not trigger asthma attacks.
3. Emphysema, pneumonia, and laryngitis are all diseases which affect the ability of the alveoli to act as sites of gas exchange.
4. Chemical digestion begins with saliva.
5. Gallstones can cause serious blockages in a person's large intestine.
6. Systolic pressure is greatest when the ventricles are contracting.
7. Red blood cells are important disease-fighting cells for your body.
8. Arteries carry blood to the heart and veins carry blood away from the heart.
9. The way food is cooked does not affect its vitamin content.
10. To be used by your body, minerals must be digested and absorbed.

FOR DISCUSSION

Read the paragraph below and answer the questions that follow.

Consider the following situation. You have been sitting at the table, enjoying a large meal of spaghetti (carbohydrate) and salad (vitamins, minerals, fibre). Suddenly, your best friend arrives at the door and invites you for a bike ride. Off you go, pedalling for all you're worth. It's a beautiful summer evening, but you soon work up a sweat. After an hour or so, you feel tired and decide it's time to go home.

1. Describe what was happening in your digestive system before you left the table.
2. (a) How would your breathing rate and heartbeat change from when you were at the table to when you are riding your bike?
   (b) Why are these changes necessary?
   (c) List three other changes which you would probably notice occurring in your body after exercising vigorously.
3. There is only a certain amount of energy available in your body at any one time. if you need energy for your muscles, what do you think happens in your digestive system while you ride your bike?
4. Even though you lose water as perspiration when you exercise, your body actually produces more water through respiration. Write the word equation that explains how this happens.
5. Once you stop exercising, it takes some time before your breathing and heart rate return to their resting levels. Why do you think this is so?

Continuity

For this great-grandmother, this is a very special baby. She wonders what the baby will be like. Perhaps the baby will have flaming red hair, as she did when she was younger. Or perhaps the baby will have talent in music, like her old uncle who died 100 years ago. She does know one thing, however. The baby will not be exactly like her, her uncle, or anyone else in the world!

Why do people produce human babies, dogs produce puppies, and oak trees produce oak seedlings? How do differences in offspring appear? In this unit, you will find out how plants and animals produce offspring. You will look inside cells to explain why offspring resemble their parents. And then you will consider how modern technology is affecting human reproduction and inheritance.

9

Reproduction

Key Ideas

- Living things produce more of their own kind by sexual or asexual reproduction.
- In asexual reproduction, one parent produces offspring that are exactly like itself.
- In sexual reproduction for both plants and animals, a male parent provides a sperm cell and a female parent provides an egg cell.
- The offspring produced by sexual reproduction resemble both parents but are not exactly like them.

A gardener can grow tulip bulbs so that all their flowers have identical characteristics. The plants develop from identical bulbs. All the bulbs are the **offspring** (next generation) of a single parent plant. This ensures that there will be no variation in the offspring. Each and every flower will be a copy of the one original.

For variety among offspring, two parents are required. Each parent contributes some characteristics to the offspring. Chance determines which of these characteristics are inherited. All the offspring are different from the two parents and from each other.

What are the advantages of producing offspring exactly like the parents? Are there any advantages in having a variety of individuals? In this chapter, you will find the answers to these and other questions about reproduction and inheritance.

Comparing Asexual and Sexual Reproduction

For organisms to exist generation after generation, they must be able to produce offspring of their own kind. In other words, they must be able to **reproduce**. The offspring always resemble their parents. This is because the characteristics, or **traits**, of the parents are passed on to the next generation.

There are two kinds of reproduction: asexual reproduction and sexual reproduction (Figure 9.1). In **asexual reproduction**, a single organism produces offspring that are identical to itself. Every trait of the offspring is the same as its one parent.

Figure 9.1 *The patterns of asexual and sexual reproduction*

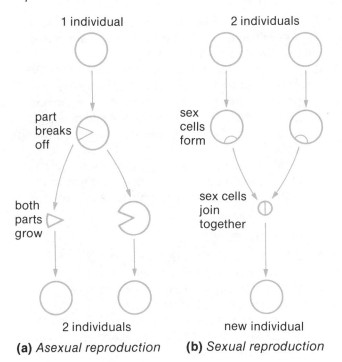

(a) *Asexual reproduction* **(b)** *Sexual reproduction*

Sexual reproduction requires two parents. Traits are passed on to the offspring by both parents. The offspring will resemble the two parents but will not be exactly like either one. Except for identical twins, the offspring also differ from each other. They inherit a variety of traits (Figure 9.2).

Figure 9.2 *Among the kittens in a single litter, there are many different traits.*

Is One Type of Reproduction Better Than the Other?

Asexual reproduction may benefit organisms that are already well adapted to their environment. Many offspring can be produced in a short time. While conditions remain favourable the offspring can thrive.

In some situations, however, the variety produced by sexual reproduction may be an advantage. If there is variety among members of a species, some may not be killed by a sudden change in the environment. Some individuals, for example, may be able to resist a new disease or withstand a severe winter that kills off most members of the species. By being different, some individuals can survive to produce more of their own species.

Depending on the organism and on the environment, there are advantages and disadvantages to both types of reproduction.

Asexual Reproduction

Animals

Only very small and relatively simple animals can reproduce themselves asexually. Planaria, a small flat animal about as long as your thumbnail, is one species that can reproduce in this way. Normally planarian worms live in clear streams and ponds and hide under leaves and rocks. If a planaria is injured and is cut into several pieces, each part can grow into a new individual (Figure 9.3).

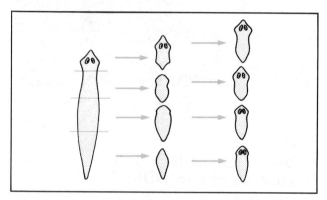

Figure 9.3 *Planarian worms can grow from any piece of the cut or injured animal.*

Yeast

Yeast is a single-celled organism that is classified as a fungus. Living yeast cells produce the bubbles of gas that cause bread to be light and fluffy. Yeast cells are able to reproduce using a type of asexual reproduction called **budding**. In this process a bulge forms in the body wall of the parent cell. The bulge grows larger and then pinches off from the parent, forming a new organism.

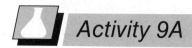

Activity 9A

Problem

How can you observe budding in yeast?

Materials

yeast cake or package of dry yeast
sugar
beaker, 250 mL
compound microscope
microscope slide and coverslip
iodine in a dropping bottle

> **CAUTION** Iodine is a corrosive liquid that will stain the skin, clothing, desk tops, and floors. Take care to avoid spilling. Quickly wipe up any accidental spills and rinse with water.

Procedure

1. Follow the directions on the label of your yeast. You will need to mix the yeast with warm water and sugar to start it growing.
2. Note the smell and appearance of the yeast as it grows (Figure 9.4). When you are sure that it is growing, prepare a wet mount of the liquid and observe the yeast cells under the microscope. Add a drop of iodine to the slide to make viewing easier.
3. After the yeast has been growing for a day, again make a wet mount of the liquid. Add a drop of iodine and view the slide under the microscope.

Observations

1. What do you see in the beaker as the yeast is growing? What do you smell?
2. On the first day, make a drawing in your notebook of a typical yeast cell.
3. On the second day, find on the slide some cells which have formed buds. Draw two or three of these in your notebok.

Figure 9.4 *You will know the yeast is growing even though you can't see the tiny organisms.*

Questions

1. Draw a sequence of diagrams showing the following:
   (a) a single yeast cell
   (b) a bud beginning to form
   (c) a bud ready to pinch off from the parent
   (d) the two yeast cells that result

Plants

The most successful asexual reproducers are plants. Some plants produce runners. These are special stems that grow outward along the ground (Figure 9.5). At their tips, the runners produce buds. The buds develop leaves and roots. In time the buds become individual plants.

(a)

(b)

Figure 9.5 (a) *Strawberry begonias and* **(b)** *spider plants send out runners that start new plants.*

Many plants have underground stems that grow horizontally. Have you ever seen grass growing in the middle of a paved driveway? The underground stem of grass has a sharp, hard point at its tip that can penetrate even asphalt. A new plant can grow from the tip where the stem breaks the surface of the ground.

Other types of underground stems are produced by potatoes, onions, and flowering plants such as tulips. These stems contain stored food. Even when conditions are not suitable for growth—during a cold winter or a hot, dry summer—these stems can remain alive. The life processes slow down and almost stop. Then, when better conditions return, the stems develop buds and start new growth (Figure 9.6).

Figure 9.6 *The food energy stored in potatoes can be used to support the growth of new plants.*

Even leaves are often able to start new plants. *Kalanchoe* is called "mother of thousands" because it produces so many "baby plants" (Figure 9.7). All along the edges of the leaves, new little plants form. When they fall off onto suitable soil, they can grow into plants identical in every way to the parent.

In some species of plants, a cutting from a stem or leaf can grow into a complete plant. Many plants are started this way in commercial nurseries.

Figure 9.7 *A species of Kalanchoe often called* "mother of thousands"

Ideas and Applications

You cannot reproduce yourself asexually. But the cells in your body are reproducing asexually all the time. As cells grow old and die, they are replaced by other cells that grow and divide into two. The production of new cells that are exactly like the original cells can happen because of a process called *mitosis*. You will review mitosis in Chapter 10.

Ideas and Applications

Although large animals cannot reproduce asexually, some can grow new parts to replace parts of their body that have been removed. When an earthworm is cut in half, the front half can grow a new tail. A crayfish can grow a new claw if one is broken off or lost. At first the new claw is smaller than the one it replaces. In time, the new part grows to normal size.

This crayfish is growing a new claw to replace one that was lost.

Self-check

1. What are the two main differences between sexual and asexual reproduction?
2. What are traits?
3. (a) Give an example of a situation where asexual reproduction would be an advantage to an organism.
   (b) Explain one advantage that sexual reproduction has over asexual reproduction.
4. Describe three different types of stems that some plants use for asexual reproduction.
5. Explain why growers in commercial nurseries use cuttings to produce many kinds of flowering plants.

Sexual Reproduction in Animals

All species of animals can reproduce sexually. Two individuals are required in order to produce offspring.

In sexual reproduction each parent contributes one special cell, called a **gamete** (Figure 9.8). The two gametes, the **egg** and the **sperm**, join together to produce the first cell of the offspring. The process of joining the egg and sperm together is called **fertilization**. The newly fertilized cell is called a **zygote**.

The zygote grows larger and the single cell divides into many cells which continue growing. While this is happening, the tiny organism is called an **embryo**. In time the embryo develops into an adult. This new organism will have some traits similar to each parent but will not be exactly like either one.

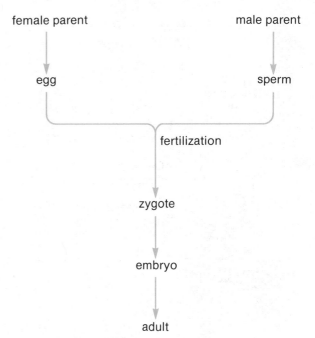

Figure 9.8 *Sexual reproduction. Two gametes, an egg and a sperm, join together to form the first cell of a new individual.*

Simple Animals

Some simple animals have both male and female sex organs within the same individual. You might think this would save the animal the time and trouble of looking for a mate, but this is not always so. Individuals usually cannot produce offspring sexually on their own. They must mate with another animal and exchange gametes. Each individual functions as both a male and a female.

EARTHWORMS

Every earthworm produces both eggs and sperm. When two individuals mate, each passes sperm cells to the other (Figure 9.9). The fertilized eggs are left in the ground to develop. Inside the egg cocoon the zygote grows, forming an embryo. When the embryo has completed its development in about three weeks, a young earthworm emerges.

More Complex Animals

In more complex animals, individuals are either male or female. The gametes produced by the two sexes are quite different. The egg is relatively large, while the sperm cells are much smaller.

ANIMALS THAT LIVE IN THE WATER

For many animals that live in the water, mating is a simple process. A male and a female come together and release the eggs and the sperm into the water at the same time.

The sperm cells swim to the eggs and fertilize them. Vast numbers of these gametes must be produced, because many do not survive. Some sperm cells do not find an egg to join with, some eggs are not fertilized, and many of the developing eggs are eaten by predators. Codfish produce up to 9 000 000 eggs. Only a few will survive to adulthood. One female frog may produce 15 000 eggs.

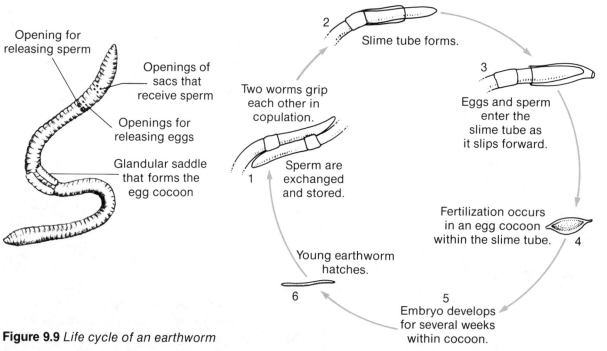

Figure 9.9 *Life cycle of an earthworm*

LAND ANIMALS

Sperm cells cannot survive dryness. For animals that breed on land, sperm must be transferred directly inside the body of the female. The males of mammals have an organ called a penis which is used for this purpose. Sperm cells leave the penis and swim inside the female until they meet with an egg cell.

Once *internal fertilization* has occurred, the next stage of development varies in different types of animals. The sexual reproduction and development of one type of mammal, the human, is described in Section 9.5.

Self-check

1. In sexual reproduction, what does each parent contribute to the offspring?
2. Define (a) zygote, (b) embryo, and (c) fertilization.
3. (a) Describe how fertilization occurs in animals that live in water.
   (b) What is one disadvantage of this method?
   (c) Why can most land animals not use this kind of fertilization?
4. Why is it helpful for some animals to produce large numbers of both male and female gametes?

Sexual Reproduction in Plants

As with animals, sexual reproduction in plants requires the joining of gametes from two parents. It also allows variation to occur in the offspring. The new generation inherits traits from both parents. The reproductive structures of plants are in the flower (Figure 9.10). Most individual flowers contain both male and female parts.

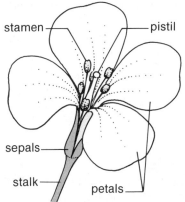

Figure 9.10
A simple flower

Challenge

How many flowers have you seen that look like the flower shown in Figure 9.10? Can you think of *any* that look like this? How can this diagram help you to understand sexual reproduction in other flowers? Flowers are obviously not all the same. Yet, in spite of their different shapes, colours, and designs, you may find that all contain the same parts. To test this idea, collect three or four different flowers and try to find the male and female structures in each. Sketch and label what you find. Some suitable flowers to examine are tulips, daffodils, dandelions, chrysanthemums, daisies, poinsettias, snapdragons, and orchids. You may find that books from your school library are helpful.

Problem

What reproductive structures of a simple flower can you find?

Materials

fresh flower
hand lens
compound microscope
microscope slides
coverslips
forceps
scalpel or single-edged razor blade
needles
prepared microscope slides of pollen grains and
  ovule section

> **CAUTION** The scalpel is very sharp. Be very careful.

Procedure

1. Examine a flower and identify the stamen and the pistil. Refer to Figure 9.11.
2. Remove a stamen. Examine it under a hand lens or the low power of the microscope. Sketch it and label the parts of the stamen shown in Figure 9.11.
3. Tap the anther onto a clean microscope slide. Did any pollen grains fall onto the slide? If not, slit the anther with the scalpel or razor blade. Again, tap the anther on the slide.
4. Examine the pollen grains under the microscope, using low and medium power. Make a sketch of a pollen grain. Compare with the pollen grains on the prepared microscope slide.
5. Remove the petals and sepals from a flower and examine the pistil, using a hand lens or the low power of the microscope. Are there any pollen grains sticking to it? Refer to Figure 9.11 and make a labelled diagram of the pistil of your flower.
6. Examine a prepared microscope slide of a section through an ovule. Sketch and label what you see.

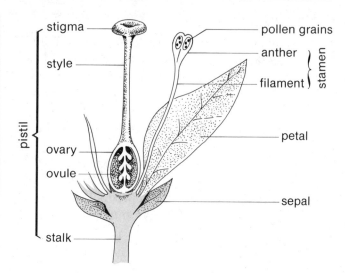

Figure 9.11 *The stamen and pistil of your flower may look different from the ones shown here, but the flower will have the same parts.*

Observations

1. Describe the arrangement of anthers in your flower.
2. List any differences between your flower and the one shown in Figure 9.10.

Questions

1. If you were watching for the development of seeds, what part of a flower would you consider to be of most importance? Explain your answer.

Ideas and Applications

A scientist wondered how many years seeds could survive. He put weed seeds in the ground in jars. Every 5 or 10 years someone dug up a jar and planted the seeds. Some seeds were still alive after 75 years.

Steps in the Sexual Reproduction of a Flowering Plant

1. A plant produces a flower containing a male part (**stamen**) and a female part (**pistil**). See Figure 9.11.
2. The stamen produces a powdery substance called **pollen**. The pollen travels, on the wind or on the body of an insect, to the pistil of another flower. This process is called **pollination** (Figure 9.12).

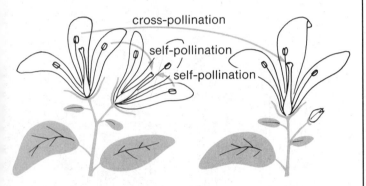

Figure 9.12 *There are two types of pollination. If the pollen comes from the same plant, the process is called self-pollination. If the pollen comes from another plant, the process is called cross-pollination. Cross-pollination is more common and produces more varied and stronger offspring.*

3. When a grain of pollen sticks to the pistil of the same species of flower, it absorbs moisture and starts to grow (Figure 9.13). The pollen tube grows down the pistil and produces sperm nuclei.
4. The pistil produces an egg nucleus.
5. The sperm fertilizes the egg. The fertilized egg is called the zygote.

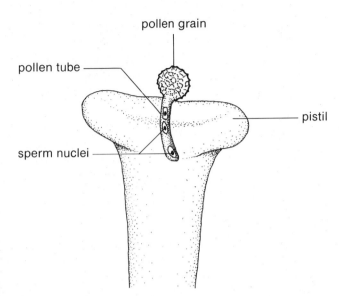

Figure 9.13 *Sperm nuclei are produced in the pollen tube.*

6. A series of changes begins. The zygote develops into an embryo, which remains only partly developed for some time. It goes into a resting stage. The embryo, along with a food supply, is enclosed in a seed (Figure 9.14). At this time the life processes slow down and the seed can survive hot, dry spells or extreme cold. It may be carried by animals or by the wind to a place far from where it was produced.

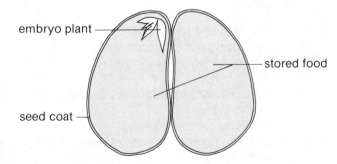

Figure 9.14 *When a lima bean seed is opened, the embryo plant can be seen.*

7. If suitable conditions for growth return, the seed absorbs moisture and the embryo completes its development. It grows into a plant which can then produce flowers to continue the cycle (Figure 9.15).

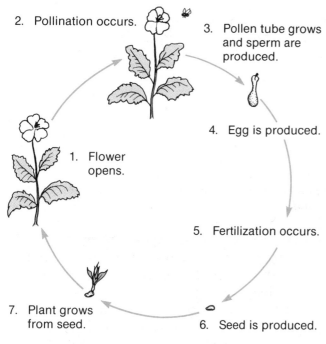

Figure 9.15 *Life cycle of flowering plants*

1. Flower opens.
2. Pollination occurs.
3. Pollen tube grows and sperm are produced.
4. Egg is produced.
5. Fertilization occurs.
6. Seed is produced.
7. Plant grows from seed.

Self-check

1. How are pollen and sperm related?
2. If you were using a microscope to examine the parts of a flower, where would you look for the zygote?
3. Explain the difference between cross-pollination and self-pollination.
4. (a) Name three parts of a seed.
   (b) What is the function of each of these parts?
5. Arrange the following events in the order in which they occur in the life cycle of a plant: seed formation, fertilization, growth of plant from seed, pollination, opening of flowers.

Human Reproduction

Figure 9.16 shows part of the plaque on the Pioneer 10 spacecraft, which was launched in 1972. This was the first manufactured object to be sent beyond the solar system. If intelligent beings from outer space ever examine the plaque, they can find out what humans look like and how males and females appear different.

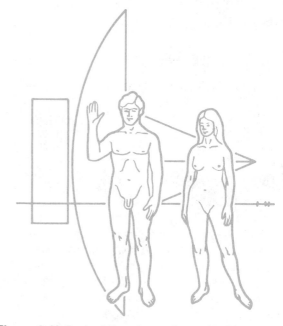

Figure 9.16 *Part of the plaque from the Pioneer 10 spacecraft*

These visible differences are the **secondary sexual characteristics**. They are the result of the action of hormones on various parts of the body during growth. Males generally have a larger body with stronger muscles and bones. In addition, males usually have hair on the face, chest, and body, and they have deeper voices. In females, the mammary glands are enlarged, forming breasts. As well, the pelvis of females is wider, to allow for the birth of a child. This makes the hips broader.

The **primary sexual characteristics** are the differences between the female organs (Figure 9.17) and the male organs (Figure 9.18). In the female, the sexual organs are

- the ovaries that produce the egg cells
- the oviducts (fallopian tubes) that carry the eggs
- the uterus where the fetus develops
- the vagina that connects the uterus to the outside.

In the male, the primary sexual organs are

- the testes that produce the sperm cells
- the tubes that carry sperm
- glands and storage sacs
- the penis that transfers the sperm into the female.

Figure 9.17 *The human female reproductive system*

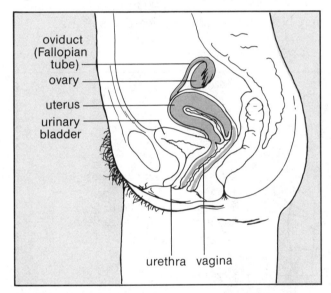

(a) *side view*

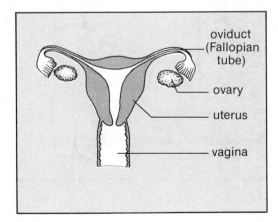

(b) *front view*

Figure 9.18 *The human male reproductive system*

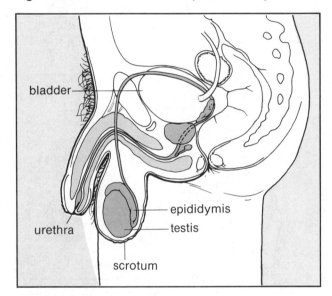

(a) *side view*

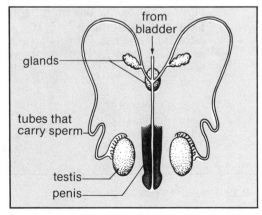

(b) *front view*

In late childhood, hormones from the thyroid and pituitary glands complete the development of the reproductive systems.

Reproductive maturity in young women is marked by the beginning of menstruation. **Menstruation** refers to the periodic flow of blood from the uterus (Figure 9.19). Menstruation occurs because hormones cause the uterus to build up a thick lining of soft material in preparation for pregnancy. The ovary releases an egg which travels to the uterus. If the egg is not fertilized by a sperm cell, the level of hormones decreases. This causes the uterus to shed its lining, and there is bleeding from the vagina. The time while there is bleeding is called a **menstrual period**. As the hormone level again increases, the cycle continues. This cycle of menstruation—preparation of the uterus, release of the egg, and shedding of the lining—occurs every three to five weeks for about 40 years. During pregnancy, menstruation does not occur.

In sexually mature males, sperm cells are produced in the testes. Fluid containing sperm cells is released, or ejaculated, from the penis. Between 300 million and 500 million sperm cells may be contained in one release of sperm.

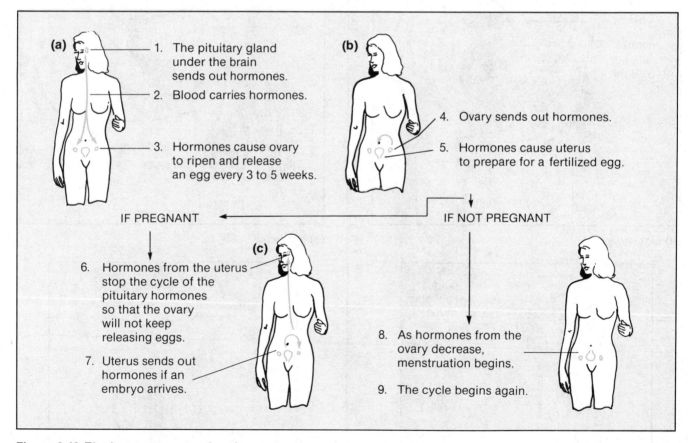

Figure 9.19 *The human menstrual cycle*

Fertilization

A sperm cell and an egg must meet for fertilization to occur. Fertilization is also called **conception** in humans. See Figure 9.20. Fluid containing sperm is released from the penis inside the vagina. The sperm cells travel to the oviduct and may remain active for about two days. If there is an egg present, if the uterus lining is prepared, and if the sperm fertilizes the egg, then a woman becomes pregnant. Conception is most likely to occur at about the middle of the menstrual cycle, but in some women it may occur at other times.

Figure 9.20 *Only one of these many sperm will enter the egg to fertilize it.*

Pregnancy

When a woman becomes pregnant, hormones are sent from the uterus to all parts of the body. These are the signal to stop the regular menstrual cycle. The uterus keeps its thick lining *and* the developing embryo. The hormones also stop the ovary from releasing more egg cells during pregnancy. The normal length of time for a pregnancy is 40 weeks, counted from the date of the beginning of the last menstrual period.

Development of the Embryo

Once fertilization has occurred, the zygote begins to grow and divide. Figure 9.21 shows some of the steps as the single-celled zygote develops into a human being. Early in the pregnancy the ball of cells is called an embryo. After the eighth week it is called a **fetus**. By the third month, the mother-to-be can feel the fetus moving its legs and arms.

TIME (WEEKS)	SIZE (mm)		APPEARANCE (3X ACTUAL SIZE)
0	0.2	°	Single-celled zygote
1	0.2		Ball of 100 cells implants itself in the uterus.
2	1.5		Ball folds to form inner layer.
3	2.5		Umbilical cord has formed, connecting the placenta. Heart is beating; segments form along back; gill pouches appear; a fold is forming the spinal cord and brain.
5	5.0		Embryo is not recognizably human yet.
8	30.0		Now the embryo is called a fetus; human features are appearing.

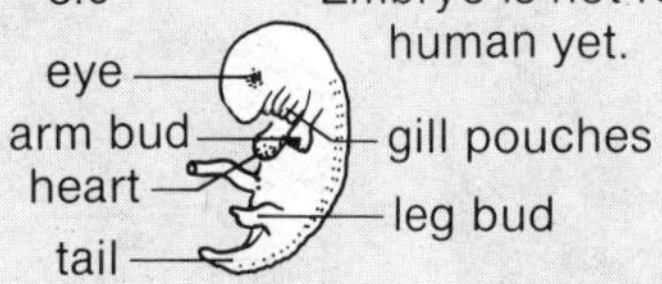

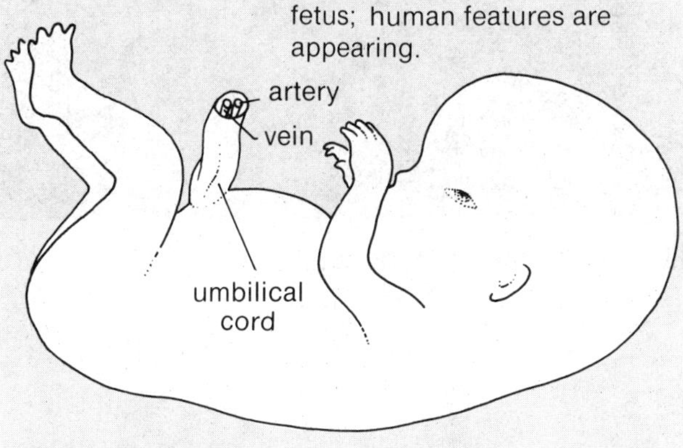

eye
arm bud — gill pouches
heart — leg bud
tail

artery
vein
umbilical cord

Figure 9.21 *Some stages in the development of the human fetus*

Birth

Muscular contractions of the walls of the uterus push the baby out into the world. The new human being must suddenly cope with variable temperatures, bright light, and strange sounds. It must breathe air, eat, eliminate waste, and adjust to separation from its mother (Figure 9.22).

The sex hormones that control the female reproductive cycle ensure that the mammary glands of the mother's breasts will be ready to feed the baby. The breasts enlarge during pregnancy, and after the birth they produce milk. The glands continue to produce milk for as long as the baby is nursing.

In Chapter 11 you will learn more about human reproduction and about traits that a baby may inherit from its parents.

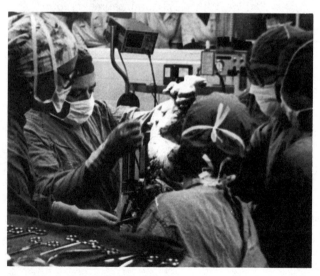

Figure 9.22 *Taking that first breath*

Self-check

1. List at least three secondary sexual characteristics of human males and females.
2. (a) What evidence shows that the reproductive system of a female has reached maturity?
   (b) Describe the reproductive cycle of the human female.
   (c) What changes take place in the reproductive cycle when a female becomes pregnant?
3. (a) What is a developing baby called during the first eight weeks of pregnancy?
   (b) What is a developing baby called from the eighth to the fortieth week of pregnancy?
4. What prevents menstruation from occurring during pregnancy?

Ideas and Applications

In the 1600s, after the discovery of the egg cell and the sperm cell, many scientists of the time thought the egg carried a miniature embryo. Others thought the sperm contained a completely formed, miniature human that started to grow once it was deposited in the womb.

Chapter Objectives

NOW THAT YOU HAVE COMPLETED THIS CHAPTER, CAN YOU DO THE FOLLOWING?	FOR REVIEW, TURN TO SECTION
1. Explain the difference between sexual and asexual reproduction.	9.1
2. Describe three types of asexual reproduction.	9.2
3. Identify asexual reproduction of plants.	9.2
4. Explain what must happen for an animal to produce offspring by sexual reproduction.	9.3
5. Describe the life cycle of a flowering plant.	9.4
6. List the primary and secondary sexual characteristics of human males and females.	9.5
7. Explain the menstrual cycle in human females.	9.5
8. Describe the development of a human fetus from fertilization to birth.	9.5

Words to Know

offspring
reproduce
trait
asexual reproduction
sexual reproduction
budding
gamete
egg
sperm
fertilization
zygote
embryo
stamen
pistil
pollen
pollination
secondary sexual characteristic
primary sexual characteristic
menstruation
menstrual period
conception
fetus

Tying It Together

1. What advantage is there in having offspring that are not identical to the parents?
2. (a) What type of asexual reproduction does yeast use?
   (b) Describe what happens during this process.
3. Name one way in which the sexual reproduction of earthworms is different from the sexual reproduction of more complex animals.
4. (a) What are gametes?
   (b) Describe how the two kinds of gametes differ.
5. (a) How does fertilization in land animals differ from fertilization in animals that live in water?
   (b) Explain why this difference is necessary.
6. (a) Draw and label a diagram of the four main parts of a simple flower.
   (b) Of the four parts, which two are essential for sexual reproduction?
7. (a) What is pollination?
   (b) Describe what happens in a flower after pollination occurs.
   (c) At what stage in the life cycle of a plant does it go into a "resting stage"?

8. In your notebook, make two columns with these headings: "Both Animals and Plants" and "Plants Only." Write each word from the following list in the correct column: egg, zygote, embryo, seed, sperm, flower, fertilization, pollination.

9. (a) Explain the difference between primary and secondary sexual characteristics.
   (b) Which of these characteristics are caused by hormones?

10. (a) Name the female organs in which (i) eggs are produced and (ii) the fetus develops.
    (b) Name the male organs (i) in which sperm is produced and (ii) from which sperm leaves the body.

11. (a) At what time in the menstrual cycle is a woman most likely to be able to conceive a child?
    (b) Why does menstruation stop during pregnancy?

12. (a) After how many weeks is an embryo recognizably human? How large is it at this stage?
    (b) What causes the baby to leave the uterus when it is fully developed?

Applying Your Knowledge

1. Give an example of a change in environment that could affect the growth of plants
   (a) on an apartment balcony
   (b) in a city garden
   (c) beside a highway
   (d) in a northern Ontario forest.

2. For one of your examples in question 1, explain why it would be an advantage for a species to have individual plants with a variety of traits.

3. (a) Suppose you have one especially beautiful geranium plant, and you want to have more plants like it next year. Describe how you could produce several identical plants from this single plant.

   (b) Suppose you give away two of the new plants to friends. One plant grows well, producing more leaves and flowers. The other just barely survives. Explain how this could happen.

4. To ensure that each species continues, each pair of adults should leave exactly two offspring. Most species produce many more offspring than this. What happens to most of the offspring? How is this useful in the balance of nature?

5. Gardeners who have wonderful gardens often snip off old flowers. Use your knowledge of what happens after fertilization to suggest how the removal of old flowers may keep plants blooming.

Projects for Investigation

1. Have you ever seen a science fiction movie about *clones*? Clones are identical copies of an organism. Clones of some organisms have been produced in laboratories from a single cell. For some time scientists have been able to clone carrots, frogs, and salamanders. More recently they have succeeded in making clones of mice. Do you think they should try to produce clones of humans? What type of person would be cloned—soldiers, athletes, scientists? Would *you* like to be cloned? With a friend, make up a plot for a movie in which a scientist develops the means to clone people. Or, watch a science fiction movie about clones and report the plot to your class.

2. Hay fever sufferers have a difficult time in spring and in early fall. Could their problems be related to plant reproduction? Find out what causes much of the hay fever at these seasons of the year. Be as specific as you can. Then, explain why sufferers have fewer problems in the middle of the summer.

10

Inheritance

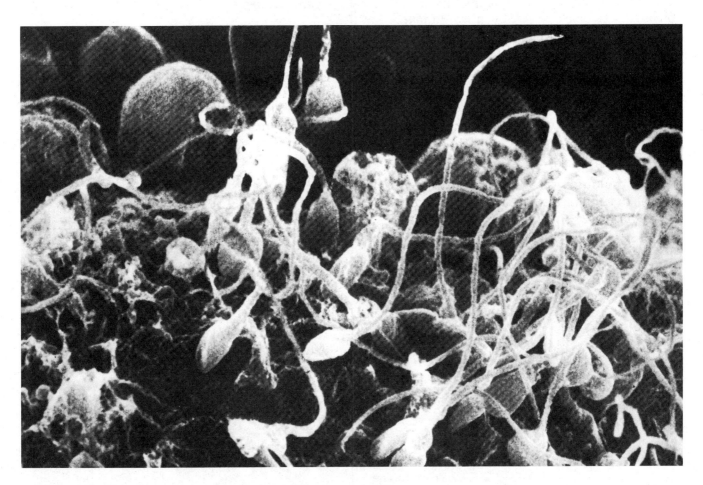

Key Ideas

- The hereditary material in a cell is contained in the cell nucleus.
- When an egg or sperm is produced, it receives exactly half of the genes of the parent organism.
- The patterns of inheritance, first studied in pea plants, are similar in all organisms.
- People make use of their knowledge of genetics in the selective breeding of plants and animals.

Traits are inherited from parents in sexual reproduction. But what exactly is it that parents pass on to their offspring? In Chapter 9, you learned that each parent contributes only one cell—an egg or a sperm. Can all the information be contained in these two gametes? What causes certain traits to be passed on to some offspring but not to others? How can a trait "disappear" in one generation and turn up again in the next? In this chapter, you will look inside cells to find the answers to these questions.

Cells

All living things are made of **cells**, which are the basic units of life. The simplest organisms consist of only one cell. A fully grown human might have 60 million million cells.

Structure of Cells

You know from your previous studies that each cell has three essential parts.

1. The **cell membrane** is the outer living surface of the cell.
2. The **nucleus** is the control centre of the cell.
3. The **cytoplasm** is the part of the cell outside the nucleus.

Although the cytoplasm appears to be uniform under a compound microscope, it actually contains many complex structures (Figure 10.1).

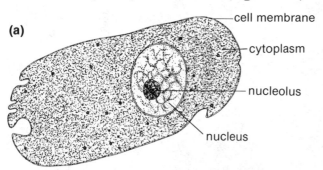

(a)

cell membrane

cytoplasm

nucleolus

nucleus

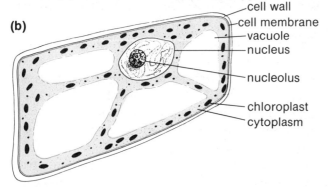

(b)

cell wall
cell membrane
vacuole
nucleus

nucleolus

chloroplast
cytoplasm

Figure 10.1 *An animal cell and a plant cell. Can you tell which is which?*

Note: Plant cells have an additional structure called the **cell wall**. The cell wall is really outside the living part of the cell. It gives a plant cell its shape.

INSIDE THE NUCLEUS

The **chromosomes** in the nucleus contain all the instructions that are passed from parent to offspring. Every body cell of an organism has the same number of chromosomes, called the **diploid number**. Humans have 46 chromosomes in every cell. In other words, the diploid number for humans is 46. The diploid number for pea plants is 14. For corn, it is 20, and for fruit flies it is 8. Privet, a common plant used in hedges, has a diploid number of 46, the same as for humans. Note that the number of chromosomes is not significant. It is the *information* contained in them that is important.

Along the chromosomes, like beads on a string, are the **genes** (Figure 10.2). Each gene contains coded instructions for one particular trait. It is the total of all the genes that determines what a cell and an organism are like.

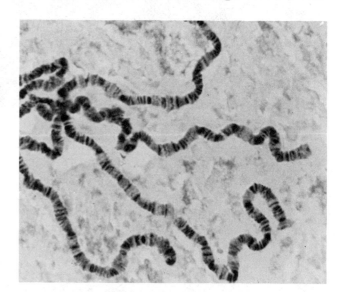

Figure 10.2 *These chromosomes are in cells of the fruit fly,* Drosophila. *The darker bands are genes.*

Cell Growth and Division

When a cell grows to a certain size it divides into two cells. Each cell must contain an exact copy of each chromosome so that each new cell contains identical instructions. **Mitosis** is the duplication of the chromosomes and the division of the nucleus. Mitosis and cell division occur regularly as cells grow.

MITOSIS

Chromosomes are not usually visible in the nucleus of cells, even under a microscope. They are very thin threads, spread out and tangled up with one another. When the cell is preparing to divide, a copy is made of each chromosome. Then the chromosomes coil up, get thicker, and become visible.

At this stage it is possible to see the two identical copies, which are still attached together at a single point (Figure 10.3). All the copies line up along the centre of the cell. Finally, the two identical copies separate completely (Figure 10.4).

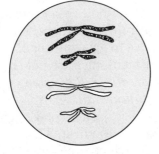

Figure 10.3 *The four chromosomes in this cell have already been copied, but the copies are still attached.*

Figure 10.4 *Toward the end of mitosis, the two sets of chromosomes move apart.*

There are now two complete sets of new and identical chromosomes. They move to each end of the cell and begin to get thinner and more difficult to see under the microscope. When mitosis is complete they are no longer visible.

CELL DIVISION

After the chromosomes have been copied and moved to each end of the cell, the cytoplasm divides into two parts. Two new cells form. Each cell has an *exact* copy of all the original chromosomes. Since these new cells have the same genes, they will have the same traits as the parent cell.

Challenge

You can review mitosis by viewing a prepared slide of animal embryo cells under a compound microscope.

PROCEDURE
1. Place the slide of the animal embryo cells on the stage of the compound microscope.
2. Examine the slide under the low-power lens.
3. Change to the high-power lens. Locate the animal cells undergoing mitosis.
4. Move the slide *very slowly* along the microscope stage. Find the cells at different stages of cell division.
5. Sketch and label at least three cells at different stages of cell division.

Life Cycle of a Sexually Reproducing Organism

During mitosis, the complete set of chromosomes is duplicated. Every new cell produced by mitosis receives a full set of genes that control its development.

Sexual reproduction, however, introduces a problem. Suppose that an egg nucleus contains one full set of chromosomes. Let the symbol N represent the number of chromosomes in this set. Then the sperm nucleus will bring another set, another N.

egg + sperm   →   zygote
N + N   →   2N

When the egg and sperm unite, the zygote will contain 2N—a double set of chromosomes. Suppose the process of mitosis were to maintain this double set of chromosomes in every cell of the embryo and eventually the adult. At the next fertilization, if the number of chromosomes doubled again, then

$$2N + 2N \rightarrow 4N$$

and, if in the next generation it doubled again, then

$$4N + 4N \rightarrow 8N$$

You can see that eventually there would be too many chromosomes for the space in the nucleus. Fortunately, there is a process to keep the chromosome number from doubling at every generation. It is called meiosis.

Meiosis: Diploid to Haploid

Meiosis is a special kind of nuclear duplication of the cell. It occurs only when gametes (egg and sperm cells) are being produced. In humans, the egg is produced in the ovary of the female, and the sperm is produced in the testis of the male. In meiosis, the double set of chromosomes (2N or diploid number) is reduced to a single set. The number of chromosomes in the single set is called the **haploid number** (N). Both the egg and the sperm contain the haploid number. For example, in humans the diploid number is 46. The haploid number is 23 (46 ÷ 2 = 23). Egg cells and sperm cells contain only 23 chromosomes.

Meiosis resembles mitosis in some ways. Both processes begin with the chromosomes duplicating, thickening, and shortening. But in meiosis there are two steps that do not occur in mitosis.

- There is a difference in the way the duplicated chromosomes line up at the middle of the cell. In meiosis, the chromosomes line up in matching pairs (Figure 10.5). Some chromosomes may break and exchange parts with their partners. When they separate and move to opposite ends, the two sets of chromosomes are not the same. *This means that, after cell division, new cells will not have identical traits.*
- In meiosis, a second cell division immediately follows the first. This results in *four* haploid cells which are formed from the one original cell. In humans, each of the four haploid cells would contain 23 chromosomes. You can see from Figure 10.5 that the chromosomes in each of these four cells are different. (In mitosis, the chromosomes are the same—there is no "swapping" of chromosome material.)

Figure 10.5 *Steps in the process of meiosis*

(a) *The chromosomes coil up, get thicker, and become visible.*

(b) *The two identical copies of each chromosome are still attached together. This step is similar to mitosis.*

(c) *The chromosomes now come together in matching pairs. They may break and exchange parts.*

(d) *The cell divides. The two new cells contain new combinations of chromosome material.*

(e) *These new cells immediately divide again, forming four haploid cells.*

Problem

What steps of meiosis can you observe using a compound microscope?

Materials

compound microscope
prepared slides of sections of testis, ovary, anther, ovule

Procedure

1. Under low power, examine one of the prepared slides. Scan the field of view for cells with noticeable chromosomes. The chromosomes will appear as black lines inside cells.
2. Move one of the cells with chromosomes into the centre of the field of view. Carefully switch to medium, then to high power.
3. Repeat steps 1 and 2 until you have found cells in all the stages of meiosis.
4. Repeat steps 1, 2, and 3 for each slide—testis, ovary, anther, and ovule.

Observations

Make diagrams of cells found in each of the following stages:

   (a) the pairing of matching chromosomes
   (b) the duplication of the chromosomes into groups of four
   (c) the separation of the groups of four at the first division
   (d) the final separation at the second division

Questions

1. List any similarities that you found on the different slides.
2. What were the differences in meiosis on the different slides?

Fertilization: Haploid to Diploid

A haploid cell produced by meiosis develops into an egg cell in a female, or into a sperm cell in a male. When an egg cell and a sperm cell unite, the zygote contains the complete diploid number of chromosomes. Half the chromosomes came from one parent, and half from the other. Figure 10.6 shows how meiosis and fertilization fit into a typical life cycle.

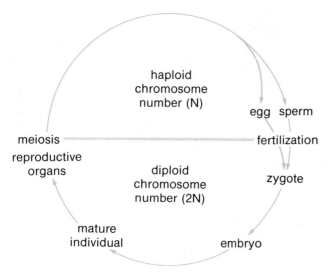

Figure 10.6 *Life cycle of a sexually reproducing organism*

Self-check

1. What are the three essential parts of all cells?
2. How are genes and chromosomes related?
3. (a) What is one similarity between mitosis and meiosis?
   (b) What are two differences between mitosis and meiosis?
4. Explain the meaning of 2N and N in meiosis.
5. Name two kinds of cells that contain the haploid number of chromosomes.
6. (a) Where does meiosis occur in your body?
   (b) Where does meiosis occur in the body of a member of the opposite sex?

Inheritance of Traits

Heredity is the tendency of offspring to resemble their parents. Because of meiosis, the offspring do not inherit every trait of their parents. Instead, the offspring inherit *some* traits from each parent.

Think of your own family. What traits do you share with your mother? In what ways are you like your father? Do you have any traits that are different from both your parents?

By examining two or three generations of a family you can discover whether there is a pattern to inheritance of traits. You can look at various plants and animals to find out whether inheritance works in a similar way for them.

Challenge

WHAT IS CHANCE?

Five students should work together to answer this question. Each should toss a coin ten times. Record how many times "heads" turns up. How many times did you get "tails"? What *percentage* of the time did you get heads? What percentage of the time did you get tails? (Remember: To calculate percentages, divide the number by the total and multiply by 100. Example: 6 heads out of 10 tosses = 6 ÷ 10 = 0.60 or 60%.)

Now add *your* numbers for heads and tails to the numbers obtained by the other four members of your group. What percentage of the *total* was heads? tails?

Extend this exercise to a genetics question. Approximately the same number of human males and females are born. Thus, there is a 50:50 chance, or *probability*, of being born male or female.

Why, then, are there not always equal numbers of boys and girls in every family?

Activity 10B

Problem

What is the pattern to inheritance of traits?

Materials

Procedure

1. Clasp your hands together, with the fingers interlocking (Figure 10.7). Which thumb is on top? Try clasping your hands with the other thumb on top. Which way feels more comfortable?
2. Prepare an observation sheet with your name at the top. Beside your name, write down which thumb you placed on top when you first clasped your hands.
3. At home, have the other members of your family try step 1. Add their names to your observation sheet. Record your findings on your observation sheet. Bring the results to the next class.

left thumb on top   right thumb on top

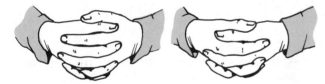

Figure 10.7 *Hand clasping*

Observations

1. Record the number of people you surveyed about this trait. How many of them clasped with their left thumb on top, and how many clasped with their right thumb on top? Your teacher will record the numbers of each type surveyed by everyone in the class. Calculate the total number of left-thumb-over claspers and the total number of right-thumb-over claspers.

2. In a family where both parents put their right thumbs on top, how do the children clasp their hands?
3. In a family where both parents put their left thumbs on top, how do the children clasp their hands?
4. In a family where the parents differ in the way they clasp their hands, in which way do the children clasp?

Questions

1. (a) Which form of this trait is more common among the people surveyed by your classmates?
   (b) Do you think the same would be true for the whole population of your school district? Explain.
2. Have you found any reason to believe that this trait is inherited? Explain.

Problem

What similarities can you find in inheritance among plants and animals?

Materials

class results from Activity 10B
data from Figure 10.8
package of mixed dry peas
large tray
ear of corn with various coloured kernels

Procedure

1. Make a table in your notebook like Table 10.1.
2. Record the total number of left-thumb-over claspers and right-thumb-over claspers that your class found in Activity 10B.
3. Examine Figure 10.8. *Drosophila*, or fruit flies, inherit a gene for wing type. The wings may be normal or *vestigial*. Vestigial means small and not fully developed. The results of one experiment have been entered for you into Table 10.1.
4. Use the beaker to scoop a random sample of peas from the package. Spread them on the tray. Sort them into yellow and green and record the number of each in your observation table.
5. Using the same peas again, sort them into smooth and wrinkled. Record the numbers of each in your observation table.
6. On the ear of corn, count the numbers of kernels of each colour. Record the numbers in your observation table.

normal wings: 920 flies   vestigial wings: 317 flies

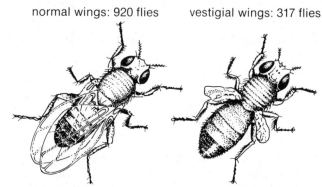

Figure 10.8 Drosophila, *or fruit flies, are often used to study inheritance. In a recent study, the wings of more than 1000 fruit flies were examined. The flies with normal wings and the flies with vestigial (undeveloped) wings were counted.*

Observations

1. For each of the five sets of data obtained, divide the smaller number into the larger. Round off the results to the nearest whole number, and express it as a ratio in the last column of the table. For the *Drosophila* data the calculation has been done for you.

Questions

1. What similarity is there among the five ratios that you have calculated?
2. Explain how a similar pattern of inheritance could have occurred in these four different organisms.

Table 10.1 *Data for Activity 10C*

TRAIT	MORE COMMON FORM		LESS COMMON FORM		RATIO
	DESCRIPTION	NUMBER	DESCRIPTION	NUMBER	
Hand clasping					
Drosophila wing type	Normal	920	Vestigial	317	$\frac{920}{317} = \frac{2.9}{1} = \frac{3}{1}$
Pea colour					
Pea shape					
Colour of corn kernels					

Discovering the Pattern of Inheritance: Gregor Mendel

The traits you observed in Activity 10C showed similar patterns of inheritance. As you have discovered, there are two forms of each trait. One form of a trait occurs in three out of four individuals. The other form of the trait occurs in one out of four individuals. This pattern or ratio of 3:1 was first discovered in 1865 by an Austrian monk named **Gregor Mendel** (Figure 10.9). Mendel discovered the pattern, and he was also able to explain it.

Figure 10.9 *Gregor Mendel*

Inheritance in Pea Plants

Mendel's success was based on simple experiments and careful recording of observations. He studied inheritance of seven separate traits in pea plants. For eight years he grew peas, observed the traits of the plants, and harvested the seeds. Since a new generation of peas is produced each year, he gathered information for about eight generations.

Mendel understood that two parents are necessary for the pea plant to produce seeds. He was able to control this sexual reproduction because he realized that pollen from the stamen of one parent moved to the pistil of the other parent.

Mendel removed the stamens from some flowers and transferred pollen by hand (Figure 10.10). Using this method he could be certain which plants were the parents of which seeds. In the fall he collected the seeds and stored them until spring. The following year he planted these seeds and observed the traits of the next generation.

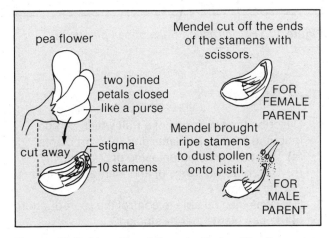

Figure 10.10 *How Mendel controlled pollination*

Of the seven traits that he studied, he found that there were only two forms of each trait (Figure 10.11). Plants were either short *or* tall, seeds were either yellow *or* green, etc. And, most important, the ratio 3:1 kept occurring in his results. The explanation for this pattern of inheritance is the subject of the next section.

TRAIT	TWO FORMS OF TRAIT	
Seed shape	 smooth	 wrinkled
Seed colour	 yellow	 green
Seed coat colour	 gray	 white
Pod shape	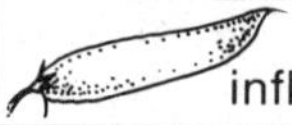 inflated	 constricted
Pod colour	 green	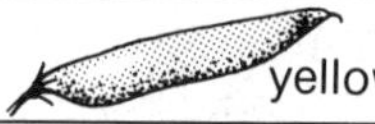 yellow
Flower position	at sides 	 at tips
Stem height	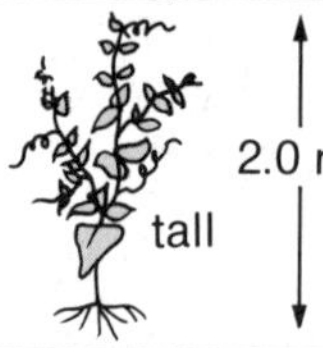 tall 2.0 m	short 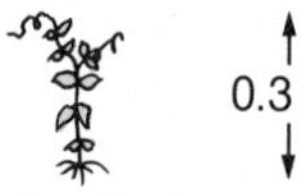 0.3 m

Figure 10.11 *Contrasting traits of pea plants*

Self-check

1. Describe the two forms of a trait which can be inherited by (a) pea plants and (b) corn plants.
2. (a) What is the common name of *Drosophila*?
   (b) Describe two forms of an inherited trait in this organism.
3. How was Mendel able to control the reproduction of the pea plants that he studied?

Genetics: The Science of Heredity

You have observed that there is a pattern to inheritance. The explanation for the pattern of inheritance is called **genetics**. To understand genetics, you must again look inside cells at the chromosomes and genes.

The material that controls the inheritance of an offspring comes from two parents. Whatever the species, a set of N chromosomes comes from the female parent, and a set of N chromosomes comes from the male parent. The fertilized egg contains a double set of instructions. An organism has *two* genes for every trait. One is inherited from the mother, and one is inherited from the father. This is true for all plants and animals that reproduce sexually.

When both genes contain the code for the same form of a trait, that form of the trait is the one that is present in the organism. For example, if a pea plant has two genes that code for wrinkled seeds, the seeds will be wrinkled. What happens when the two genes code for a *different* form of the same trait? Which form of the trait shows up in the offspring?

For many traits, one form of the gene dominates the other. This **dominant gene** is the one that affects the appearance or behaviour of the individual. The other gene of the pair is called the **recessive gene**. Although it may not affect the appearance or behaviour, it may be passed on to the next generation.

In this activity you will use pieces of plastic to represent dominant and recessive genes. You will come to understand how the effect of one gene can dominate the other.

Problem

If the genes of one parent are unlike the genes of the other parent, what will the offspring be like?

Materials

two identical pieces of coloured transparent plastic (each 5 cm x 10 cm)
two identical pieces of clear, colourless transparent plastic (each 5 cm x 10 cm)
two paper bags

Procedure

1. Put two pieces of plastic together and hold them up to the light (Figure 10.12). Repeat this with all the other combinations of two pieces of plastic.

Figure 10.12

2. Put the two coloured pieces in one bag and the two colourless pieces in the other. The bags represent two parents, and the pieces of plastic represent two genes for one trait. Take one piece of plastic from each bag, put the two pieces together, and look through them to the light. These pieces will represent the offspring.

Observations

1. In your notebook, record whether each combination appeared coloured or clear.
2. When the two pieces of plastic are different, which one *dominates* the other?

Questions

1. Which type of plastic represents the dominant gene? Explain.
2. Which type of plastic represents the recessive gene? Explain.

Genotype and Phenotype

Genotype is the word used to describe the kind of genes an individual has. Let us use a capital C to represent the gene for coloured, and a small c to represent the gene for colourless. Suppose the genotype of one parent is CC, and the genotype of the other parent is cc. Their genotypes are both **pure strain**—their two genes for the trait are the same. All the offspring have the genotype Cc (Figure 10-13). The offspring genotype is **hybrid**. This means that the individuals have two different genes for the same trait. Hybrid offspring may *appear* to be identical to one of the parents.

The appearance of a trait in an individual is called the **phenotype**. In the example in Figure 10.13, the phenotype of the offspring is the same as the phenotype of *one* of the parents.

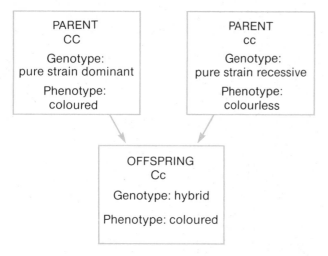

Figure 10.13 *Each parent passes on to the offspring only one gene of the pair.*

In this activity you will observe the phenotype of the offspring when the parents are hybrids.

Problem

What will the offspring of two hybrid parents be like?

Materials

two identical pieces of coloured transparent plastic (each 5 cm x 10 cm)
two identical pieces of clear, colourless transparent plastic (each 5 cm x 10 cm)
two paper bags

Procedure

1. Make a table in your notebook similar to Figure 10.14. Include three columns, labelled "CC," "cc," and "Cc." A capital C represents coloured, and a small c represents colourless.
2. In each bag put one coloured (C) and one clear (c) piece of plastic. The pieces of plastic in the bags now represent the genes of hybrid parents (Cc).
3. Without looking, draw one piece of plastic from each bag. The pieces you have withdrawn represent the genes passed on to the *second* generation. Make a mark in your table to record the type of offspring (Figure 10.14).
4. Repeat steps 2 and 3 a total of 30 times.

	CC	cc	Cc
Number of offspring	ЖЖ |||	ЖЖ ||	///

Figure 10.14 *Keep a count of the results by making marks in groups of five.*

Observations

1. Count the numbers of marks in each column and record the totals.
2. (a) What was the total number of combinations that appeared coloured (CC + Cc)?
   (b) What was the total number of combinations that appeared colourless?
3. Using the two numbers from Observations question 2, divide the smaller number into the larger one. Round off the answer to the nearest whole number. You have done this type of calculation before, in Activity 10C. This number is the ratio of coloured to colourless offspring.

Questions

1. Draw a table like Table 10.2 in your notebook. Fill in the blank squares to show all the possible combinations of genes for the second generation.
2. A hybrid genotype is used in this activity. Why does one phenotype occur more often than the other?
3. (a) What is the ratio that resulted from your observations?
   (b) Is this ratio the same as that predicted by Mendel? Why?

Table 10.2 *The top line represents the two genes that can be passed on from the female parent. The left column represents the two genes of the male parent.*

	C	c
C		
c		

Mendel and His Study of Pea Plants

In his work with peas, Mendel worked with one trait at a time. He also tested plants to be sure that he could produce several generations that had the same traits. For example, if he bred pure strain tall plants among themselves, all the offspring were tall. If he bred pure strain short plants among themselves, all the offspring were short.

Mendel then cross-pollinated the pure strain tall plants with the pure strain short plants. He found that the plants in the next generation were all of the same phenotype. *All* the offspring were tall, just like *one* of the parents. It did not matter which was the female or male parent. The gene for tallness dominated. However, these first generation plants *must* have received a different gene from each parent. They must have been hybrids.

When these hybrid plants were used as parents, their offspring (the second generation) were three-quarters tall and one-quarter short (Figure 10.15). Here is the 3:1 ratio again, which

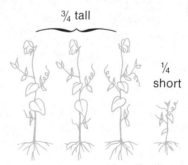

¾ tall

¼ short

second generation offspring

Figure 10.15 *The result of a cross between hybrid plants*

177

kept appearing in Activity 10C. Figure 10.16 shows a type of diagram called a *Punnett square*. A Punnett square is an easy way of showing the different genotypes which can be produced by hybrid parents. It is similar to Table 10.2, which you used in Activity 10E.

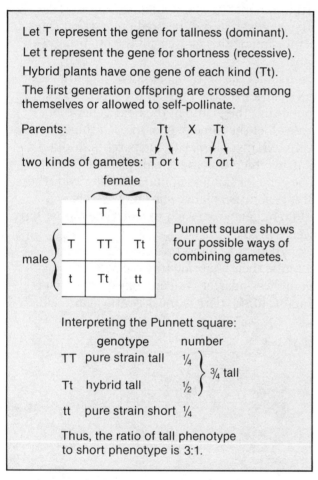

Let T represent the gene for tallness (dominant).

Let t represent the gene for shortness (recessive).

Hybrid plants have one gene of each kind (Tt).

The first generation offspring are crossed among themselves or allowed to self-pollinate.

Parents: Tt   X   Tt

two kinds of gametes: T or t   T or t

female

	T	t
T	TT	Tt
t	Tt	tt

male

Punnett square shows four possible ways of combining gametes.

Interpreting the Punnett square:

genotype	number
TT pure strain tall	¼
Tt hybrid tall	½
tt pure strain short	¼

¾ tall (TT + Tt)

Thus, the ratio of tall phenotype to short phenotype is 3:1.

Figure 10.16 *The explanation of height inheritance in peas*

Self-check

1. (a) What is meant by "dominant gene for a trait"?
    (b) What is meant by "recessive gene for a trait"?
2. (a) Explain the meaning of "genotype."
    (b) How does the genotype of an individual affect its phenotype?
3. In guinea pigs, the gene for black hair (B) is dominant. The gene for white hair (b) is recessive.
    (a) Write the genotype of a hybrid guinea pig.
    (b) What will be the phenotype of this guinea pig?
4. In pea plants, the gene for smooth seeds (S) is dominant over the gene for wrinkled seeds (s).
    (a) List the three possible genotypes for this trait of seed shape. For each genotype, tell whether the seeds would be smooth or wrinkled.
    (b) Draw a Punnett square like the one in Figure 10.16, showing the offspring of two plants that are hybrid for seed shape.
5. In fruit flies, the gene for normal wings (N) is dominant over the gene for vestigial wings (n).
    (a) Draw a Punnett square showing the offspring of a pure strain normal parent and a pure strain vestigial-winged parent. Describe the offspring.
    (b) Draw a Punnett square showing the offspring of two hybrid parents. Describe the offspring.

Challenge

SYMBOLS	MALE	FEMALE
Right thumb on top	☐	◯
Left thumb on top	■	●

(a) *The shape of the symbol indicates the sex of the individual. The colour indicates which form of the trait the individual has.*

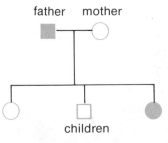

(b) *This type of diagram is called a pedigree.*

More about Genetics

Incomplete Dominance

Mendel found that there were two forms of each gene for all the traits he studied. The phenotype was determined by the dominant gene. Since the hybrid plants looked like the ones with a pair of dominant genes, he could not tell them apart. Only plants with two recessive genes had a different and distinctive phenotype. All these traits showed complete dominance of one form of the gene.

In Activities 10D and 10E you may have been able to see a difference between two pieces of coloured plastic, CC, and one coloured and one colourless piece, Cc. Even though the coloured piece still dominated the effect of the clear piece, the dominance may not have been complete.

In nature there are many examples of both complete and incomplete dominance. Complete dominance is shown when humans cross their hands with the left *or* the right thumb on top, and when pea plants are short *or* tall.

On the other hand, there are also many cases of blending, or incomplete dominance. Some hybrid plants produce pink flowers, not red flowers like one parent or white like the other (Figure 10.17). A girl may have one tall parent

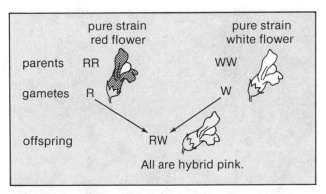

Figure 10.17 *Inheritance in snapdragons does not show dominance. If these pink hybrid offspring are crossed among themselves, what will the next generation look like?*

and one short one, and grow to an in-between height. Think of other examples of human traits that show incomplete dominance.

Mutations

Occasionally an offspring may have a trait that is unlike the traits of any of its relatives. This sudden change in a trait is called a **mutation**.

Chromosomes are made up of two types of chemical substances—protein and **DNA (deoxyribonucleic acid)**. DNA contains the code that determines the traits. During cell division, the DNA *must* be copied exactly. If a mistake is made during meiosis, the offspring may contain an altered copy of the DNA. This change in the DNA of the chromosomes causes the mutation.

Many mutations are harmful. A change in the DNA might change one of the chemical processes in an organism, killing it. However, it might cause only a small change, such as altering the colour of an animal or plant. "Mutation mink" has resulted in minks with blond fur. Sometimes a mutation will cause a white flower to appear in a clump that had only purple ones in previous years (Figure 10.18).

Figure 10.18 *The white anemone is the result of a mutation.*

Selective Breeding

Long before there was any knowledge of cell structure, chromosomes, genes, or DNA, farmers knew that offspring tended to resemble their parents. For this reason they would use **selective breeding**. In other words, they allowed only animals and plants with desirable traits to reproduce.

Animals

A farmer might observe that some particular hens are laying more and larger eggs than usual. By allowing only these hens to reproduce, the farmer raises the probability that more of the chicks will also lay more and larger eggs. Some of them will have inherited the same ability from their mothers.

The dog was the first animal to be bred for specific traits. All the *pure breeds* that exist today are the result of selective breeding. They are called pure breeds because they are known to

Figure 10.19 *The dachshund is a pure breed dog.*

pass on to their offspring all the characteristics of their breed. Careful records of the parents are kept in the form of *pedigrees*. Dogs have been selectively bred for hunting, guarding, guiding, and for intelligence, as well as for companionship. The dachshund, with its short legs, was bred to be able to pursue wild animals into their burrows (Figure 10.19).

Scientific selective breeding of domestic animals began more than 200 years ago. In Australia, merino sheep that produce a lot of wool have been developed by selective breeding (Figure 10.20).

The pedigrees of many cattle are well known. Registered bulls are rarely taken to farms to be mated with specific cows. Instead, their sperm is collected, frozen in liquid nitrogen, and transported worldwide. The sperm can then be used to fertilize thousands of cows. This practice, called **artificial insemination**, is becoming more and more common.

Plants

Corn has been grown by humans for food for at least 7000 years. We don't know how ancient peoples improved their crops, but we do know that during those 7000 years, ears of corn have changed greatly. Originally there were fewer than 50 kernels on a cob of corn. The cobs were also tiny—only about 5 cm long. Now there may be 1000 kernels on a cob, and the cob may be 20 cm long. The early farmers probably selected the seeds from the best cobs for planting in the following season. Over thousands of years the cobs have gradually grown bigger and bigger. In modern times, scientists continue to develop better corn. Using their knowledge of genetics, they have also developed high-yield corn plants that can resist attack by diseases and insects, as well as produce corn stalks with increased numbers of corn cobs.

Other plants used for food are also modified by selective breeding. Cucumber plants have been bred to produce fruit that is exactly the size required for dill pickles. Tomatoes have been bred with tough skins that can withstand automatic pickers and long distance transport (Figure 10.21).

Figure 10.20 *The sheep on the left, with its thick fleece, was developed by selective breeding. The sheep on the right is the original type.*

Figure 10.21 *Machines like this one are used to harvest tomatoes.*

Problems with Selective Breeding

Animals or plants can be selectively bred through many generations. Desirable characteristics are more and more likely to appear in the offspring. There is less and less variation. However, other less-desirable traits may also appear. For example, race horses are fast but easily frightened. Many selectively bred plants and animals are not as hardy as wild species. For example, lawn grass needs watering and fertilizing, while wild prairie grasses can survive with no care.

The traits desired by humans do not always benefit the animals themselves. Selective breeding of turkeys has produced birds with an increased amount of white breast meat (Figure 10.22). These birds are profitable for the farmers who grow them. However, the male turkeys have such wide chests that they have difficulty keeping their balance. They fall over when they attempt to mate so they cannot reproduce in the natural way. Offspring must be produced by artificial insemination.

Figure 10.22 *A change in a breed of animal that benefits the farmer may not benefit the animal itself.*

STERILE OFFSPRING

Occasionally organisms of closely related species have been mated to produce hybrid offspring. Usually the offspring are sterile. **Sterile** organisms cannot reproduce themselves.

The offspring of a horse and a donkey is a *mule*. This animal inherits useful traits from both parents. It has the strength and stamina of a horse. It has the donkey's surefootedness and ability to eat raw vegetation.

The *beefalo* is the result of a cross between a cow and a buffalo (Figure 10.23). This could be a profitable animal because it is bigger than a cow, and it can live outside in Canadian winters. However, since beefalo themselves are sterile, they are difficult to produce.

Figure 10.23 *Beefaloes*

Self-check

1. What is meant by incomplete dominance of a gene? Give an example.
2. (a) What is a mutation?
   (b) Give an example of a mutation that is apparently harmless.
3. (a) What is selective breeding?
   (b) List five organisms that have been used in selective breeding experiments. For each, describe what characteristic was desired in the offspring.

Northern Dancer: A Selective-Breeding Success Story

In May of 1964, a record was set at the Kentucky Derby. Northern Dancer, a Canadian three-year-old, ran the course in exactly two minutes. He became the Horse of the Year in Canada and Champion Three-Year-Old in the United States. Unfortunately, a few months after his victory, Northern Dancer was slightly injured. Rather than risk further damage to a bowed tendon in his leg, his owners decided to retire him. He would be kept as a *stud* and used only for breeding purposes.

Northern Dancer is one of the most successful studs of all time. As racers, his sons and daughters have done exceptionally well. They have also produced exceptional offspring. The descendants of Northern Dancer are having a lasting effect on thoroughbred racing.

Northern Dancer

Chapter Objectives

NOW THAT YOU HAVE COMPLETED THIS CHAPTER, CAN YOU DO THE FOLLOWING?	FOR REVIEW, TURN TO SECTION
1. Describe the essential structure of plant and animal cells.	10.1
2. Describe the process of mitosis.	10.1
3. Explain how and why haploid cells are produced in meiosis.	10.2
4. Tell what Mendel did in his experiments with pea plants and what he found.	10.3
5. Explain the result of Mendel's experiments with pea plants.	10.4
6. Draw Punnett squares to show the genes that may be inherited by offspring.	10.4
7. Distinguish between phenotype and genotype.	10.4
8. Give examples of complete and incomplete dominance.	10.5
9. Define mutation, and give an example.	10.5
10. Explain why selective breeding has both advantages and disadvantages.	10.6
11. Give examples of animals and plants that have been selectively bred.	10.6

Words to Know

cell
cell membrane
nucleus
cytoplasm
chromosome
diploid number
gene
mitosis
meiosis
haploid number
heredity
Mendel
genetics
dominant gene
recessive gene
genotype

pure strain
hybrid
phenotype
mutation
DNA (deoxyribonucleic acid)
selective breeding
artificial insemination
sterile

Tying It Together

1. (a) What is a gene?
   (b) How is a gene related to a chromosome?
2. Privet hedges and humans have the same number of chromosomes in their cells (Figure 10.24). Explain why they are not alike.
3. What is mitosis? In what part of the cell does mitosis occur?
4. Define the following:
   (a) meiosis
   (b) haploid (N)
   (c) diploid (2N)
5. Explain how meiosis differs from mitosis.
6. (a) What type of cells contain the diploid number of chromosomes?
   (b) What type of cells contain the haploid number of chromosomes?

Figure 10.24 *Cells in these privet plants contain 23 pairs of chromosomes. Cells in humans contain the same number.*

7. (a) List at least five traits that may be different in individual pea plants.
    (b) When Mendel removed the stamens from certain flowers, what was he trying to avoid?
    (c) Why did he want to avoid this?
8. (a) What is meant by the genotype of an individual?
    (b) How does genotype affect an individual's appearance?
9. (a) Draw a Punnett square showing the results of a cross between two pea plants. One parent has two genes for green pods (GG) and one has two genes for yellow pods (gg). The gene for green pods is dominant. Describe the phenotype of the offspring.
    (b) Draw a Punnett square showing the results of a cross among the offspring of part (a). Describe the phenotype of this second generation of offspring.
10. What is incomplete dominance? Give an example.
11. (a) What two types of substances make up chromosomes?
    (b) When there is a mutation, which of these two substances has changed?

12. (a) How does selective breeding increase the chance of offspring with desirable traits?
    (b) List three animals that have been modified by selective breeding. For each animal, describe one trait that has been changed over the generations.
    (c) List three plants that have been modified by selective breeding. For each plant, describe one trait that has been changed over the generations.
13. What is the name for the offspring of a horse and a donkey? Why are these offspring not used in further selective breeding?

Applying Your Knowledge

1. Refer to your results from Activity 10C. Which gene for pea colour, yellow or green, is the dominant one? Which gene for pea shape, round or wrinkled, is dominant? Explain your answer.
2. (a) Use a Punnett square to work out the possible types of offspring following a cross between a hybrid gray mouse (Gg) and a pure strain white mouse (gg). Grayness is dominant.
    (b) Describe the phenotypes of the offspring.
3. Pea plants that are hybrid for both pea colour and pea shape have the genotype YyRr. Yellow (Y) is dominant over green (y), and round (R) is dominant over wrinkled (r). When two traits are considered in breeding experiments, this is called a dihybrid cross. Table 10.3 shows all the possible gametes that could be produced by these parents.
    (a) Describe the different phenotypes of the offspring.
    (b) How many different phenotypes are possible?
    (c) Count the number of each phenotype that occurs in the Punnett square and express the numbers as a ratio.

Table 10.3 *Offspring of dihybrid cross.*

	YR	Yr	yR	yr
YR	YYRR	YYRr	YyRR	YyRr
Yr	YYRr	YYrr	YyRr	Yyrr
yR	YyRR	YyRr	yyRR	yyRr
yr	YyRr	Yyrr	yyRr	yyrr

4. When a snapdragon with red flowers (RR) is crossed with one having white flowers (rr), the offspring are pink. Predict the results of crossing a pink flower with a white one. Draw a Punnett square to explain your prediction.
5. List several physical traits that have many forms. Use your family or a friend's family to find examples of these traits. For each trait, give an example of some possible variations.
6. Wheat rust is a fungus disease that attacks the stems, leaves, and kernels of wheat. In a typical year, this disease reduces the value of the wheat crop by about ten percent. How would scientists go about producing varieties of wheat that can resist the disease?

Projects for Investigation

1. How can all the instructions for a complete individual be included in the tiny amount of material contained in a fertilized egg? What kind of code can contain so much information in such a compact form? Scientists have discovered that a chemical substance called DNA contains the instructions that are passed from generation to generation. Find out how the DNA code controls the activities of the cell. Draw diagrams to show how this happens.
2. Biologists use the symbols shown in Figure 10.25 to indicate "male" and "female." Astronomers use the same symbols for the planets Mars and Venus. Discover the connection between Mars and male and between Venus and female. Do you think these symbols accurately reflect "male" and "female"? Explain.

female   male

Figure 10.25

Human Genetics

Key Ideas

- Inheritance in humans follows the same pattern as inheritance in other organisms.
- Modern technology applied to human reproduction raises many moral dilemmas.
- Genetic engineering is used to produce many valuable substances. But this technique may also pose problems for the future.

On Sunday, July 6, 1986, the human population of the planet earth reached 5000 million. There are now more than 5000 million people on this planet. All of these people are similar in some ways. Yet each person is a distinctly different individual. How can there be so many differences? Are there ever two people exactly alike? Can we predict what characteristics a newborn child will have? Could we produce people with certain traits "made to order"? Would we want to?

Inheritance in Humans

In Chapter 10, you saw that the manner in which a person clasps hands is determined by a single gene. If a person has one or both genes coding for left thumb on top, then that is the way the hands will be clasped. Only if a person has *both* genes coding for right thumb on top will the hands be clasped that way. This trait follows the pattern of dominant and recessive genes that Mendel discovered. There are other human characteristics that follow the same pattern. See Figure 11.1.

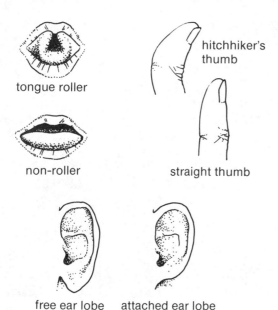

Figure 11.1 *Some contrasting pairs of human traits*

Activity 11A

Problem

What human traits follow the pattern of dominance?

Materials

Procedure

1. Try rolling your tongue into a U-shape with a groove down the middle (Figure 11.1). If you can do this, then you have the trait for tongue rolling.
2. Record how many people in your class have this trait and how many do not have it.
3. Hold your hands in front of you with thumbs spread out. Are the thumbs fairly straight, or do they curve like those of a hitchhiker (Figure 11.1)? Repeat step 2 for this trait.
4. Do you have a "free" ear lobe? Examine the shape of the bottom of your ear. Note whether the lobe hangs below the point where your ear joins your face (Figure 11.1). Repeat step 2 for this trait.
5. Refer to the pedigree diagram in the Challenge on page 179. Have four or five volunteers prepare a pedigree diagram showing the appearance of one of these traits in their families.

Observations

1. For each of the three traits examined, which one is the most common phenotype?

Questions

1. From the pedigree diagrams, which is the dominant form of each trait?
2. In your notebook, make a table similar to Table 11.1 and fill it in. If you have the dominant form of the trait, there may be two possibilities for your genotype.

3. For one of the traits studied, examine the family records. Try to find a class member who must be hybrid for the trait.
4. Why is it not always possible to determine the genotype of an individual?

Table 11.1 *Possible Results from Activity 11A*

TRAIT	DOMINANT FORM	MY PHENOTYPE	MY POSSIBLE GENOTYPE
Tongue Rolling			
Hitchhiker's thumb			
Ear lobe shape			

SAMPLE ONLY

Challenge

Could two tongue-rolling parents produce children who could not roll their tongue? Use a Punnett square to show how this would be possible.

Complex Patterns of Inheritance

In Activity 11A you observed some inherited human traits which follow the simple pattern of dominant and recessive genes that Mendel discovered in pea plants. Not many human traits follow this simple pattern. There are other human traits that follow other patterns.

Often, many genes work together to determine a single visible trait. Fair skin and blue eyes occur when there are few genes coding for colour. More genes coding for colour make the skin and eyes darker. Since several genes work together, there are many possible variations in colouring.

For some traits, there is still uncertainty about inheritance. For example, in some families many people develop diabetes. Diabetes is a disease in which the body cannot properly use or store sugar. In other families the disease does not occur. But doctors have found that even in the families where the disease is more probable, it can sometimes be prevented. Sensible food and exercise can reduce the chances of the disease occurring. The disease itself may not be inheritied, but a *tendency* to develop the disease may be inherited.

Twins

One out of every 96 human births results in twins. See Figure 11.2 on page 190. Some twins, called **fraternal twins**, are no more alike than any two children of the same parents. When fraternal twins are conceived, two eggs are fertilized by two sperm cells. The two individuals may be quite different and may even be of different sexes.

Identical twins develop from the same fertilized egg. All their genes are exactly the same, and it is often very difficult to tell them apart. Identical twins are always of the same sex.

Figure 11.2 *Can you match the twins? Answers are at the end of the chapter.*

Blood Type: An Inherited Trait

As you learned in Unit 2, blood consists of cells in a liquid called *plasma*. Both cells and plasma contain many chemical substances that differ from person to person. The differences are caused by the inheritance of different genes.

One of the most important characteristics of the red blood cells is the ABO blood type. There are four types of red blood cells—O, A, B, and AB. See Table 11.2.

Table 11.2 *The four blood groups*

PHENOTYPE	GENOTYPE	PERCENTAGE OF CANADIAN POPULATION
O	OO	46%
A	AA or OA	42%
B	BB or OB	0.9%
AB	AB	0.3%

The four possible phenotypes shown in the table are caused by one gene that has *three* forms. There are two equally dominant forms, A and B, and one recessive form, O. Gene A causes the formation of substance A on blood cells. Gene B causes the formation of substance B on blood cells. The recessive form of the gene, O, does not cause the formation of any substance. If both genes A and B are present, both substance A and substance B are produced on the blood cells. All the possible genotypes are shown in Table 11.2.

Why are medical people concerned about blood type? If you require a blood transfusion, you must receive the correct type of blood (Table 11.3). If the wrong type is given, there could be a reaction between your blood and the transfused blood. This could cause destruction of red blood cells and could be fatal. In Canada, the Canadian Red Cross Society collects blood from volunteer blood donors (Figure 11.3) and supplies the blood free to hospitals. The blood from these donors is thoroughly tested to be sure of its safety.

Table 11.3 *Types of Blood Used in Transfusions. Which Type Could Be Called the Universal Donor?*

BLOOD FROM DONOR	CAN BE GIVEN TO PERSON OF TYPE
O	O, A, B, AB
A	A, AB
B	B, AB
AB	AB

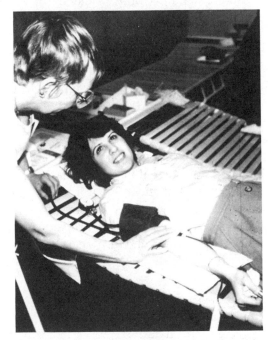

Figure 11.3 *A blood donor at a Canadian Red Cross blood donor clinic*

Sex Determination

You know that human cells contain 46 chromosomes. In all normal individuals, 44 of these chromosomes can be seen to match up into 22 pairs. In females the twenty-third pair also matches (Figure 11.4). However, in males the twenty-third pair consists of two unlike chromosomes. One is an X-shaped chromosome like those in the twenty-third pair of females.

The other is shorter and is called a Y chromosome (Figure 11.4). The X and Y chromosomes are called the sex chromosomes.

Since females are XX, every egg must contain an X chromosome. Since males are XY, a sperm cell will contain either an X chromosome or a Y chromosome. The sex of a fertilized egg is determined by the sex chromosome it receives from the sperm cell. Figure 11.5 shows the probability that an offspring will be a son or a daughter.

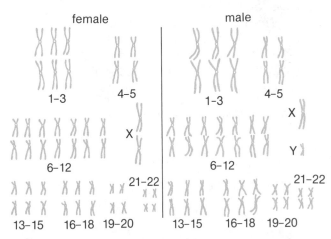

Figure 11.4 *Two sets of pairs of human chromosomes. Find the difference between the female set and male set.*

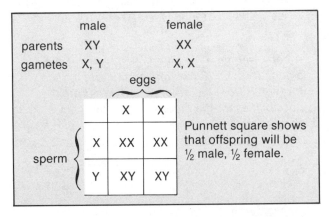

Figure 11.5 *What is the probability of a child being a son or a daughter?*

Your genes make every cell in your body different from the cells of every other person in the world. Many of these differences can be detected even on traces of blood or saliva. A cup found at the scene of a crime might be sent to a police laboratory. There, technicians can analyze saliva left on the cup. That saliva can be compared with saliva from the suspect. If the two saliva samples match, that could suggest that the suspect was actually at the scene of the crime.

The inheritance pattern of blood groups can also be used to indicate relationships between individuals. For example, if a baby has type AB blood, a man with type O blood could not possibly have been the father.

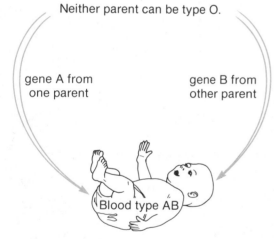

Neither parent can be type O.

gene A from one parent

gene B from other parent

Blood type AB

A baby with type AB blood must have received a gene for type A from one parent and a gene for type B from the other parent. What are the possibilities for the blood types of the baby's parents?

Sex-Linked Inheritance

The X and Y chromosomes carry other genes as well as those that determine sex. Because the genes are on the sex chromosomes, the traits are called **sex-linked traits**. Since the X chromosome is larger than the Y chromosome, it carries more genes. Females have two X chromosomes, so they will always have two genes for every trait. Males, with only one X chromosome, will have only *one* gene for certain traits. That one gene will determine the trait for that person.

COLOUR-BLINDNESS

The most common kind of colour-blindness is an example of a sex-linked trait. People with this kind of colour-blindness cannot distinguish red from green. Males have this trait far more often than females.

The gene for normal vision is located on the X chromosome. This means that a male will have only one of these genes, while a female will have two. A female who receives the defective gene may also have a gene for normal vision (Figure 11.6). Since the normal gene is dominant,

N = gene for normal vision (dominant)

n = gene for colour-blindness (recessive)

	NORMAL MALE	CARRIER FEMALE
Parents	$X^N Y$	$X^N X^n$
Gametes	X^N, Y	X^N, X^n

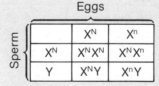

Eggs

Sperm

	X^N	X^n
X^N	$X^N X^N$	$X^N X^n$
Y	$X^N Y$	$X^n Y$

Punnett square shows that half of the females will carry the gene for colour-blindness but will have normal vision; half of the males will be colour-blind.

Figure 11.6 *Inheritance of colour-blindness. Why are males more likely than females to be colour-blind?*

she will carry the recessive gene without being colour-blind. If a male receives a defective gene, he will be colour-blind. A female would have to have two defective genes in order to be colour-blind.

HEMOPHILIA

Hemophilia is another condition that is controlled by a gene on the X chromosome. Individuals with hemophilia have blood that does not form clots. A slight scratch can bleed for days. A bruise can cause severe internal bleeding.

Queen Victoria (1819–1901), who ruled the British Empire for 63 years, was a carrier of this disease. She had nine children (Figure 11.7). Of these, two daughters were carriers of the disease, and one son had it. Seven of her grandchildren and six of her 34 great-grandchildren were affected by the disease.

In the past, most hemophiliacs (people with hemophilia) died young. Now, treatment is available and hemophiliacs may live fairly normal lives (Figure 11.8). No cure has yet been found for this condition.

Figure 11.8 *Hemophiliacs can, with care, take part in some sports activities.*

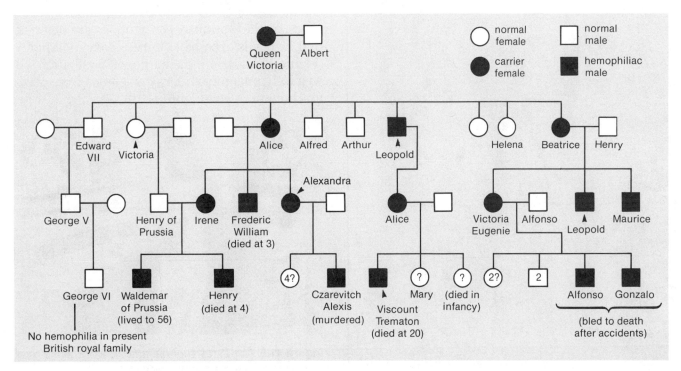

Figure 11.7 *Queen Victoria's family pedigree*

Self-check

1. Two friends find that one has "hitchhikers thumb" and one does not. Explain why one friend can be sure of her genotype, while the other would have to make further investigations to determine hers.
2. (a) What is different in blood cells of different types?
   (b) What causes this difference?
   (c) Which is the most common blood type in Canada?
3. In a paternity suit a woman with type AB blood sues a man with type A blood. The child has type B blood. Could this man be the father?
4. When a baby is conceived there is approximately a 50% chance that it will be male, and approximately a 50% chance that it will be female. Explain why.
5. What is the function of the X and Y chromosomes in humans?
6. What are sex-linked traits? Give two examples of traits that are sex-linked.

Genetic Mutations and Chromosome Errors

Cell division is a very complex process. Copying the DNA, separating the chromosomes, and constructing other chemical substances involve many complicated steps. Sometimes mistakes occur.

Mutations

Mutations, as mentioned in Chapter 10, are one source of differences that we see among individuals. We all probably carry large numbers of new mutations in addition to those of our parents and ancestors. The frequency of occurrence of mutations has been measured. The mutation that causes hemophilia, for example, appears about 50 times in every 1 000 000 people. Exposure to radiation and certain drugs and chemicals increases the rate of mutation of genes. In the workplace, precautions are taken so that no one is exposed to unnecessary radiation (Figure 11.9). Before the nature of X radiation was fully understood, X-ray machines were used much more freely (Figure 11.10).

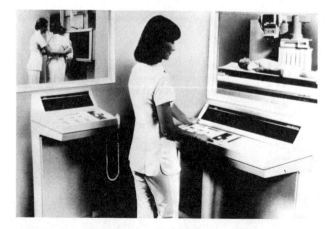

Figure 11.9 *The X-ray technician can work while remaining protected from stray radiation.*

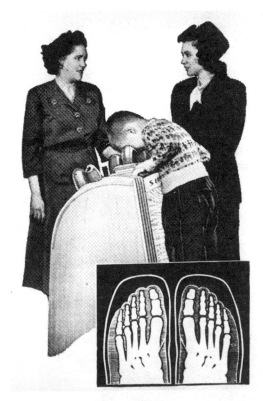

Figure 11.10 *In the 1940s and 1950s, people used X-ray machines in shoe stores to check that children's shoes fit correctly.*

Chromosome Errors

Another kind of mistake occurs when chromosomes are sorted during cell division or when gametes are formed. A **chromosome error** results when a cell does not receive the correct number of chromosomes. If an extra copy of chromosome 21 ends up in a zygote, a child with Down's syndrome is born. People with Down's syndrome have varying degrees of mental retardation. They may have large tongues, unusual eye folds, short stature, and stubby hands and feet (Figure 11.11).

Figure 11.11 *Teenager with Down's syndrome*

Mistakes occur with the sex chromosomes, too. The cells of normal females are XX, and those of normal males are XY. Occasionally an individual who appears female will have only one X chromosome in all her body cells (Turner's syndrome). A male may have an extra Y chromosome and thus be XYY. Or, a person may appear to be male, but actually be XXY or even XXXY (Klinefelter's syndrome). The abnormal chromosomes cause a variety of other physical and mental effects in the individuals.

When chromosomes are missing or when extra chromosomes are present, the upset chemical balance may cause the developing fetus to die, or may cause the baby to die in infancy. Many pregnancies end in miscarriage, perhaps because of such abnormalities.

Activity 11B

Problem

What can you find out about genetic errors?

Materials

Procedure

Select two diseases from Table 11.4 and do research on them. Make a chart showing the following information:

Cause—For example, is the error in a gene or in a chromosome? Is it a dominant or recessive trait? Is it sex-linked?

Symptoms—For example, at what age do symptoms occur? Can the person live a normal life?

Treatment

Table 11.4 *Diseases and Conditions Caused by Genetic Errors*

Huntington's disease
Cystic fibrosis
Sickle cell anemia
Spina bifida (open spine)
Galactosemia
Tay-Sachs disease
Phenylketonuria (PKU)
Club foot
Cleft palate
Muscular dystrophy

Dr. Irene A. Uchida is a professor at McMaster University in Hamilton, Ontario. One day, while browsing around in the library, Dr. Uchida came across an old article claiming that exposure to X rays can increase abnormal chromosome separation in the eggs of old female flies. She wondered if the same problem could occur in humans. Down's syndrome was known to occur most often with older human mothers. Dr. Uchida made a study of mothers who had given birth to abnormal children. She found that mothers of Down's syndrome children had indeed had more abdominal X-ray examinations than the mothers of other types of abnormal children.

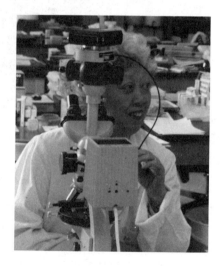

Some Moral Questions

Our heredity is determined at the moment of fertilization. Does that mean that our intelligence, health, emotional development, and future life are all pre-programmed in the zygote? Does "nature" alone determine what we become? Or does "nurture" influence us also? Does the care, nutrition, and education of the baby and child affect what sort of person will develop? Scientists still debate exactly how many human characteristics are due strictly to heredity.

Prenatal Nutrition

One answer in the "nature or nurture" controversy is now well known. Whatever its genetic makeup, a baby may be severely disadvantaged before it is born. The **prenatal period**, the time spent by the baby in the uterus of the mother, is very important. Many diseases, such as AIDS or venereal diseases, can be passed on to the unborn child. If a woman does not eat the proper foods during pregnancy, or if she smokes heavily, drinks excessive amounts of alcohol, or uses various drugs, the development of the baby will likely be affected.

Will the Baby Be Normal?

If you know that a member of your family has a genetic disease, you might be concerned about whether you too might be a *carrier* of the disease. If you are a carrier, you will have a gene for that disease. There is still no procedure to change the genetic make-up of a fetus, but prospective parents can get advice from medical specialists.

They may choose to discuss their concerns with a **genetic counsellor**. This is a highly trained person who has a wide knowledge of human genetics. The genetic counsellor works with the prospective parents, examining the family history of each parent for *any* possible hereditary disease. The counsellor can then tell the couple what the chances are that they might bear a child with a genetic defect.

If the parents do conceive a child, they may want to find out early in the pregnancy whether it is normal. Genetic researchers have developed many methods to diagnose genetic defects before birth.

ULTRASOUND

One of the most widely used methods of checking the development of the fetus uses sound waves (Figure 11.12). These sound waves,

Figure 11.12

(a) *Ultrasound equipment allows the growth of the fetus to be monitored. X-rays are not suitable because they could cause harm to the fetus.*

(b) *Can you detect the blurred outline of the fetus in this ultrasound picture? The baby's head is at the bottom left.*

beyond the wavelength of sounds we can hear, are called **ultrasound**. Doctors can learn the size, age, and position of the developing fetus using this technique. Some abnormalities can also be detected.

SAMPLING CELLS FROM THE FETUS

Amniocentesis is a procedure that doctors use to obtain cells from a developing fetus. They insert a long hollow needle into the uterus of the pregnant woman (Figure 11.13). A small amount of the fluid surrounding the fetus is removed in this way. The fluid contains fetal cells from the fetus. By growing and then examining these cells, scientists can tell whether the normal number of chromosomes is present. They also examine the chromosomes for evidence of abnormalities. While examining the chromosomes they also find out the sex of the baby.

Amniocentesis is usually conducted in the sixteenth week of pregnancy. There is a very small risk involved in the procedure.

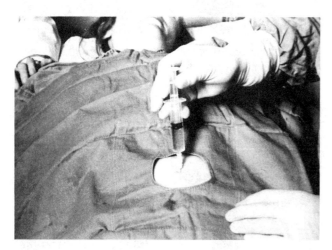

Figure 11.13 *Amniocentesis*

Occasionally a fetus may be spontaneously aborted after amniocentesis. This risk must be weighed against the benefits of knowing whether or not the fetus is normal.

One of the newest techniques, *chorionic villus biopsy*, can be done earlier in the pregnancy, in the tenth week. In this technique, a sample of fetal cells is removed using a catheter inserted through the vagina. Growth and examination of the cells gives the same information as that yielded by amniocentesis. The risks using this newer technique may be greater than the risks using amniocentesis. However, because it can be done so much earlier in the pregnancy it may be preferred by some parents.

BLOOD TESTS

Some disorders can be revealed by a simple test of the pregnant mother's blood. A protein called AFP, produced by the fetus, gets into the mother's blood and can be detected there. Large amounts of AFP may indicate an abnormal fetus, but other tests can be done to confirm the results.

Unfortunately, diagnosis of genetic defects has not led to treatment or cure in most cases. Genetic research may in the future make it possible to avoid or treat genetic problems.

Whose Baby Is This?

There are many medical reasons why an otherwise normal couple cannot together produce a child. For many couples it may be heartbreaking to realize that they will never produce a baby in the normal way. They may choose to adopt a baby or may choose to have a doctor help with alternatives. The field of *fertility research* has made many advances. However, the advances have raised many questions.

ARTIFICIAL INSEMINATION

The chances of fertilization occurring increase with the number of sperm. Sometimes there are not enough sperm produced by the male for fertilization to take place easily. Sperm from a healthy donor can be inserted by a doctor into a woman's vagina during the most fertile period of her menstrual cycle. If fertilization occurs, the fetus will be genetically like both the mother and the donor of the sperm.

In Canada, donors of sperm for artificial insemination have always remained anonymous. The woman would never know who the donor was, and the donor would never even know if his sperm had been used. In this way the individuals can keep their privacy. The resulting child, however, will never be able to learn the identity of its genetic father.

In some places today, human *sperm banks* exist. Here, sperm of particularly intelligent and athletic individuals has been stored for possible use in the future. Specific desired traits can be selected, and the appropriate sperm used. While human sperm banks have not yet been widely used, their very existence raises many moral questions.

What do you think about this issue? Should artificial insemination be used for human beings? Under what conditions would it be acceptable to you? When would it be unacceptable? Should sperm donors remain anonymous? Should stored sperm be used for selective breeding of humans? In Activity 11C your class will hold a debate about one of these questions.

Activity 11C

Your teacher will provide suggestions on holding a class debate.

Problem

What are your opinions about artificial insemination?

Materials

stop watch

Procedure

1. Agree on the resolution to be debated.
2. Decide what resources (books, magazines, newspapers, audiovisual tapes, etc.) you will need to help you argue for or against the resolution. Then hold the debate.

Observations

1. State one main point made by the "For" team that was not successfully argued against by the "Against" team.
2. State one main point made by the "Against" team that was not successfully argued against by the "For" team.

Questions

1. You have now had an opportunity to consider carefully both sides of the issue of artificial insemination. In a brief paragraph, state your own opinion about this issue, giving your reasons.

Legal Questions

The questions raised by modern science and by technologies like artificial insemination cannot be answered by scientists alone. They are questions that all members of society must consider. At the present time there are no laws about many of these activities. The technology of genetics has moved faster than the legal system. These questions will be of concern to all of us in the future.

Self-check

1. What causes Down's syndrome?
2. Name three things that a pregnant woman can do to increase her chances of having a healthy baby.
3. Describe the work of genetic counsellors.
4. Name three procedures that can be used to study characteristics of a fetus before birth.
5. Describe two situations in which it might be unclear exactly who are the parents of a baby.

Genetic Engineering

Why is business interested in genetics? Why are companies being formed and millions of dollars being invested in genetic research? Many opportunities are becoming available because of **genetic engineering**. This refers to the application of genetic knowledge for practical purposes (Figure 11.14).

In the technique called **gene splicing**, a gene is taken from the chromosome of one individual and joined to a chromosome of another organism. The organism most used is a simple bacterium, *E. coli*, which is normally found in the human intestine. These harmless bacteria can grow and reproduce every 45 minutes. Scientists have found a way of tricking these bacteria into accepting totally unrelated pieces of chromosomal DNA. Every time the *E. coli* divides, so will the new piece of DNA.

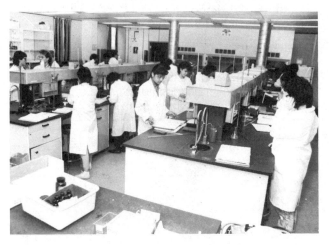

Figure 11.14 *These community college students are preparing for careers as laboratory technicians.*

Ideas and Applications

Gene splicing has been used to produce *human growth hormone*. A certain gene in human cells codes for the production of this substance. If a baby lacks this gene, it cannot produce the hormone, and dwarfism (small size) and mental retardation can result. Treatment with human growth hormone can prevent these effects. In the past, the only source of this hormone was dead bodies. Only the bodies of the few people who had willed their organs to medical science could be used. So little was available that many babies could not be treated with it.

Now, by gene splicing, scientists can insert the gene for human growth hormone into *E. coli*. While the *E. coli* lives, it makes the hormone. As the bacteria grow and reproduce, all the newly produced bacteria also make the hormone. A large amount of it is thus produced and collected. Today, in Canada, all babies requiring human growth hormone can receive it because of genetic engineering.

Bacteria have been engineered to produce many chemical substances. Various industries are using the technique. Some bacteria can now produce alcohols for fuel. The possible benefits are far-reaching. However, as with most new technologies, problems do emerge.

Gene Splicing: A Mixed Blessing?

Many people are extremely concerned about the potential dangers of gene splicing. For example, a bacterium could be programmed to produce deadly substances in great quantities. What are some other possible hazards?

Presently, scientists are using strains of bacteria that cannot survive outside the laboratory environment. Yet there is still the possibility of a strain being used that *could* survive and rapidly multiply outside the laboratory.

Imagine, for example, that a bacterium has been altered so that it can consume large quantities of crude oil. These bacteria may be used to clean up oil spills. After this, they die. What would happen if someone were to obtain a sample of these bacteria and alter them so that they could consume all types of oil? What if these bacteria got into crude oil supplies?

Scientists around the world have agreed to proceed with extreme caution in this area because of the potential hazards (Figure 11.15).

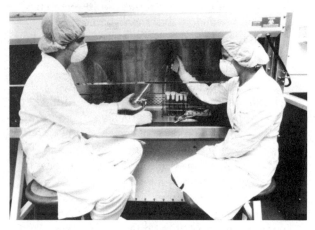

Figure 11.15 *In a laboratory where there are disease-causing organisms, workers must take extra care. How many safety precautions can you see in this picture? Other precautions are also taken. The laboratories may be constructed with air-lock doors and special washing-up rooms. There may be special air currents to carry any free organisms to air filters. Workers must follow careful safety procedures when entering or leaving the laboratory.*

Chapter Objectives

NOW THAT YOU HAVE COMPLETED THIS CHAPTER, CAN YOU DO THE FOLLOWING?	FOR REVIEW, TURN TO SECTION
1. Describe three inherited human traits that follow the pattern of dominance.	11.1
2. Make a chart showing the phenotype and genotype of the four major blood types.	11.1
3. Explain what determines whether an individual is female or male.	11.1
4. Give two examples of sex-linked inheritance in humans.	11.1
5. Distinguish between mutations and chromosome errors and give an example of each.	11.2
6. Explain what prenatal nutrition is and why it is important.	11.3
7. List three ways in which genetic defects can be detected in a fetus.	11.3
8. Give examples of cases where the exact legal relationship of parents to their child may not be clear.	11.3
9. Tell why the field of genetic engineering has great potential for both good and evil.	11.4

Words to Know

fraternal twins
identical twins
sex-linked trait
hemophilia
chromosome error
prenatal period

genetic counsellor
ultrasound
amniocentesis
genetic engineering
gene splicing

Tying It Together

1. In your notebook, write the sentences (a) to (g). Fill in the missing words from the following list: prenatal period, conception, genetic engineering, genetic counsellor, sex-linked traits, chromosome errors, conceive, mutations, test tube, chorionic villus biopsy.

    (a) If a couple knows there is an inheritable disease in the family, they may talk to a _____ before they decide to _____ a baby.

    (b) If _____ occurs outside the human body, the resulting individual is called a _____ baby.

    (c) Cells of the fetus can be sampled in the tenth week of pregnancy using a new technique called _____.

    (d) Scientists agree that _____ has great potential for both benefits and dangers to life on earth.

    (e) The health of a baby can be greatly influenced by the activities of its mother during the 40-week _____.

    (f) Because they do not have a pair of X chromosomes, _____ appear more often in males.

    (g) Genetic defects may be due to _____ or to _____.

2. Hold your hands out in front of you with the palms upward. Roll your fingers in to make fists. Bend the fists upward, and watch the cords in your wrists. Are there two cords or three (Figure 11.16)? The number of cords in the wrist is an inherited trait. Table 11.5 lists the individuals in the Polso family according to whether they have this trait. Draw a pedigree diagram, like that shown in the Challenge on page 179, to show the occurrence of this trait in the Polso family.

3. A woman can roll her tongue, but her husband and son cannot roll theirs. What are the genotypes of each of the three members of this family?

two cords   three cords

Figure 11.16 *People may have two or three cords in their wrists.*

Table 11.5 *Cords in Wrist in the Polso Family*

FAMILY MEMBER	NUMBER OF CORDS IN WRIST
Mother	3
Father	2
Son	3
Son	2
Daughter	2
Daughter	3
Daughter	2
Son	2

4. Give two examples of human traits that show incomplete dominance.

5. What are the four main types of human blood? For each blood type, list all the possible genotypes.

6. The ratio of male to female offspring is predicted to be 1:1 (Figure 11.5). How is it possible for a family to have three children all of one sex?

7. (a) Queen Victoria was a carrier of the gene for hemophilia. She had five sons but only one had the disease (Figure 11.7). How could this happen?

    (b) Explain why hemophilia is much more common among males than among females.

8. (a) Why do police look for traces of blood or saliva at the scene of a crime?
   (b) In the 1940s, a paternity suit was brought against the actor and director Charlie Chaplin in California. The mother, whose blood was type A, claimed that he was the father of her child. The baby's blood was type B and Charlie Chaplin's was type O. If you were judging this case today, how would you decide the outcome? Explain your answer. See the note on the real outcome of the case at the end of this chapter.
9. Describe two types of genetic mistakes that can occur.
10. (a) What is meant by "nature or nurture"?
    (b) What evidence is there that nurture can affect a baby even before it is born?
11. (a) What can be determined about a fetus using ultrasound?
    (b) What can be determined from a sample of cells from a fetus?
    (c) Why can a test on the blood of a pregnant woman reveal information about the fetus?
12. Describe one benefit that genetic engineering has already supplied.

Applying Your Knowledge

1. A pedigree diagram can include more than two generations of a family (Figure 11.7). Prepare a pedigree diagram showing at least three generations for your family or for the family of a friend. You could use the trait studied in Activity 10B, or one of the traits studied in Activity 11A.
2. Some people have six fingers and six toes. This is a dominant trait. Why does it not occur in a large part of the human population?
3. A boy has blood Type O. His father has blood Type B.
   (a) What must be the father's genotype?
   (b) What are the possible genotypes of the mother?

4. Examine Figure 11.6 and then draw a Punnett square showing the offspring of a colour-blind male and a normal female.
5. Selective breeding of humans is possible. If selective-breeding experiments on humans were carried out, what would be the response of the public? What are some benefits that could result from selective breeding? What objections might be raised?
6. In the past, "biological parents" meant the genetic father and mother of a child. "Adoptive parents" meant the father and mother who raised the child but who had no genetic relationship to it. With modern reproductive technology, these distinctions are no longer so clear. Give examples of situations where it may not be clear exactly who are the parents of a child.
7. Some people believe that genetic engineering is dangerous and that all experimenting should be stopped. Others believe that the possible benefits outweigh the dangers. Hold a class debate on this topic.

Projects for Investigation

1. Persuade an adult member of your family to attend a blood donor clinic of the Canadian Red Cross Society. Accompany your relative to the clinic and observe what is done when blood is donated. Report back to your class about the procedure.
2. Sickle cell anemia is a genetic disease. Individuals with two genes for this condition have blood cells that have an abnormal shape (Figure 11.17). Malaria is a disease caused by a parasite injected into human blood by mosquitoes. In parts of the world where malaria is common, sickle cell anemia is also common (Figure 11.18). Find out why these two diseases occur in the same areas of the world.
3. Research has been done on the effects of "nature and nurture" on identical twins. The twins have grown up in different places with different adoptive parents. Investigate the results of these studies.

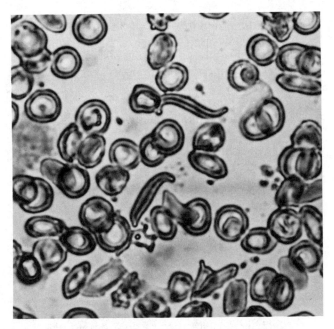

Figure 11.17 *Normal and sickled red blood cells*

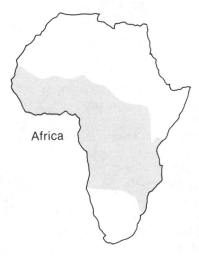

Africa

Figure 11.18 *Both malaria and sickle cell anemia are common in the part of Africa that is shaded on this map.*

Unit 3: Continuity

MATCH

In your notebook, write the letters (a) to (f). Beside each letter, write the number of the word in the right column that corresponds to each description in the left column.

(a) a developing organism made up of many cells but not yet in adult form
(b) application of genetic knowledge for practical purposes
(c) method used to find the size and position of a developing fetus
(d) female part of a flower
(e) characteristic that may be passed on to offspring
(f) structure found in a cell nucleus

1. pistil
2. trait
3. chromosome
4. ultrasound
5. sperm
6. genetic engineering
7. genotype
8. embryo
9. stamen

MULTIPLE CHOICE

In your notebook, write the numbers 1 to 10. Beside each number, write the letter of the best choice.

1. Which of the following is *not* involved in sexual reproduction?
   (a) gamete
   (b) flower
   (c) budding
   (d) zygote
2. Which process does *not* occur in the sexual reproduction of animals?
   (a) fertilization
   (b) production of egg
   (c) development of the embryo
   (d) pollination
3. What part of a plant contains the embryo?
   (a) pistil
   (b) stamen
   (c) leaf
   (d) seed
4. Which of the following is a primary sexual characteristic?
   (a) Females have enlarged breasts.
   (b) Males generally have deeper voices than females.
   (c) Males produce sperm.
   (d) Females generally have broader hips than males.
5. If N represents the number of chromosomes, which of the following represents fertilization?
   (a) $N + N \rightarrow 2N$
   (b) $2N \rightarrow N + N$
   (c) $2N + 2N \rightarrow 4N$
   (d) $46N \rightarrow 23N$
6. If you had one month to conduct an experiment in genetics, which of the following organisms would be the most suitable?
   (a) turkeys   (c) fruit flies
   (b) pea plants   (d) corn
7. Which is most likely to be an example of mutation?
   (a) Human parents with brown eyes produce a child who has blue eyes.
   (b) Two tall pea plants produce offspring that are both tall and short.
   (c) A farmer selectively breeds only hens that are good egg producers.
   (d) In a field of primroses where all flowers had been yellow for many years, a red primrose appears.
8. Which of the following is a sex-linked trait in humans?
   (a) colour-blindness   (c) blood type
   (b) hitchhiker's thumb   (d) diabetes
9. Which may affect the development of an unborn baby?
   (a) diet of the pregnant mother
   (b) genes inherited from the father
   (c) drugs prescribed for the pregnant mother by her doctor
   (d) all of the above
10. Which of the following is *not* a method used to check the development of an unborn baby?
    (a) chorionic villus biopsy   (c) ultrasound
    (b) artificial insemination   (d) amniocentesis

TRUE/FALSE

Write the numbers 1 to 10 in your notebook. Beside each number, write T if the statement is true and F if the statement is false. For each false statement, rewrite it as a true statement.

1. Asexual reproduction requires two parents.
2. There are two types of gametes: egg and sperm.
3. Within a seed, there is a stored food supply and a tiny egg.
4. Mitosis is the duplication of the chromosomes and the division of the cell nucleus.
5. A fertilized egg cell contains the diploid number of chromosomes.
6. Inherited characteristics are always present in every member of a family.
7. The offspring of two different pure strain parents may appear to be different from one of the parents.
8. Fraternal twins always have the same hair colour.
9. Sometimes gametes are formed that contain an incorrect number of chromosomes.
10. A test tube baby is conceived in a test tube but develops inside a mother's uterus.

FOR DISCUSSION

Read the paragraphs below and answer the questions that follow.

Susan and David are first cousins. They are concerned because some members of their family have diabetes. Diabetes is a serious disease caused by a lack of insulin in the body. In healthy people, insulin is produced by the pancreas and circulates in the blood. Insulin controls the use of sugar by the body. It keeps the amount of sugar in the blood at a steady level. Diabetics (people with diabetes) might have too much sugar in the blood after a meal, and not enough between meals.

Before the function of insulin was understood, diabetes was a fatal disease. Even now there is no cure, but diabetics can be treated and can lead fairly normal lives. There are different forms of the disease. A tendency to develop one type of diabetes *may* be inherited as a recessive gene. There is still much to be learned about whether diabetes is really an inherited trait.

Susan and David's 62-year-old grandmother has diabetes. An uncle, who is 41, has just developed the disease. Susan and David decide to visit a genetic counsellor to discuss the chances that they might have inherited genes for diabetes.

1. Explain how first cousins are related to each other.
2. Examine the family tree.
   (a) How many relatives do Susan and David have in common?
   (b) How many people could have inherited a gene for diabetes?

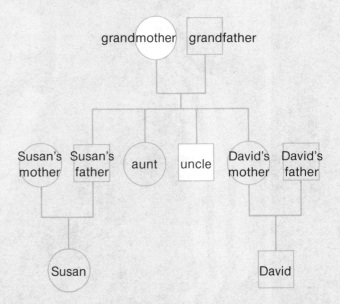

3. Susan's father has not developed diabetes. Does that mean he has not inherited a gene for diabetes? Explain.
4. Suppose David's mother never develops diabetes. Does that mean David does not have a gene for the disease? Explain.
5. Do you think that Susan or David will develop diabetes? Explain your answer.

Magnetism and Electricity

If not for the work of such scientists as Benjamin Franklin, William Gilbert, Charles Du Fay, and many others, you would not be able to listen to the radio or your favourite cassette tape. Without an understanding of magnetism and electricity, modern engineers would not be able to design and produce stereo loudspeakers, floppy disks for computers, and many other modern conveniences.

In this unit, you will find out about magnetism and electricity and how they are related. You will also have the chance to perform some of the experiments that have helped scientists understand more about these important forces.

When you wake up tomorrow morning, think about magnetism and electricity. How would your day be different without them?

Static Electricity

Key Ideas

- Static electricity is electricity at rest.
- There are laws that describe the behaviour of static charges.
- Static electricity can be used to increase the efficiency of many industrial processes.
- If not handled with care, static electricity can be dangerous.

The comb in this photograph is just an ordinary comb. It is not coated with glue or any other sticky substance. But the sawdust from the dish appears to be stuck to it just the same. What force causes this to happen? What theory can we devise to explain it? In this chapter, you will investigate static electricity—what it is, how it occurs, and how it is part of your daily life.

What Is Static Electricity?

Do you ever have trouble getting your hair to stay down after you've brushed it? Do your clothes crackle when you remove them from the dryer? Do you ever get a shock from touching a door knob after you walk across a carpet or rug? Have you ever put your hand close to a television set and observed the tiny hairs on your hand move toward the screen? Have you ever seen or experienced a situation similar to the one shown in Figure 12.1? If you answered yes to any of these questions, then you are already familiar with static electricity.

The cause of these strange occurrences is **static electricity**. Static means "at rest" or "not moving." You can observe many of the effects of static electricity in your classroom. In Activity 12A, you will generate static electricity in several different ways. In Activity 12B, you will find out what materials produce strong electrical charges.

Figure 12.1
Where else might you see a demonstration such as this?

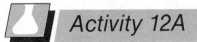

Activity 12A

Problem

How can static electricity be generated?

Materials

comb
small pieces of paper (confetti-sized)
piece of normal notebook paper (19 cm x 26 cm)
felt or woollen cloth
balloon

(For teacher demonstration)
static electricity generator
insulated metal rod
puffed rice cereal or styrofoam packing chips
iron ring clamp
retort stand
newspapers

Procedure

1. Make a table in your notebook similar to Table 12.1 to record your observations.
2. Place a pile of the small paper pieces on the larger piece of paper.
3. Comb your hair for 2–3 min with a plastic comb.
4. Bring the comb close to the paper pieces. Observe and record the results.
5. Blow up a balloon and tie the end.
6. Rub the balloon vigorously against a piece of woollen or felt cloth.
7. Bring the balloon close to the wall. Record your observations.

The remaining steps will be demonstrated by your teacher.

CAUTION Only the teacher may operate the static electricity generator.

8. Your teacher will place a handful of puffed rice or styrofoam packing chips on the dome of the static electricity generator.
9. The generator will be turned on. Record all observations.

10. The generator will be turned off. Your teacher will touch the dome of the generator with an insulated metal rod to remove any excess static charge.
11. An iron ring will be attached to a retort stand and placed on a stack of newspapers near the generator. The iron ring should be level with the dome of the generator.
12. The lights will be turned off and the generator turned on. Record your observations.
13. The generator will be turned off and the dome will once again be touched with an insulated metal rod.

Observations

Table 12.1 *Results of Static Electricity Demonstrations*

ACTIVITY	RESULT
Comb brought close to paper pieces	
Balloon rubbed on sweater brought close to wall	
Puffed rice placed on static electricity generator	
Iron ring placed close to static electricity generator	

SAMPLE ONLY

Questions

1. Did you detect any similarities among the various demonstrations? If so, describe them.
2. The puffed rice or styrofoam packing chips behaved in two different ways in the demonstration. What was responsible for changing their behaviour?

Activity 12B

You can produce static electricity from many common household materials. In this activity, you can try some combinations of materials to find out which ones produce a static charge. Once you begin, you will think of others to try.

Problem

Which combination of materials results in the strongest electrical charge?

Materials

styrofoam packing chips

GROUP A	GROUP B
comb	paper towel
plastic ruler	hair
soda straw	fur
glass rod	wool
ebonite rod	cotton
styrofoam cup	silk
steel rod	plastic garbage bag
copper wire	sandwich wrap
aluminum rod	nylon
vinyl plastic strip	
Plexiglas rod	

Procedure

1. Make a table in your notebook similar to Table 12.2.
2. Choose an object from Group A.
3. Rub it vigorously with a material from Group B.
4. Bring the rubbed end of the object from Group A close to a small pile of styrofoam packing chips.
5. In the table in your notebook, record the combination of materials tested. Beside each combination, state the number of styrofoam pieces picked up by the object.
6. Remove the styrofoam chips from the rod and hold them in your hand to remove any charge from them.
7. Repeat steps 2–6 for at least 20 different combinations of materials.
8. When all combinations of these materials have been tested, indicate in the table whether the charge was STRONG, GOOD, FAIR, POOR, NOT PRESENT.

Observations

Table 12.2 *Strength of static charges generated*

OBJECT A	MATERIAL B	NUMBER OF CHIPS PICKED UP	STRENGTH OF CHARGE
Ebonite	Fur	3	Strong

SAMPLE ONLY

Questions

1. Of all the combinations you tried, which pair of materials seemed to produce the most static electricity when they were rubbed together?
2. With which materials were you unable to produce a static charge?
3. Why was it necessary to hold the styrofoam chips in your hand in between each test?
4. If you have experienced any small "shocks" at home or in school, describe the situation in which they occurred. What pair of materials do you think might have been responsible for producing this static electricity?

Self-check

1. What is meant by the term static electricity?
2. How can you tell when an object has been statically charged?
3. What must be done to an object to make it become charged with static electricity?

Behaviour of Charged Objects

William Gilbert (1544-1603) was a physician to Queen Elizabeth I. See Figure 12.2. He was also one of the first truly experimental scientists. His investigations into static electricity included experiments much like the one you did in Activity 12B.

Gilbert learned that he could produce a static charge on some materials. He called this strange process "the electrifying of objects." He made the first device to test objects for "electrification." He called it an electroscope.

Figure 12.2 *William Gilbert at work*

Much has been learned about static electricity since Gilbert's time. In the early eighteenth century, a French scientist named Charles Du Fay (1698-1739) carried out several experiments with static electricity. Du Fay knew that glass rubbed with silk could be "electrified" (or charged). When another substance, amber, was rubbed with fur, it also became charged.

213

An **electroscope** is a device that is specially designed to detect static electricity. Figure 12.3 shows four types of electroscopes that can be found in school science laboratories. Your teacher will show you how to use the type available in your school.

In the next activity, you will construct an electroscope to study the effect of charged objects on each other.

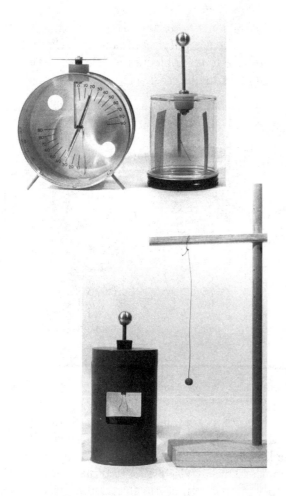

Figure 12.3 *Electroscopes are used to detect the presence of static electricity.*

Activity 12C

Problem

How do two charged objects behave when brought close together?

Materials

2 iron ring clamps
2 retort stands
stirrup
2 pieces of thread, each one 10-15 cm in length
soda straw
2 glass rods
2 ebonite rods
fur
silk

Procedure

1. Make a table in your notebook similar to Table 12.3.
2. Attach the iron ring clamp to the retort stand. Tie the thread around the middle of the soda straw and suspend it from the iron ring. This is an electroscope.
3. Attach another iron ring clamp to the second retort stand. Suspend the stirrup from the iron ring. Your equipment should look like that shown in Figure 12.4.

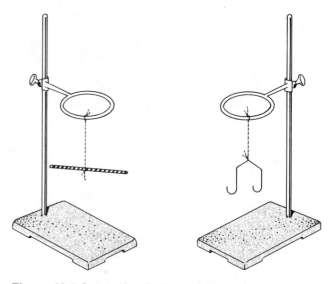

Figure 12.4 *Set-up for Activity 12C*

4. Charge one end of an ebonite rod by rubbing it vigorously with the fur. Place the ebonite rod in the stirrup. Do not touch the charged end of the rod.
5. Charge the second ebonite rod in the same way and hold it in your hand. Do not touch the charged end of the rod.
6. Bring the electroscope close to the charged end of each ebonite rod to make sure that each is electrically charged. If the straw contacts the rod, hold the straw in your hand for a few seconds to remove the charge.
7. Bring the charged end of the second ebonite rod close to (but not touching) the charged end of the ebonite rod in the stirrup.
8. Observe the effect of the two charged ebonite rods on each other.
9. Repeat steps 4–8 using glass rods and silk instead of ebonite rods and fur.
10. Charge an ebonite rod with fur.
11. Slowly move the charged end of the ebonite rod toward the charged end of the glass rod in the stirrup.
12. Observe the effect of the rods on each other.

Observations

Table 12.3 *Summary of Results of Activity 12C*

ROD IN STIRRUP	ROD IN HAND	BEHAVIOUR WHEN BROUGHT CLOSE TO EACH OTHER
Ebonite rod rubbed with fur	Ebonite rod rubbed with fur	
Glass rod rubbed with silk	Glass rod rubbed with silk	
Glass rod rubbed with silk	Ebonite rod rubbed with fur	

Questions

1. How do two rods that have been charged in the same way behave when brought close together?
2. If the ebonite rod and glass rod had been given the same charge after rubbing, what should have happened when the ebonite rod was brought close to the glass rod? Did this happen?
3. What would you predict would happen if an ebonite rod rubbed with fur was placed in the stirrup and a glass rod rubbed with silk was brought close to it?
4. Based on this experiment, would you say that there is only one kind of charge or that there are at least two kinds of charges? Explain your reasoning.

Electrical Charge

All matter is made up of tiny particles called **atoms**. The electrical nature of matter is due to the structure of these atoms.

The **nucleus**, or centre, of an atom contains positively charged particles called **protons**. The force that holds the nucleus together is so strong that the atom does not easily lose protons. Also present in the nucleus are **neutrons**. Neutrons are particles that have no charge. Tiny, negatively charged particles called **electrons** orbit around the nucleus. They are the only particles in an atom that can move. The forces holding electrons in place are relatively weak. Thus, an atom can gain or lose electrons relatively easily. If the number of negatively charged electrons is equal to the number of positively charged protons, the atom is said to be electrically neutral.

Figure 12.5(a) shows a simple model of an atom of the element helium. Figure 12.5(b) shows a model of an oxygen atom. In a neutral helium atom, the number of protons equals the number of electrons. Is this true for a neutral oxygen atom?

When the atoms of two different materials are brought into close contact, electrons may move from one to the other. You can see the effect of this electron movement when you comb your hair. If the material your comb is made of has a stronger attraction for electrons than your hair, your comb will take electrons from your hair. See Figure 12.6.

Examine Figure 12.6 closely. Count the number of positively charged protons and negatively charged electrons on the comb and the hair before combing. Count the number of protons and electrons on the comb and the hair after combing. You can see that the comb has more negative charges than positive charges. It is now **negatively charged**. Since the hair has lost electrons, it has more protons (positive charges) than electrons (negative charges). The hair is now **positively charged**.

(a) *helium*   **(b)** *oxygen*

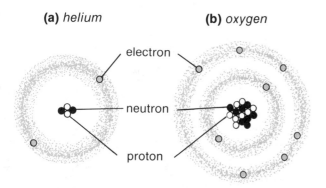

Figure 12.5 *A neutral helium atom and a neutral oxygen atom. Count the number of protons and electrons in each atom. What do you notice?*

(a)

(b)

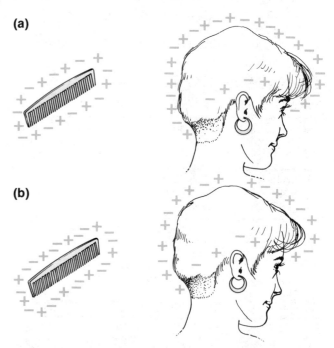

Figure 12.6 (a) *The comb and hair are neutral.*
(b) *After combing, electrons from the hair have moved onto the comb.*

Self-check

1. What two types of particles are found in the nucleus of an atom?
2. Why can an atom lose electrons easily?
3. Why is an atom unlikely to lose protons?
4. Under what conditions is an atom electrically neutral?
5. What charge is on an atom if
   (a) it loses electrons?
   (b) it gains electrons?

Challenge

You have just walked into your science class. The teacher has a large insulated stand at the front of the room. On top of the stand is a metal sphere. The teacher tells you that there is a charge on the sphere. Your assignment is to determine what type of charge is on the sphere. Explain how you would go about this assignment.

Laws of Static Charge

After completing his experiments with static electricity, Monsieur Du Fay noted that when two glass rods were rubbed with silk, they became charged. If these two rods were brought close to each other, they seemed to push away from each other. In other words, they **repelled** each other. Likewise, two pieces of amber that were charged by rubbing with fur would also repel each other. When he brought the charged glass rod near the charged amber, however, he found that the two materials **attracted** each other.

Du Fay concluded that there were two kinds of static charge. Later in the eighteenth century, the American inventor Benjamin Franklin gave these two types of charge their present names: positive and negative. A glass rod rubbed with silk is said to have a positive charge. An amber rod or an ebonite rod rubbed with fur is said to have a negative charge.

Based on the results of your own experiments as well as those of Du Fay and Franklin, it is possible to predict what will happen when two charged objects are brought close to each other. If the objects have been charged in the same way, they will have the same charge. Such objects have like charges. What happens if two objects with like charges are brought close together? If two objects have received different charges, they are said to have unlike charges. What happens if two objects with unlike charges are brought close together? In Activity 12D, you will study the effect of a charged object on a neutral object.

Activity 12D

Problem

What effect does a charged object have on an electrically neutral object?

Materials

plastic ruler
watch glass
ebonite rod
fur
glass rod
silk
electroscope

Procedure

1. Set up the ruler and watch glass as shown in Figure 12.7. Make sure that the ruler can swing freely on the watch glass.
2. Make sure that the ruler is electrically neutral. Use an electroscope to check this.
3. Charge an ebonite rod by rubbing it with fur.
4. Use the electroscope to make sure that the ebonite rod is charged.
5. Bring the ebonite rod close to one end of the ruler. Do not touch the ruler with the ebonite rod.

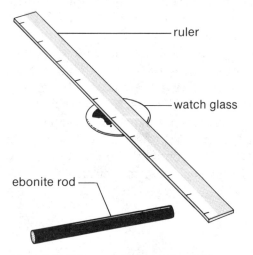

Figure 12.7 *Set-up for Activity 12D*

6. Observe the behaviour of the ruler.
7. Make sure that the ruler is still electrically neutral. Use an electroscope to make sure of this.
8. Charge a glass rod by rubbing it with silk.
9. Use the electroscope to make sure that the glass rod is charged.
10. Bring the glass rod close to one end of the ruler. Do not touch the ruler with the glass rod.
11. Observe the behaviour of the ruler.

Observations

1. What did the ruler do when the charged ebonite rod was brought close to it?
2. What did the ruler do when the charged glass rod was brought close to it?

Questions

1. Did the ruler remain electrically neutral throughout the entire activity? Explain.
2. What is the effect of a positively charged object on an electrically neutral object?
3. What is the effect of a negatively charged object on an electrically neutral object?

Ideas and Applications

Words such as *electricity*, *electron*, and *electronics* all come from the same Greek word, *elektron*. Elektron was the Greek word for *amber*. As long ago as 600 B.C., the Greeks knew that amber, a fossilized resin from trees, would pick up small bits of dust, lint, and other light materials when the amber was rubbed.

Charging By Induction

When you rubbed a balloon with a piece of woollen or felt cloth in Activity 12A and brought it near the wall, the balloon was attracted to the wall. The balloon, like the ebonite rod, becomes negatively charged when rubbed with wool. The wall is electrically neutral. Why is there an attraction between these two objects?

The wall is made up of atoms. These atoms are grouped into larger units called molecules. Each molecule has an equal number of positive protons and negative electrons. When the balloon is rubbed with wool or felt, some of the negative electrons are transferred to the balloon. The balloon becomes negatively charged. When the negatively charged balloon is placed near the wall, some electrons in the molecules on the wall's surface are repelled by the negative electrons in the balloon. The surface area becomes positively charged. See Figure 12.8. Since the surface of the wall and the balloon have opposite charges, they attract each other.

In previous examples, an object became charged when brought in contact with another object, usually by rubbing. In the example in Figure 12.8, the surface of the wall became charged when a charged object was held near without contact being made. This type of electrifying is called charging by **induction**.

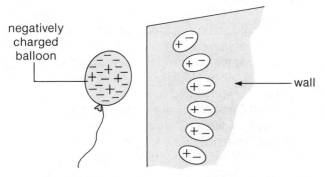

Figure 12.8 *The negative charges on the surface of the wall are repelled by the negative charges on the balloon.*

The effects of a charged object on other objects can be summarized in the following laws of static charge:

1. Like charges repel each other.
2. Unlike charges attract each other.
3. A charged object attracts an electrically neutral object.

Grounding

Our planet is very large compared with any of the objects on it. Because of its size, the earth can gain or lose relatively small numbers of electrons without developing a charge. When a positively charged object is brought into contact with the ground, it will take electrons from the earth and become neutral. When a negatively charged object is brought into contact with the ground, it will release electrons into the earth and become neutral. This process of making an object electrically neutral by placing it in contact with the earth is called **grounding**.

Self-check

1. If a positively charged comb attracts a balloon, which of the following conclusions could you definitely make? Explain your answer.
    (a) The balloon is positively charged.
    (b) The balloon is negatively charged.
    (c) The balloon is electrically neutral.
    (d) The balloon is either positively charged or electrically neutral.
    (e) The balloon is either negatively charged or electrically neutral.
2. How is an induced charge different from a charge made by contact?
3. What are the three laws describing the behaviour of charged objects?
4. What is grounding?

Applications of Static Electricity

Scientists are constantly finding new ways to put static electricity to work. Some of these may surprise you.

Electrostatic Spray Painting

When a spray gun is used to paint a wire mesh fence, a lot of paint is usually wasted. If the fence is given a static charge and the paint is given the opposite charge, the paint will be attracted to the wire mesh. The paint will now be attracted to the wire instead of going through the holes. See Figure 12.9.

Figure 12.9 *Static electricity can be put to use when spray painting.*

Electrostatic Sandpaper

The paper backing for sandpaper can be coated with adhesive and given a strong static charge. The grit particles will then be attracted to the sandpaper.

Insecticide Powders

When electrically charged, insecticide powders can be applied very efficiently to certain plants. There is very little waste of insecticide.

Electrostatic Precipitators

Tall chimneys in chemical plants, smelters, and mills may have electrically charged parts inside them. These attract dust particles and polluting droplets before they can escape from the smokestack. As much as 99.5% of the large particles can be removed from the air before they leave the smokestack.

Dust particles can prevent sensitive electrical parts from functioning properly. Small **electrostatic precipitators** are used to remove dust from the air of the factories where electrical parts are being made. Similar devices remove dust from hospital air.

Plastic Food Wrap

The thin plastic used for wrapping foods clings to itself because of static electricity. This makes it easy to get an airtight package.

Self-check

1. How would static electricity be useful in helping to purify polluted air?
2. Here are some common problems caused by static electricity. How do you think they can be reduced or eliminated?
   (a) Dust gathers on your phonograph records, causing scratchy sounds.
   (b) You have dry, "fly-away" hair.
   (c) Your clothes have "static cling."

The Dangers of Static Electricity

Lightning

Do you remember how the negatively charged balloon brought about a positive charge on the surface of the wall near it (Figure 12.8)? The same thing can occur on a larger scale in nature. The motion of the particles in the clouds high above the earth may result in the clouds becoming negatively charged. This may induce a positive charge on the surface of the earth. See Figures 12.10 and 12.11.

If the difference between the size of the negative charge in the cloud and the positive charge on the earth is large, negative electrons are attracted to the earth's surface and may "jump" from cloud to earth. If this happens, you will see a giant spark. This spark is lightning.

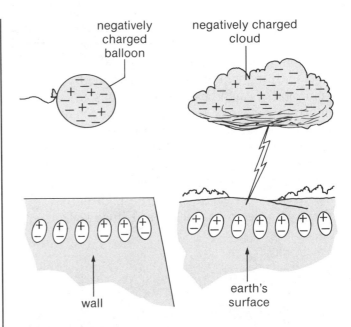

Figure 12.11 *The balloon induces a positive charge on the surface of the wall. The cloud induces a positive charge on the surface of the earth.*

Figure 12.10 *Lightning near the city of Kamloops, B.C.*

A bolt of lightning may be up to 3 km in length and 30 cm in width. The heat generated from the electron movement may reach 30 000°C.

Lightning will usually strike the highest point on the earth below. For this reason, lightning rods may be attached to the top of houses and tall buildings. An insulated conductor connects the lightning rod to a cable buried in the ground. If lightning strikes the rod, the charge is carried along the conductor to the earth. Since the earth is so large, it "absorbs" the excess electrons safely. See Figure 12.12.

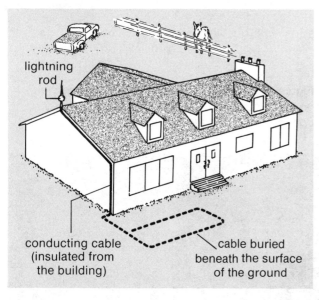

lightning rod

conducting cable
(insulated from
the building)

cable buried
beneath the surface
of the ground

Figure 12.12 *How a lightning rod protects buildings*

Explosions

Ether is a gas that is sometimes used as an anaesthetic in operating rooms. It burns easily. If there is a buildup of static charge in the operating room, small sparks may cause the ether to explode. Doctors and nurses working in the operating room must wear "conducting" boots to prevent this from happening.

The motion of car and truck tires on the road can also build up a static charge. This could be a problem for gasoline trucks. The heat from a spark can ignite the vapours from the gas tank. To prevent this from happening, a metal chain is dragged along the ground. Any excess charge is drained into the earth. There is little danger of sparks occurring.

Self-check

1. What is a lightning bolt?
2. Where does lightning most often strike?
3. Why does the earth not become electrically charged when it is struck by a bolt of lightning?
4. How could a buildup of static charge in a moving vehicle be prevented?

Chapter Objectives

Words To Know

static electricity
electroscope
atom
nucleus
proton
neutron
electron
negatively charged

positively charged
repel
attract
induction
grounding
electrostatic precipitator

Tying It Together

1. Describe two situations in which static electricity has affected you.
2. What charge, if any, will be on each of the following objects? How do you know?
   (a) a comb after you have combed your hair
   (b) an ebonite rod after being rubbed with fur
   (c) a glass rod after being rubbed with silk
   (d) an object that has lost electrons
   (e) the earth after being struck by lightning
3. Use the words proton, neutron, electron, or none to answer each of the following questions.
   (a) What part or parts of an atom are positive?
   (b) What part or parts of the atom orbit the nucleus?
   (c) What part or parts of the atom cannot be easily lost or gained?
   (d) What part or parts of the atom can be found in the nucleus?
   (e) What part of the atom is most likely present in the largest number in a negatively charged atom?
4. An atom of the element fluorine contains 9 protons and 10 neutrons. If it is electrically neutral, how many electrons will it have?

5. What would be observed in each of the following situations?
   (a) Two negatively charged objects approach each other.
   (b) Two positively charged objects approach each other.
   (c) A negatively charged object approaches a neutral object.
   (d) A negatively charged object approaches a positively charged object.
   (e) Two neutral objects approach each other.
   (f) A positively charged object approaches a neutral object.
6. How can a charge be produced on an object
   (a) by touching it with another object?
   (b) without touching it with another object?
7. Describe three ways in which static electricity can be helpful.
8. Describe three ways in which static electricity can be harmful.

Applying Your Knowledge

1. (a) You may have noticed that you get more static electrical shocks on a dry winter day than you do on a moist summer day. Why is this?
   (b) What can be done at home to reduce static shocks in winter?
2. A student placed two tin cans on top of three inverted styrofoam cups. Styrofoam is an excellent insulator. It keeps excess charges from flowing out of the cans. The student rubbed an acetate strip with silk and touched it to the can on the left. This was repeated ten times. She then rubbed a vinyl strip with fur and touched it to the other can. This was also done ten times. She then placed the tin cans about 2 cm apart by touching only the styrofoam. A neutral plastic electroscope ball was lowered between the two cans as shown in Figure 12.13.
   (a) What charge will be on each can?
   (b) What will happen when the plastic ball is placed between the two cans? Explain your reasoning.

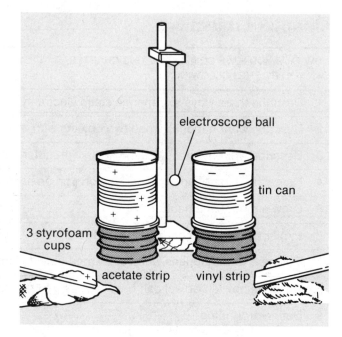

Figure 12.13 *What will happen in this experiment?*

Projects For Investigation

1. Benjamin Franklin performed a very dangerous experiment involving a kite, a key, and a lightning storm. Go to the library and find out more about this famous experiment. **Caution: Do not attempt this experiment yourself—at least one scientist has been killed trying to do this experiment at home**.
2. There are a number of products on the market today that prevent "static cling." Research these products to see how they work. Find out as many uses as possible for similar antistatic products.

Current Electricity

Key Ideas

- Current electricity is electricity in motion.
- There are many ways to generate current electricity.
- Electrical circuits can be designed so that electric current can be used to run machines and many of the appliances in your home.
- It is important to understand how current electricity works in order to use it safely.

Electricity is such a common part of our daily lives that we often take it for granted. Imagine what it would be like if your community had no electric power for a whole month. How would you adjust to this situation?

You have already learned about one kind of electricity, called static electricity. Now you will find out about a more useful form of electricity. In this chapter, you will investigate current electricity.

13.1

What Is Current Electricity?

When you hear the word "electricity," the kind of electricity you probably think of is current electricity. **Current electricity** flows when charges move from one place to another. This is different from static electricity, where electrical charges remain at rest. Light bulbs, ovens, toasters, televisions, computers, and many other devices work because of electrical current.

An electrical current usually consists of electrons moving along a metal wire. Materials like metal wires that allow electrons to flow through them easily are called **conductors**. The most commonly used conductor is copper. Aluminum, graphite, gold, and silver are also good conductors.

Materials that do not allow electrons to flow through them easily are called **insulators**. Rubber, paper, glass, and many plastics are examples of useful insulators. What examples of conductors and insulators can you see in Figure 13.1?

Figure 13.1 *Part of a high voltage electrical distribution system. What conductors and insulators can you see?*

13.2

Generating Electrical Current

Electrical current can be detected using an instrument called a **galvanometer**. When current is flowing, the needle of the galvanometer moves. A small current results in a small movement of the needle. A larger current causes a greater movement of the needle.

There are many ways to produce electrical current. Some of these ways are described below.

Thermocouple

A **thermocouple** is one way in which an electrical current can be generated. *Thermo* means "heat," and *couple* refers to "two." A thermocouple consists of two different metals in close contact with each other. One of these metals has a stronger attraction for electrons than the other. Heat encourages electrons to move from the metal with the weaker attraction for electrons to the metal with the stronger attraction for electrons. The movement of electrons results in a weak current.

Solar Cells

Solar cells use light energy to provide current for camera light meters, satellites, some wristwatches, and some calculators. When light falls on a solar cell, it causes electrons to move. This produces an electrical current. Mariner IV, the spacecraft that took the first photographs of Mars, carried over 28 000 solar cells. Near Mars, the light from the sun falling on these cells produced enough power to light up five 60-W lightbulbs. Many researchers are trying to design homes that use solar energy for all daily needs.

Generators

A simple **generator** consists of a wire coil that is held in place and a magnet that moves rapidly in and out of the coil. Some generators have a stationary magnet and a coil that moves forward and back. Generators are used in many places. How many can you think of?

In the following activities, you will use a thermocouple, solar cell, and generator to produce electrical current.

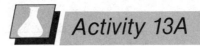

Activity 13A

Problem

How can heat be used to produce an electrical current?

Materials

ice water
hot water
iron coat hanger
sandpaper
2 pieces of bare copper wire (each piece 50 cm)
pliers
cork stopper
retort stand
utility clamp
galvanometer
2 beakers
Bunsen burner
safety goggles

Procedure

1. Make a table in your notebook similar to Table 13.1.
2. Obtain a piece of iron coat hanger.
3. Clean the paint off the last 5 cm of both ends of the hanger with sandpaper.
4. Take one piece of copper wire and wind 8 cm of it *tightly* around the bared iron, beginning at one end of the hanger. Wind the second piece of copper wire around the other end of the hanger in a similar way. The areas where the copper wire is in contact with the bare iron hanger are known as *junctions*.
5. Tighten the windings using a pair of pliers.
6. Use the cork stopper to support the iron wire. Mount the cork in a utility clamp on a retort stand as shown in Figure 13.2.
7. Connect the free end of each copper wire to the galvanometer. Record the galvanometer reading.

Challenge

Find out the location of the generator that supplies electricity to your community. How far away is it from your community? At what voltage is the electricity transmitted from the generator to your community?

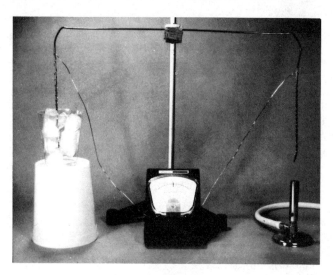

Figure 13.2 *This is a thermocouple.*

Table 13.1 *Galvanometer Readings Using a Thermocouple*

STEP NUMBER	JUNCTION 1	JUNCTION 2	GALVANOMETER READING
7	In air	In air	
8	In ice water	In air	
9	In ice water	In hand	
10	In ice water	In hot water	
11	In ice water	In burner flame	
12	In ice water	In ice water	

8. Place one junction (Junction 1) into a beaker of ice water as shown in Figure 13.2. It may be necessary to raise the beaker of ice water on some support. Record the galvanometer reading.
9. Warm the other junction (Junction 2) by holding it in your hand. Record the galvanometer reading.
10. Remove your hand and place Junction 2 in a beaker of hot water. Record the galvanometer reading. Remove the beaker of hot water.

CAUTION Wear safety goggles for the next step of this Activity. Do not touch the hot junction with your hands.

11. Light the Bunsen burner, and use it to heat Junction 2. Record the galvanometer reading.
12. Cool Junction 2 by placing it in a second beaker of ice water. Record the galvanometer reading.

Questions

1. What happens to the current when the difference in temperature between the two junctions increases?
2. What do you think would happen to the current if you heated Junction 1 and left Junction 2 in ice water? Test your prediction.

Challenge

In many ovens and pottery kilns, the "thermometer" is actually a galvanometer that is hooked up to a thermocouple. Explain how this set up could be used to measure the temperature in the oven.

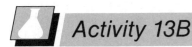

Problem

How can light be used to generate an electrical current?

Materials

solar cell
galvanometer
flashlight
overhead projector or sunlight

Procedure

1. Make a table in your notebook similar to Table 13.2.
2. Attach a solar cell to a galvanometer as shown in Figure 13.3. Record the galvanometer reading.
3. Shine a light from a flashlight onto the solar cell. Record the galvanometer reading.
4. Let the sun shine on your solar cell. If it is cloudy, use the light from an overhead projector. Record the galvanometer reading.

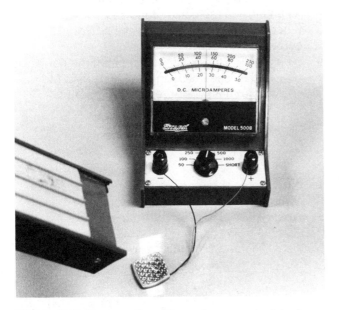

Figure 13.3 *Can a solar cell produce an electrical current?*

Observations

Table 13.2 *Galvanometer Readings Using a Solar Cell*

DESCRIPTION	GALVANOMETER READING
Room light	
Flashlight	
Sunlight/overhead projector	

Questions

1. What relationship exists between the intensity (strength) of the light and the size of the current generated?
2. Suppose that you measured the current produced when a 60 W lightbulb was held 100 cm away from the solar cell. What do you predict would happen to the galvanometer reading if
   (a) the light was placed 200 cm away from the solar cell?
   (b) the light was placed 50 cm away from the solar cell?
   (c) the 60 W bulb was replaced with a 100 W bulb and placed 100 cm away?

Activity 13C

Problem

How can a magnet be used to produce a current?

Materials

2 bar magnets
generator coil
galvanometer
2 connecting wires

Procedure

1. Make a table in your notebook similar to Table 13.3.
2. Connect the generator coil to a galvanometer as shown in Figure 13.4. Record the galvanometer reading.
3. Slowly place the south pole of one magnet inside the coil, as shown in Figure 13.4. Record the galvanometer reading.
4. Slowly remove the magnet. Record the galvanometer reading.
5. Quickly push the magnet in and pull it out of the coil repeatedly. Record the galvanometer reading.
6. Hold two magnets side by side with like poles together.
7. Repeat steps 3–5 using both magnets.

Figure 13.4 *This is a simple generator.*

Observations

Table 13.3 *Galvanometer Readings using a Simple Generator*

DESCRIPTION	GALVANOMETER READING
Magnet not in place	
Magnet moved in slowly	
Magnet moved out slowly	
Magnet moved in and out quickly	
Two magnets moved in slowly	
Two magnets moved out slowly	
Two magnets moved in and out quickly	

Questions

1. What must be done with the magnet in order to generate a current?
2. What would you expect to see if the magnet was resting inside the coil, not moving?
3. What can you do to increase the size of the current?
4. What would you expect to happen if the north pole was placed inside the coil instead of the south pole? Test your prediction if possible.

Self-check

1. What factor or factors determine the size of the current produced by a thermocouple?
2. What type of equipment is often run by solar cells?
3. What are the two main parts of a generator?

More Ways of Generating Electrical Current

Piezo-electric Effect

Certain crystals, such as Rochelle salt and quartz, respond to very slight changes in pressure. When the crystal is "squeezed," positively charged atoms are forced in one direction while negatively charged atoms are forced in the opposite direction. If the crystal is connected to a conductor, a current results. This is known as the **piezo-electric effect**.

Sound waves can cause the crystals to vibrate (or squeeze and unsqueeze). If you speak into a microphone containing such a crystal, the sound waves will "squeeze" the crystal and a current will be produced. The current can travel along a conductor to an earphone that also contains a crystal. The current causes the crystal in the earphone to vibrate and produce sound waves.

During earthquakes in areas rich in quartz rock, large flashes of light may be seen in the night sky. Some scientists have suggested that the piezo-electric effect could be the source of the electricity needed to produce these flashes. Some scientists have suggested that many of the UFO (unidentified flying object) sightings that have been reported may have been nothing more than flashes of light due to the piezo-electricity at night.

Hydro-electricity

In Canada, most electricity used in the home is **hydro-electricity** produced by hydro-electric generators. When large quantities of water flow from behind dams or over waterfalls, the energy is used to make electricity. The electrical energy you obtain by plugging appliances into your wall outlets may have come from a generator hundreds of kilometres away. Examine Figure 13.5 to see how the energy of falling water is converted into an electrical current.

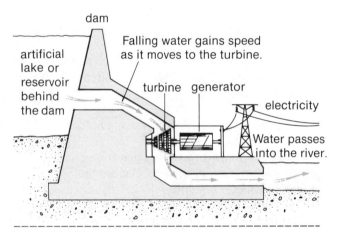

Figure 13.5 *A hydro-electric power plant. The turbines and generators are usually located at the base of the falls or the dam. Why do you think this is the case?*

Batteries and Cells

Cells are devices that are able to store energy. A combination of two or more cells is called a **battery**. When you buy a small flashlight "battery," you are usually buying a single cell. Cells are used to run flashlights, watches, toys, radios, hearing aids, and many other items that we use daily. All cells and batteries need three essential ingredients in order to function: two different metals and a conducting solution. In the next activity, you will be able to make a simple cell using an ordinary lemon.

Activity 13D

Problem

How can a lemon be used to produce a current?

Materials

lemon
2 iron paper clips
2 pieces of bare copper wire (each piece 10 cm)
2 alligator connectors
galvanometer
styrofoam cup

Procedure

1. Make a table in your notebook similar to Table 13.4.
2. Place a lemon on top of an inverted styrofoam cup.
3. Insert a straightened iron paper clip and a 10 cm piece of copper wire into the lemon as shown in Figure 13.6.
4. Record the galvanometer reading before attaching it to the lemon.
5. Connect the two wires to a galvanometer as instructed by your teacher. Record the galvanometer reading.
6. Remove the copper wire and replace it with another straightened paper clip.
7. Connect the 2 paper clips to the galvanometer and record the galvanometer reading.
8. Remove the 2 paper clips and replace them with 2 pieces of copper wire.
9. Connect the 2 wires to the galvanometer and record the galvanometer reading.

Observations

Table 13.4 *Galvanometer Readings From Lemon Cell*

DESCRIPTION	GALVANOMETER READING
Before hooking up to lemon	
One paper clip and one piece of copper wire	
Two paper clips	
Two copper wires	

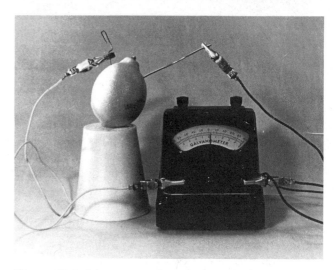

Figure 13.6 *A lemon can be used to produce electricity.*

Questions

1. Must both wires be made of the same material in order to produce a current? How do you know?
2. Do you think a current would be produced if the lemon was replaced with a beaker of lemon juice? Why or why not?

Challenge

What other fruits might you expect to produce an electrical current? With your teacher's permission, design and carry out an experiment to test your hypothesis.

Self-check

1. How can electricity be generated from quartz crystals?
2. What are the three main parts of a cell?
3. What is a battery?

More About Cells

If you examine a flashlight cell that has been cut open, you will see its main parts: a zinc case (metal 1), a carbon rod (metal 2), and a black paste made of ammonium chloride, carbon particles, sawdust, and water. The black paste is the conducting solution. A flashlight cell is called a dry cell even though it is not totally dry. A diagram of a flashlight cell is shown in Figure 13.7.

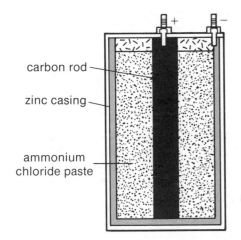

carbon rod

zinc casing

ammonium chloride paste

Figure 13.7 *A dry cell looks like this when it is cut open.*

CAUTION Do not cut open a cell or battery unless you are supervised by an adult. The substances in them are caustic and can burn your skin.

Most people call a flashlight cell a "battery" even though there is only one cell present. Some of the larger batteries are true batteries and contain more than one cell. If you break open an old 9 volt transistor radio battery, you will see six tiny cells inside that are all joined together.

Be careful not to get the paste on your hands or on the surface on which you are working. The paste contains an acid that could cause burns.

There are many different kinds of cells and batteries. Not all are made of carbon, zinc, ammonium chloride, and other dry cell ingredients. Some cells contain mercury, others contain lead, and still others are made of nickel and cadmium. Some cells are ready to work immediately and are thrown away when they are used up. New car batteries, however, cannot be used right away. They must be charged first before they can be used. These batteries are called **storage batteries**. They are able to store energy for later use. These batteries are recharged for continual use.

Challenge

Compare the prices of rechargeable batteries with those of non-rechargeable ones. Design and conduct an experiment to find out how long a regular battery lasts. How many times would you have to recharge a rechargeable battery before you began to save money?

Potential Difference of a Cell

When you buy a battery at the store, you will have to know what "voltage" you need. For example, a camera flash attachment may need a 1.5 V cell. A smoke alarm detector may need a 9.0 V battery, while an automobile battery is usually 12 V. What is the difference between these batteries and cells?

A battery or cell provides the energy for electrons to travel around a circuit. On the way back to the cell, the electrons give up their energy. This energy may be used, for example, to light lamps, ring bells, or start car engines. Different amounts of energy are needed to move electrons through different circuits. The **electric potential difference** (or **potential difference**) of a cell indicates the amount of energy available to move electrons.

A **coulomb** (**C**) is the name given to a large group of electrons. You will learn more about coulombs in Section 13.5. The **joule** (**J**) is the unit used to measure energy. You used this unit to measure food energy in Unit 2. The number of joules of energy supplied to each coulomb of electrons is known as a **volt** (**V**). A 12 V battery, therefore, will supply 12 J of energy to every coulomb of electrons that passes through it. This energy can then be used to run various appliances. A **voltmeter** can be used to measure potential difference.

In the next activity, you will be able to make several chemical cells and compare the potential difference of each.

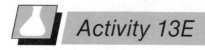
Activity 13E

Problem

What factors contribute to the potential difference of a chemical wet cell?

Materials

ammonium chloride solution
dilute sodium hydroxide solution
vinegar
distilled water
assorted metal strips (each approximately 2 cm × 10 cm)
wet cell apparatus
2 alligator connectors
voltmeter
thermometer
graduated cylinder
ruler

Procedure

1. Watch carefully as your teacher demonstrates how to use the voltmeter. The electrode marked (-) shows where electrons move into the voltmeter from the wire. This tells you the direction in which the electrons are flowing. See Figure 13.8.

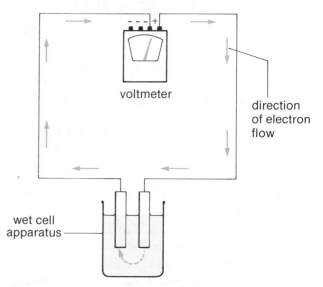

Figure 13.8 *Use the voltmeter to determine the direction of electron flow and the amount of energy in the cell.*

2. Prepare a table in your notebook similar to Table 13.5. Record all of the important conditions to make sure that these variables are always kept the same while different metals are being tested.
3. Put 200 mL of ammonium chloride solution in the wet cell apparatus. Determine the temperature of the solution. Record this in your table.
4. Select two different metallic strips to start. Measure the dimension of each strip. Record this in your table.
5. Connect the two metal strips to the wet cell apparatus and the voltmeter as shown in Figure 13.9.
6. Place the metal strips in the ammonium chloride solution to a depth of 2.0 cm. Measure the separation between the strips and record it in your table.
7. Record the reading on the voltmeter.
8. Record which metal is losing electrons and which metal is gaining electrons.
9. Keep one metal strip in one holder, but unclip the other metal and replace it with a different metal. Be sure to keep the separation between the strips and the depth in the solution the same for each trial.
10. Repeat steps 6–9 for as many combinations of metals as possible. For each combination, record which metal lost electrons, which metal gained electrons, and how much potential difference was produced.

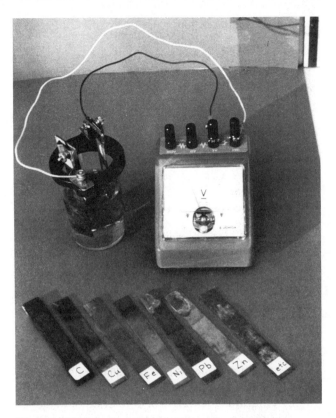

Figure 13.9 *Equipment used to make a wet cell. Make sure you connect the black terminal of the voltmeter (–) to the black terminal of the wet cell apparatus and the red terminal (+) of the voltmeter to the red terminal of the wet cell apparatus.*

Table 13.5 *Summary of Wet Cell Results*

CONTROL DATA			
Amount of solution used: 200 mL			
Temperature of solution: _____			
Size of metal strips: _____			
Depth to which strips were immersed: 2.0 cm			
Separation between strips: _____			
SOLUTION USED	METAL THAT LOST ELECTRONS	METAL THAT GAINED ELECTRONS	POTENTIAL DIFFERENCE

11. Pour the ammonium chloride solution into the storage container provided by your teacher. Wash all equipment thoroughly before using it again.
12. Repeat steps 3–10 using sodium hydroxide.

CAUTION Sodium hydroxide can burn your skin and clothes. Do not come in contact with any sodium hydroxide. If you do, inform your teacher immediately and, if necessary, flood the area with water.

13. Repeat steps 3–10 using vinegar.
14. Repeat steps 3–10 using distilled water.

Observations

(see Table 13.5)

Questions

1. (a) Which combination of metals resulted in the largest potential difference?
   (b) What was the potential difference of this cell?
   (c) Which combination produced the lowest potential difference?
2. Was there any combination of metals that did not produce a current? If so, list the combination of metals in this cell.
3. What would be the disadvantage of using your cell to run a flashlight, radio, etc.?

Challenge

In Activity 13E, you examined how the type of metal and type of solution used in the cell affected the potential difference produced. Now design an experiment to see how one of the other variables (size of metal strip, depth to which strips were immersed, separation between strips, or temperature of solution) would affect the potential difference of the cell.

Science at Work

At the University of British Columbia, a research team led by Professor Rudolph Roland Haering has been developing new batteries that will store several times as much energy as a lead-acid battery of the same mass. A lead-acid storage battery is the type used in automobiles. One type of new cell is called the *MoLi* cell. Its name comes from *molybdenum* and *lithium*, two of the chemical elements in these cells. The MoLi cell is rechargeable. During testing, it outlasted presently existing cells used to power devices that draw large currents. It uses readily available materials, so its cost to the consumer should be quite favorable.

Self-check

1. What is a storage battery?
2. What units are used to measure
   (a) energy?
   (b) potential difference?
3. A battery is marked "6.0 V." What does this tell you about the amount of energy provided by this battery?
4. What factors affect the potential difference of a chemical wet cell?

Electrical Circuits

An electrical **circuit** is a path through which electrons flow. In order for current to flow, the circuit must be continuous. There can be no gaps in the circuit. An electrical circuit can be compared to a race-track. Cars complete laps by moving around the entire race-track. It does not matter if the road is dirt, gravel, or asphalt. The car will continue as long as there is a road of some type. If the road is interrupted, the car cannot continue and it must stop.

The same is true in an electrical circuit. Electrons move along a conductor. It does not matter what type of conductor is present as long as it allows electrons to flow. If there is a gap in the conductor, electrons stop moving and the current stops.

Measuring Electrical Current in a Circuit

Imagine that you are standing beside a river during the spring flood season. You know that the river current is much stronger than normal. In order to measure it, you would have to find a way to count the number of litres of water passing you each second. This would allow you to estimate the size of the current in the river in litres per second (L/s). You could then compare this current with the normal current.

Measuring electrical current is similar to measuring river current. You need to find a way to count the number of electrons passing a certain point in a conductor in one second. If you did this, you might find that the current in your stereo would be 6 240 000 000 000 000 000 electrons per second! This would be like counting every water molecule that passed by you in the river. The number is too large to work with.

To make things simpler, scientists count "packages" of electrons. One "package" of electrons contains 6 240 000 000 000 000 000 electrons (or 6.24×10^{18}). This package of electrons is called a coulomb (C). The current in your stereo is therefore 1 C/s (one coulomb per second). A current of 1 C/s is called an **ampere** (**A**).

Table 13.6 indicates the current drawn by a few common household appliances.

Table 13.6 *Current Drawn by Household Appliances*

APPLIANCE	CURRENT
Electric kettle	12.5 A
100 W lamp	0.8 A
Radio	0.4 A
Toaster	8.3 A
Colour television	1.7 A

An **ammeter** measures current in a circuit. Most ammeters have several different scales on them so that you can measure a wide range of currents. The currents you will be measuring will be quite small so you will measure them in milliamperes (mA). One milliampere is equal to 1/1000 of an ampere. Therefore,

$$1 \text{ A} = 1 \text{ 000 mA}$$
$$1 \text{ mA} = 0.001 \text{ A}$$

Types of Current

The current provided by batteries and special electronic adaptors that plug into wall outlets flow in one direction only. This type of current is called **direct current**, or **DC**.

The giant generators that produce electricity for your home make the electrical current reverse directions very rapidly. This type of current is called **alternating current**, or **AC**. The rate at which the current reverses directions is called the **frequency**. It is measured in **hertz** (**Hz**). Most of the appliances in your home work on an alternating current.

Self-check

1. What name is given to a "package" of electrons?
2. What is meant by the term "current"?
3. What units are used to measure the size of the current in a circuit?
4. What is the difference between a direct current and an alternating current?

Simple Circuits

Figure 13.10 shows an example of a circuit. Imagine the time it would take for electricians to draw all the parts of the circuit every time they planned a circuit. It is far faster and easier to draw circuits using symbols. Each symbol represents part of the circuit. For example, Figure 13.10 (b) shows the same circuit as the one in Figure 13.10 (a). You can identify the different circuit symbols and their meaning in Table 13.7.

Table 13.7 Circuit Symbols

SYMBOL	NAME	DESCRIPTION
	Cell	Source of current. Long bar represents the positive terminal.
	Battery	Two or more cells joined together. This battery is made up of 2 cells.
	Lamp	Small lightbulb.
	Switch	Can be opened to stop current flow or closed to allow current to flow.
	Fuse	Prevents too much current from flowing through the circuit.
G	Galvanometer	Measures very small currents (milliamperes).
A	Ammeter	Measures a wide range of currents (amperes).
V	Voltmeter	Measures the amount of energy given to (or lost by) electrons in a circuit (volts).

Figure 13.10 *A basic electrical circuit*

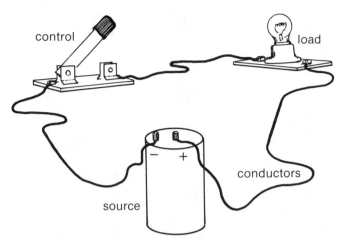

(a) *The circuit set-up*

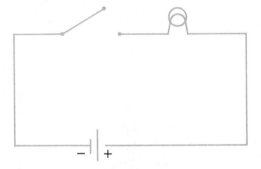

(b) *Diagram of the same circuit, drawn with standard symbols.*

Examine the circuit diagrams in Figure 13.11. Read the description accompanying each diagram. Make sure you understand what is being shown in each diagram.

Remember that current in an electrical circuit is measured using an ammeter. Make sure you are familiar with the use of an ammeter before beginning the next activity.

Circuit A

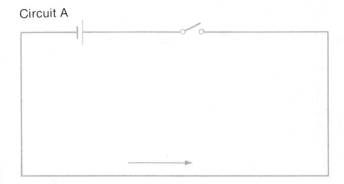

Circuit B

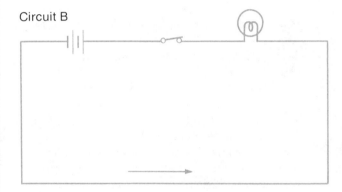

Circuit C

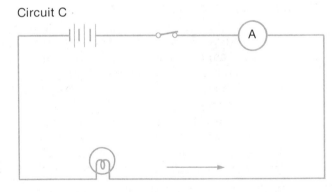

Figure 13.11 *Some simple circuits. The arrow indicates the direction of current flow. Circuit A contains a single cell and an open switch. Circuit B contains a battery of two cells, a closed switch, and a lamp. Circuit C contains a battery of three cells, a lamp, a closed switch, and an ammeter measuring the current in the circuit.*

Activity 13F

Problem

What factors affect the current in a circuit?

Materials

ammeter
button switch
battery
2 lamps
wire with alligator connectors

Procedure

1. Make a table in your notebook similar to Table 13.8.
2. Set up a circuit similar to the one shown in Figure 13.12 (a). When the switch is closed, electrons will leave the negative terminal of the battery and travel through the lamp, the ammeter, and then the switch before returning to the positive terminal of the battery.
3. Push the switch. Record the ammeter reading.
4. Change the circuit so that there are two lamps connected in **series**. This means that the electrons flow through lamp 1 and then lamp 2 before returning to the battery. See Figure 13.12 (b).
5. Push the switch. Record the ammeter reading.
6. Remove the ammeter and connect it into the circuit between the two lamps. See Figure 13.12 (c). Push the switch and record the ammeter reading.
7. Change the circuit so that the two lamps are connected in **parallel**. See Figure 13.12 (d). In this case, electrons flow through either lamp 1 or lamp 2 (but not both) before returning to the battery.
8. Push the switch. Record the ammeter reading.
9. Remove the ammeter and connect it so that it measures the current going through lamp 1 only. See Figure 13.12 (e). Push the switch and record the ammeter reading.
10. Remove the ammeter and connect it so that it measures the current going through lamp 2 only. See Figure 13.12 (f).
11. Push the switch. Record the ammeter reading.

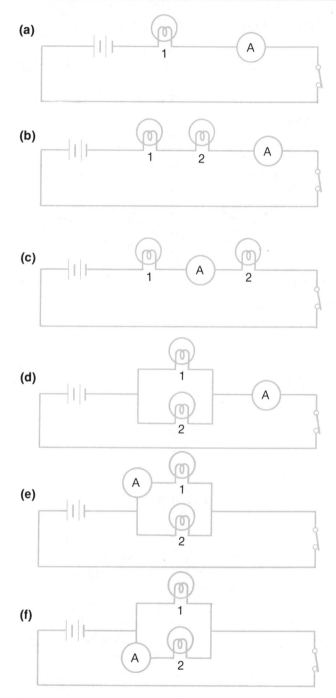

Figure 13.12 *The red terminal (+) of the battery should be nearest the red terminal of the ammeter. The black terminal (–) of the battery should be nearest the black terminal of the ammeter.*

Observations

Table 13.8 *Summary of Current Flow*

	ONE LAMP	TWO LAMPS IN SERIES	TWO LAMPS IN PARALLEL
Total current in circuit			
Current through lamp 1			
Brightness of lamp 1			
Current through lamp 2	.....		
Brightness of lamp 2	.....		

SAMPLE ONLY

Questions

1. What conclusion can you make about the relationship between the total current in a circuit and the current through each part of the circuit if it is set up
   (a) in series?
   (b) in parallel?
2. How did the brightness of the lamps differ when you had
   (a) two lamps in series?
   (b) two lamps in parallel?
3. Suppose that you set up three identical lamps in series. The total current in the circuit was 9.0 A.
   (a) What would be the current going through each lamp?
   (b) What do you think would happen if one of the lamps was removed?
   (c) Why do you think this would happen?
4. Suppose that you set up three identical lamps in parallel.
   (a) What would be the current going through each lamp?
   (b) What do you think would happen if one of the lamps was removed?
   (c) Why do you think this would happen?

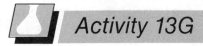

Potential difference in a circuit is measured using a voltmeter. Make sure you are familiar with the use of a voltmeter before beginning the next activity.

Problem

What factors affect the potential difference in a circuit?

Materials

voltmeter   2 lamps
button switch   wire with alligator connectors
battery

Procedure

1. Make a table in your notebook similar to Table 13.9.
2. Set up a circuit similar to the one shown in Figure 13.13 (a). The voltmeter will measure the potential difference between the two points of attachment.

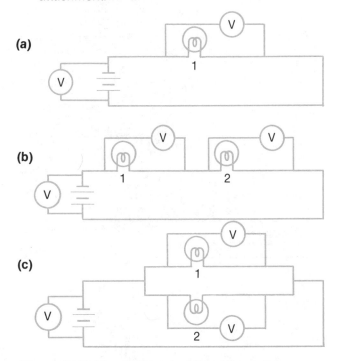

Figure 13.13 *The red terminal (+) of the battery should be nearest the red terminal of the voltmeter. The black terminal (–) of the battery should be nearest the black terminal of the voltmeter.*

3. Push the switch. Record the potential difference across the battery and across the lamp.
4. Change the circuit so that there are two lamps connected in series. This means that the electrons flow through lamp 1 and then lamp 2 before returning to the battery. See Figure 13.13 (b).
5. Push the switch. Record the potential difference across the battery, lamp 1, and lamp 2.
6. Change the circuit so that the two lamps are connected in parallel. See Figure 13.13 (c). In this case, electrons flow through either lamp 1 or lamp 2 (but not both) before returning to the battery.
7. Push the switch. Record the voltmeter reading across the battery, lamp 1, and lamp 2.

Observations

Table 13.9 *Summary of Potential Difference*

	ONE LAMP	TWO LAMPS IN SERIES	TWO LAMPS IN PARALLEL
Potential difference across battery			
Potential difference across lamp 1			
Brightness of lamp 1			
Potential difference across lamp 2	.....		
Brightness of lamp 2	.....		

Questions

1. What relationship do you notice between the potential difference across the battery and the potential difference across the lamps in series?
2. What relationship do you notice between the potential difference across the battery and the potential difference across the lamps in parallel?
3. Suppose that you set up a circuit containing three lamps and a battery. The potential difference across the battery was 6.0 V. If the lamps were identical, what would be the potential difference across each lamp if
   (a) the lamps were in series?
   (b) the lamps were in parallel?

Ideas and Applications

A galvanometer is the basic instrument used in designing both voltmeters and ammeters. Such instruments are commonly found in tape recorders, battery testers, car dashboards, and in science laboratories.

Series and Parallel Circuits

Imagine a circuit in which three lamps (or other appliances) are set up in series. If you add up the potential differences across each lamp, the sum will equal the total potential difference across the energy source. See Figure 13.14 (a). The current, however, will stay the same no matter where it is measured. See Figure 13.14 (b).

(a)

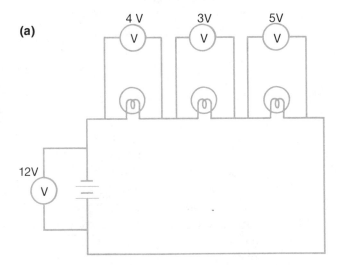

(b)

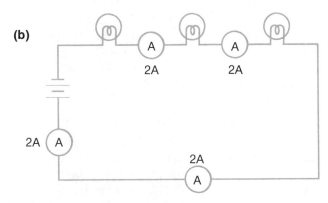

Figure 13.14 *Current and potential difference in a series circuit*

Picture another circuit in which three lamps (or other appliances) are set up in parallel. The potential difference is the same across each lamp and across the energy source. See Figure 13.15 (a). If you measure the current going through each individual lamp and through the entire circuit, you will find that the sum of the individual currents will equal the total current in the circuit. See Figure 13.15 (b).

(a)

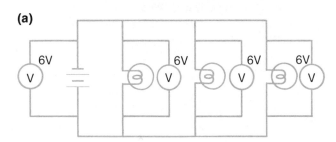

(b)

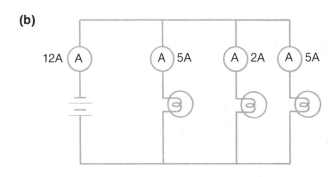

Figure 13.15 *Current and potential difference in a parallel circuit*

Self-check

1. What is the symbol used to represent the following:
   (a) an ammeter
   (b) a voltmeter
   (c) an open switch
2. Draw a circuit showing two lamps connected in series.

3. Draw a circuit showing two lamps connected in parallel.
4. Draw a circuit showing three cells hooked up in series that supply energy to three lamps in parallel. Include switches that would let you turn the lamps on and off individually.
5. Examine Figure 13.16. What would be the reading on each ammeter and each voltmeter in the circuits?
6. Some strings of Christmas tree lights are connected in series. Others are connected in parallel. Which type of lights do you think is best? Explain your answer.

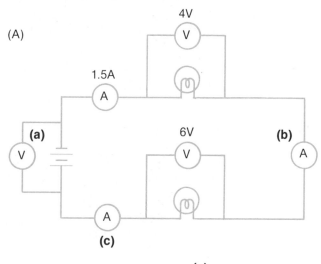

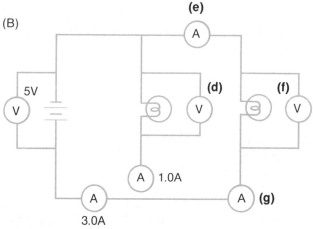

Figure 13.16 *What would be the readings on each ammeter and voltmeter?*

13.7

Electricity in the Home

Three underground cables (or overhead wires) deliver electricity to your home. Once connected to your home, the three wires first run through an electric meter. The meter, which is actually a motor, measures the amount of electric energy used in your home. As more current is drawn into the house, the counting mechanism turns faster. This meter can then be read to determine how much energy you have used. You will then be billed for the cost of this energy.

Neutral and Hot Wires

One of the wires that enters your home is connected to the ground. This wire is electrically *neutral*. The other two wires are energized, or live. They are sometimes called *hot wires*. If you were to touch a hot wire, the shock could be dangerous or even fatal.

The three wires entering your home make it possible to obtain either 120 V or 240 V. If you connect a voltmeter to one hot wire and the neutral wire, it will read 120 V. Most appliances in your home require this potential difference. If you connect the voltmeter to both hot wires, it will read 240 V. Larger appliances, such as stoves, clothes dryers, and some air conditioners, require 240 V. They must be plugged into special outlets that will connect them to both hot wires.

After going through the meter, the three wires go to the service entrance panel. See Figure 13.17. A main switch inside the panel allows you to turn off all the power to your house instantly. This should be done if you are altering or repairing the electrical circuits in your home.

The wiring in your home is made up of several separate circuits called branch circuits.

The panel distributes the electricity coming into your home into the branch circuits. If the wires carry too much current, they could overheat and cause a fire. To prevent this, fuses or circuit breakers are installed to control the amount of current in each circuit.

Fuses

A **fuse** is basically a thin piece of metal that will melt rapidly if the current passing through it exceeds a certain limit. This will break the circuit and stop the current from flowing through the wires. Fuses come in various sizes to allow different amounts of current to pass through. If the wiring of a circuit or appliance can safely handle a current up to 15 A, then a 15 A fuse is placed in the circuit. If a 20 A or 30 A fuse is substituted for a 15 A fuse, too much current will go through the circuit. This will overheat the conducting wire and could cause a fire.

The main disadvantage of fuses is that once they are burned out or "blown" (melted), they must be replaced. Figure 13.18 shows a good fuse and a blown fuse.

Figure 13.18

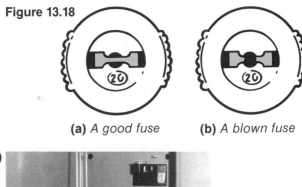

(a) *A good fuse*   **(b)** *A blown fuse*

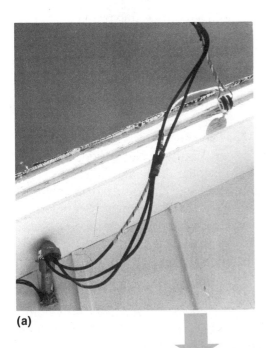

(a)

(b)   **(c)**

Figure 13.17 (a) *Three wires from the nearest power pole enter your home.* **(b)** *After entering your home, electricity goes through your electric meter, which measures the amount of energy you use.* **(c)** *From the electric meter, the three wires go to the service entrance panel. The main disconnect switch is at the top of the service entrance panel.*

Circuit Breakers

Circuit breakers are more convenient to use than fuses. A **circuit breaker** consists of a strip made of two different metals connected to a switch. See Figure 13.19. When the current goes through the circuit breaker, the strip is heated. One metal expands more than the other and so the strip bends. If the current in the circuit is too high, the strip bends enough to "trip" the switch. This breaks the circuit. When the overload is corrected, the circuit breaker can be reset.

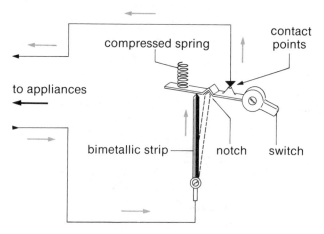

Figure 13.19 *A circuit breaker. Too much current heats the strip. Since the strip is made of two different metals, one metal expands more than the other, bending the strip. The notch in the spring loader strip drops down. This breaks the circuit and shuts off the current.*

How Grounding Protects You

The branch circuits that carry current to the wall outlets and light fixtures around your home supply 120 V. The two prongs of the plugs that go into an outlet connect to one hot wire and one neutral wire.

In a three-pronged outlet, one prong is connected to the hot wire, the second prong is connected to the neutral wire, and the extra prong is connected to a wire that leads to the ground. The hot wire and the neutral wire carry the current. The grounding wire is important if something goes wrong.

Suppose that someone drops an electric drill. You cannot see any damage, but inside, the hot wire connection is jolted loose and is now touching the metal case. The entire drill casing is now hot since the metal of which it is made conducts electricity. If you pick up the drill, your body will provide a path for the current to travel from the drill casing to the ground. If the current was 0.001 A, you would feel a shock. If the current was 0.02 A, the muscles that move your rib cage would become paralyzed and you would stop breathing. A current of 1.0 A or higher could cause severe burns throughout the body.

Luckily, the grounding wire provides an easier route for the electrical current to reach the ground. The current would flow from the drill casing, through the grounding wire, and into the earth. The very high current that results would blow the fuse or trip the circuit breaker to stop the current flow. As a result, you would not be seriously hurt. Don't be tempted to cut off the extra prong in order to connect an appliance to a two-pronged receptacle of an extension cord. If you do, you will lose the protection of the grounding wire. It is much safer to purchase a three-prong extension cord to go with the appliance.

An appliance such as an electric stove, air conditioner, or clothes dryer requires 240 V to run. The plugs of these appliances and the outlets to which they are connected have four prongs. Where does each of the four prongs lead?

Self-check

1. What is a hot wire?
2. What is the potential difference available when an appliance is hooked up to two hot wires?
3. What happens if a circuit carries too much current?
4. In what two ways can the amount of current in a circuit be limited?
5. What is the minimum current that will give you a shock if it flows through you?
6. Where does the third prong of a three-prong plug lead?
7. Why is grounding important?

Using Electricity Safely and Wisely

You know that electricity can be dangerous if it is not used carefully. Here are ten suggestions that will help you to use electricity safely.

1. Check the cords on any appliances you use. Old cords may have worn-out insulation or loose connections inside their plugs. These can cause overheating and lead to fire.
2. Do not overload extension cords. There is a limit to the amount of current they can carry safely without overheating.
3. If a fuse blows or a circuit breaker trips, find out what is causing the overload. Perhaps too many appliances have been plugged into one circuit. If this is not the case, check for frayed cords or a defect in one of the appliances.
4. If a fuse blows, replace it with one of exactly the same size. If you replace it with one that allows a higher current, the wires could overheat and a fire could result.
5. Do not use electrical appliances while you are in contact with water. For example, do not use a hair dryer in the bathtub or an electric drill while standing on a wet floor. Current flows more easily through water than through dry materials and so the current may be grounded through you.
6. Do not perform do-it-yourself electrical repairs that you are not trained to do. Call in a qualified electrician.
7. If you must perform electrical repairs, shut off the current to the circuit on which you are working. This can be done by removing the fuse or tripping the circuit breaker by hand.
8. Never remove the third prong of a three-pronged plug.

9. Use a three-prong extension with a three-pronged plug.
10. If you are working outdoors, keep all ladders (especially metal ones) away from power lines.

Ideas and Applications

Energy for home and industrial use comes from a variety of sources. At present, most of the energy used in Canada comes from burning fossil fuels. The term fossil fuels refers to petroleum, natural gas, and coal. Burning these fuels results in waste materials that can pollute the air we breathe, the water we drink, and the very earth itself. A great deal of research is being done to discover new sources of energy. Solar energy, wind energy, nuclear energy, and tidal energy are being investigated as alternatives to hydro-electricity and fossil fuels. In Unit Five, you will find out more about energy sources and methods of conserving energy.

Activity 13H

Every electrical appliance comes with a plate or sticker that provides you with information about its electrical characteristics. This information may include the potential difference at which it operates, the current it draws, the power it uses. It may also indicate the frequency at which it operates.

In this activity, you will collect information about many of the appliances in your home or in your school.

Problem

What information is found on the plates or stickers of electrical appliances?

Procedure

1. Make a table in your notebook similar to Table 13.10.
2. Examine some of the electrical appliances found in your home and at school. These might include a washer, stove, refrigerator, curling iron, microwave oven, electric typewriter, or power saw.
3. Look for the plate or sticker that gives you information about the electrical characteristics of the appliance.
4. Enter the information from each sticker in Table 13.10. You may not be able to fill in all columns for every appliance.

Observations

(see Table 13.10)

Questions

1. Which appliance draws the most current?
2. Which appliance uses the most power?
3. The electric meter measures the amount of energy used in **kilowatt hours** (**kW·h**). A kilowatt hour is equal to the number of kilowatts of energy that would be needed if the appliance ran for one hour. One thousand watts are equal to one kilowatt of energy. Make a table in your book similar to Table 13.11. Find out how much you are charged for every kW·h of energy you use. Use this information to complete Table 13.11.

Table 13.10 *Electrical Rating of Some Household Appliances*

APPLIANCE	POTENTIAL DIFFERENCE (V)	CURRENT (A)	POWER (W/kW)	FREQUENCY (Hz)	OTHER INFORMATION

Table 13.11 *Cost of Energy at Home*

DEVICE	LIGHT IN KITCHEN	CLOTHES DRYER	AIR CONDITIONER	COLOUR TELEVISION
Power (W)	100 W	4800 W	1400 W	330 W
Power (KW)				
Number of hours used daily				
Number of days used each year				
Number of hours used each year				
Total energy used each year (kW·h)				
Cost of 1 kW·h of energy ($)				
Cost of running the device for one year ($)				

Challenge

Describe five ways that you could reduce the amount of energy used by the appliances in Activity 13H.

Self-check

1. What two things should be done if a fuse blows or a circuit breaker is tripped?
2. Why is it dangerous to play a transistor radio while in the shower?
3. What should you do before attempting to repair an electrical circuit?

How Are Electronic Devices Made?

It's 4:00 p.m. on a Friday afternoon—time to get ready for the weekend. You're in a hurry today, so you're off to the bank machine to get money. Now stop for a moment. How many people have made it possible for you to be able to access your money after banking hours?

To make any one modern electronic device—whether it's a toaster, stereo receiver, or computer—many different skills are needed from many different people.

Engineers draw up basic designs and production plans for a new device in response to marketing research.

Design technicians work from the engineers' plans to develop a more detailed and exact mechanical design. The design must take into account the environment in which the device will be used, the people who will use it, and how it will be installed.

Technical writers have the job of writing operation and service manuals. These manuals must be accurate and easy to understand. They will help people use or service the new device correctly.

Assembly technicians make the first model (or prototype) of the new device. They may suggest changes that could make it work better. They may also suggest ways to make the assembly process easier or less costly.

Drafting technicians use special electronic diagrams and symbols to make accurate production and service drawings. Their work must be very precise.

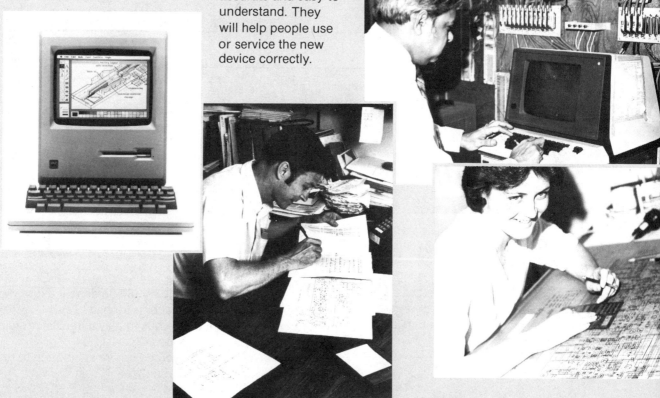

Environmental test technicians test all components to be sure that they will work properly in all the environments in which the device will be used.

Machinists and metalworkers use their knowledge of the properties of the parts of the new device. They use only materials that they know will withstand the demands of the environmental conditions to which the device will be exposed.

Assemblers work in the factory. They put together all the various parts that go into making the finished product.

Once the new product is finished, company salespeople must sell it to retail stores. Then retail store salespeople resell the product to the public. In doing so, they may be helped by large advertising campaigns launched by the marketing research personnel of the company that made the product.

The people in each of these jobs have an in-depth knowledge of their own areas. But they also have in common a certain amount of knowledge about electronics. Without these people and their knowledge, the development and production of new electronic devices—such as a computer—would be nearly impossible.

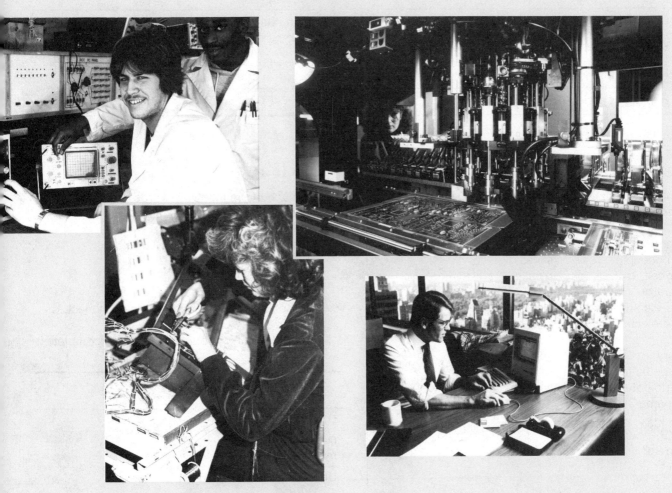

Chapter Objectives

NOW THAT YOU HAVE COMPLETED THIS CHAPTER, CAN YOU DO THE FOLLOWING?	FOR REVIEW, TURN TO SECTION
1. Explain the difference between static electricity and current electricity.	13.1
2. Describe three ways that current electricity can be generated.	13.2
3. Make an electrical cell.	13.3
4. Measure the potential difference of an electrical cell.	13.4
5. Explain the difference between AC and DC current.	13.5
6. Draw simple series and parallel circuits.	13.6
7. Compare current and potential difference in series and parallel circuits.	13.6
8. Explain how a fuse and circuit breaker work.	13.7
9. Interpret the information on the plate of an electrical appliance.	13.8
10. Explain how electricity may be used safely.	13.8

Words to Know

current electricity
conductor
insulator
galvanometer
thermocouple
solar cell
generator
piezo-electric effect
hydro-electricity
cell
battery
storage battery
electric potential difference (potential difference)
coulomb (C)
joule (J)
volt (V)
voltmeter
circuit
ampere (A)
ammeter

direct current (DC)
alternating current (AC)
frequency
hertz (Hz)
series
parallel
fuse
circuit breaker
kilowatt hour (kW·h)

Tying It Together

1. Use each of the following words in a sentence that demonstrates the meaning of the word.
   (a) hydro-electricity
   (b) battery
   (c) generator
   (d) piezo-electric effect
   (e) thermocouple
2. List the three parts needed to make an electric cell.
3. Copy this chart in your notebook and complete it.

	CURRENT	POTENTIAL DIFFERENCE	POWER
Definition			
Device used to measure it			
Units used to measure it			

SAMPLE ONLY

4. Draw a circuit diagram to show each of the following circuits. Indicate the direction of current flow.
   (a) a circuit containing a battery made up of two cells, four lamps in series, a closed switch, and an ammeter that measures the current between lamp 1 and lamp 2
   (b) a circuit containing a single cell, three lamps in parallel, an open switch, and a voltmeter that measures the potential difference across the battery
5. What is the difference between AC current and DC current?
6. (a) How are a fuse and circuit breaker similar?
   (b) How are a fuse and circuit breaker different?
7. What information can be found on the plate of an electrical appliance?
8. It takes Sonia 1.5 h to mow the lawn, using a 1500 W power mower.
   (a) Calculate the amount of electrical energy she uses in kilowatt hours.
   (b) If electrical energy costs four cents per kilowatt hour, calculate the cost of cutting the lawn.
9. List three things to look for when checking your home for electrical problems.

Applying Your Knowledge

1. What would happen if the outlets in your home were wired in series instead of in parallel?
2. The light in Miguel's hallway can be turned off at either end. To do this requires special switches, called double-throw switches. See Figure 13.20. Draw a circuit diagram showing how this can be done. Include a lamp, two switches, and a battery.
3. What do you think would be the most efficient way to use an air conditioner? Explain.

Figure 13.20
A double-throw switch has three connections for wires A, B, and C.

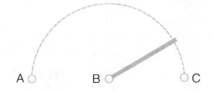

A   B   C

Projects for Investigation

1. The energy of a person pedalling a bicycle can be used to light a headlamp. A generator called a dynamo must be in place to make this happen. Use library references to find out how a dynamo works.
2. Your teacher may assign this question as a class challenge. How does your school use electrical energy? Have your teacher ask your school engineer to discuss this with your class. Could your school save more money if, for example, all unused classroom lights were turned off during lunch hour? In what other ways could the use of electricity be reduced? Use the following questions and procedures to examine your school's use of electricity:
   (a) Record the power rating in watts (W) of each light fixture in your classroom. A typical single fluorescent bulb of the size regularly used in classes has a power rating of 40 W.
   (b) Calculate the total power rating of all the lights in your classroom. If all bulbs are the same, simply multiply the rating for one bulb by the total number of bulbs.
   (c) Change the total power rating to kilowatts. (Divide by 1000.)
   (d) What is the total amount of energy consumed by your unused classroom at lunch hour? Remember that energy is measured in kilowatt hours.
   (e) What is the total amount of energy consumed by all the unused classrooms in your school at lunch hour? (Multiply by the number of unused rooms.)
   (f) If this energy costs, say 5¢/kW·h, what does it cost to keep all these rooms lit up during lunch hour?
   (g) How much would the school save in one week if these lights were turned off every lunch hour? (Multiply the answer from (f) by 5.)
   (h) How much would the school save in four weeks?
   (i) How much would the school save in one ten-month school year?

Magnetism

Key Ideas

- A magnet is able to attract many different materials.
- There are laws that describe the behaviour of magnets and magnetic objects.
- Magnets are present in a large number of appliances in the school and at home.
- Magnets and electricity work together to produce an electromagnet.

Have you used a **magnet** today? Before you say "no," consider a few possibilities. When you close the refrigerator door, a magnetic latch probably holds it shut. Can you find the "silent" magnetic door latches on your kitchen cabinet doors? When you open a can of soup with an electric can opener, a small magnet keeps the lid from falling into the can. The motor that drives the can opener also has a magnet in it. In fact, every electric motor has a magnet in it. A magnet helps shape the image on the television screen. The paper cone in the loudspeaker in your radio or stereo moves in response to pushes and pulls from the magnets at its base. Even the planet on which you live is a huge magnet. Its magnetic field turns compass needles, deflects dangerous particles from the sun away from us, and may help direct birds on their annual migrations. Now . . . have you used a magnet today?

The History of the Magnet

The first known magnet was a naturally occurring mineral ore (Figure 14.1). Miners in Magnesia, a district in ancient Greece, amazed other people with their "supernatural powers." They could lift several iron rings with pieces of this strange iron ore. A piece of this ore, when suspended from a string, was observed to swing around until one end pointed in the general direction of the North Star. We call this ore **lodestone**. The North Star was used as a direction indicator for travellers. It was known as a leading star or "lodestar." Lodestone was so named because of the way it lined up in the direction of the lodestar.

Lodestone is also known as *magnetite*. This name came from Magnesia where it was first used. The term magnetism has the same origin.

Figure 14.1 *Lodestone is a mineral found in nature that demonstrates magnetic properties.*

What Is a Magnet?

A magnet is a piece of iron, steel, or other alloy that attracts iron objects. Magnets are a source of fascination to many people. Magnetic objects seem to have supernatural power over many substances because they exert a pull on these substances. Ordinary iron objects, such as iron filings, bolts, and nails can become magnetized. Mechanical shock or heating can cause these **temporary magnets** to lose their magnetic properties quite easily. **Permanent magnets** remain magnetic for long periods of time. Good permanent magnets can be made from certain alloys of iron, such as cobalt steel. *Alnico*, an alloy that contains aluminum, nickel, cobalt, and iron makes a good permanent magnet.

Permanent magnets have many uses. You can find them in telephones, can openers, loudspeakers, generators, screwdrivers, and refrigerator doors. Every year, new products are made that use magnetism in some way.

Magnetic Poles

The ends of a bar magnet usually display the greatest force. These ends are called **poles**. If you suspend a bar magnet horizontally by a string, it will swing freely. When it comes to rest, one pole will always point in the north direction while the other will always point toward the south. The **north-seeking pole** is called the **N-pole** of the magnet. The pole that points to the south is the **south-seeking pole** or **S-pole**.

Every magnet you will use has both a north pole (N-pole) and south pole (S-pole). If you break a magnet in half, you will get two magnets. Each of the smaller magnets has its own N-pole and S-pole. It does not matter how many times you break it—the magnets will just get smaller and smaller. See Figure 14.2.

Figure 14.2 *Breaking a bar magnet*

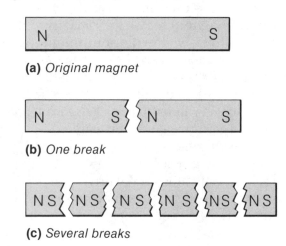

(a) *Original magnet*

(b) *One break*

(c) *Several breaks*

Problem

What materials are magnetic?

Materials

permanent bar magnet
various test materials such as silicon, sulphur, iron, nickel, steel, copper, wood, carbon, brass, tin, paper clips, pins, coins, etc.
compass
clear plastic wrap or clear plastic bag
iron filings

Procedure

1. Design a table in your notebook in which to record your observations.
2. Bring the N-pole of the magnet near a compass. What happens to the compass needle?
3. Place a pile of iron filings on a piece of paper.
4. Wrap the magnet in the plastic wrap or bag. Dip the entire bar magnet into the pile of iron filings. Draw a diagram to show what happens.
5. Return the iron filings to the container as instructed by your teacher.
6. Describe each of the test materials provided by your teacher.
7. Attempt to pick up each of the test materials with the N-pole of the magnet. Record your results in the table in your notebook.
8. Attempt to pick up each of the test materials with the S-pole of the magnet. Record your results in the table in your notebook.

Observations

1. Make a diagram to show what happens when the N-pole of the magnet is brought close to the compass.
2. Make a diagram to show what happens when a magnet is dipped into a pile of iron filings.

Questions

1. Which substances were attracted by the magnet?
2. Did the N-pole and S-pole of the magnet attract the same substances? If not, explain any differences.
3. Were all substances listed in question 1 attracted with the same strength? If not, describe any differences.
4. What do you predict would happen if you brought the S-pole of the magnet close to a compass? Test your predictions if possible.

Challenge

Adjust a water tap to give a thin stream of water. Bring the N-pole of a bar magnet close to the stream of water and observe what happens. What will happen if you bring the S-pole close to the running water?

Self-check

1. List two common uses of magnets in the home.
2. What is a temporary magnet?
3. What is a permanent magnet?
4. Around which part(s) of a bar magnet is the magnetic force strongest?

Domains

Magnetism originates inside atoms. Recall that an atom is made up of a nucleus containing positive protons and neutral neutrons. Negative electrons move in orbits around the nucleus. These electrons are also spinning much like a spinning top (Figure 14.3). This spinning action produces a magnetic force. Since all substances are made up of atoms with spinning electrons, all substances act like a magnet to some degree. Most substances, however, do not show strong magnetic properties because all electrons are not spinning in the same way. As a result, the magnetic forces produced by the electrons cancel each other out.

There are three chemical elements that are strongly magnetic when artificially magnetized —iron, nickel, and cobalt. Scientists think that there are more electrons spinning one way than the other in these three elements. As a result, the magnetic forces do not cancel each other out. Instead, they cause the element to be more magnetic than other elements. Atoms of iron, nickel, and cobalt also tend to form into groups.

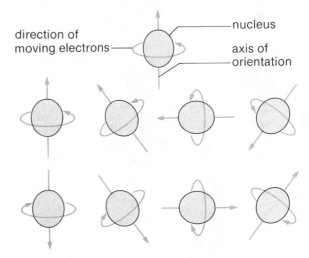

Figure 14.3 *Spinning electrons produce magnetic fields. Because electrons are spinning at different angles, the direction of the magnetic fields varies.*

The magnetic forces in each group are lined up in the same direction. These groups of aligned atoms are called **domains**. Each domain represents a miniature magnet within the element.

In unmagnetized iron, nickel, or cobalt, the domains are aimed in many different directions. This is known as random arrangement. See Figure 14.4 (a). If you stroke the iron, nickel, or cobalt with a magnet, most of the domains will line up with those of the magnetic forces in the magnet. See Figure 14.4 (b). This does not occur with most other substances, such as wood or rubber, because they do not have domains.

(a)

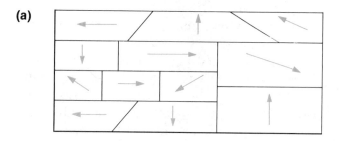

(b)

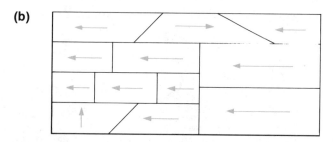

Figure 14.4 (a) *The domains of unmagnetized iron are randomly arranged.* **(b)** *Many of the domains in magnetized iron are arranged in the same direction.*

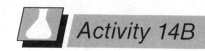

Activity 14B

Problem

Can a magnet exert its force through various substances?

Materials

bar magnet
iron filings
clear plastic wrap or a clear plastic bag
paper
glass plate
cardboard
waxed paper
steel plate
acetate sheet

Procedure

1. Place a piece of paper on your desk.
2. Make a pile of iron filings on this paper.
3. Wrap the N-pole of the magnet with plastic wrap or a plastic bag and place it 3–4 cm above the iron filings and observe the effect. Record your observations.
4. Remove the iron filings from the magnet.
5. Hold a piece of paper above the iron filings as shown in Figure 14.5.

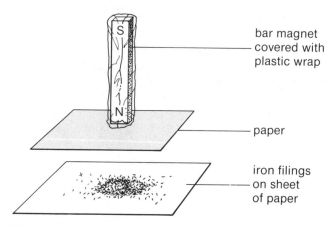

bar magnet covered with plastic wrap

paper

iron filings on sheet of paper

Figure 14.5 *Set-up for Activity 14B*

6. Hold the N-pole of the magnet as shown in Figure 14.5.
7. Observe the effect of the magnet on the iron filings. Record your observations.
8. Remove the magnet.
9. Repeat steps 5–8 for each of the remaining materials listed in the Materials section. Record your observations each time.
10. Summarize your results in a neat, organized table in your notebook.

Observations

1. Make a table in your notebook to describe the effect of the magnet through each of the materials tested. In the table, state the name of the material and describe its effect, if any, on the magnetic force of the magnet.

Questions

1. Did any of the materials affect the magnetic forces of the magnet? If so, describe the effect.

Ideas and Applications

Many animals look for landmarks and use the position of the sun and the stars to guide them in migration. It is now fairly certain that birds and other animals, such as dolphins, also have a magnetic sense. This sense, too, may help guide them, especially at times when they can't see landmarks.

Problem

How can a test tube of iron filings become magnetized?

Materials

test tube   elastic band
iron filings   bar magnet
clear plastic wrap   compass

Procedure

1. Neatly fill a test tube with iron filings. Place a piece of plastic wrap over the mouth of the test tube. Hold the wrap in place with an elastic band. Then lay the test tube in front of you.
2. Test the ends of the test tube for magnetic poles by bringing the compass close to the left end and then the right end of the test tube of iron filings. See Figure 14.6.
3. Gently rub the N-pole of a bar magnet along the test tube from left to right as shown in Figure 14.7. Be careful not to crack the test tube.

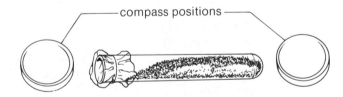

Figure 14.6 *Check the polarity of the iron filings using the compass as shown.*

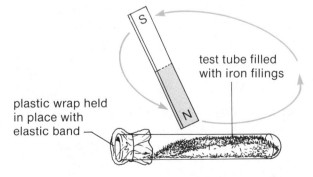

Figure 14.7 *Stroke the test tube from left to right using the N-pole of the bar magnet.*

4. Repeat step 2 to check the polarity of the iron filings.
5. Carefully shake the test tube for about 5 s.
6. Repeat step 2 to check the polarity of the iron filings.
7. Repeat steps 2–5 using the S-pole of the magnet.
8. Carefully shake the test tube for about 5 s.
9. Repeat step 2 to check the polarity of the iron filings.

Observations

1. In your notebook, make a diagram of the test tube of iron filings for each of the following situations. Each diagram should be similar to the one shown in Figure 14.6. Be sure to indicate the effect on the compass needle
   (a) before stroking with magnet
   (b) after rubbing with the N-pole of the magnet
   (c) after shaking the test tube
   (d) after rubbing with the S-pole of the magnet
   (e) after shaking the test tube.

Questions

1. (a) How did you know that the iron filings became magnetized?
   (b) When did the iron filings become magnetized?
2. Were you able to demagnetize the iron filings? If so, how did you do it?
3. Were there any differences in results when the S-pole was used? If so, describe these differences.
4. Predict what would happen if you had rubbed the test tube from right to left from the N-pole. Test your prediction to see if you were correct.

Self-check

1. What part of an atom produces a magnetic force?
2. What three chemical elements are strongly magnetic?
3. What is a domain?
4. Do all substances have domains? Explain.
5. How can you make a magnet from iron filings?

Magnetic Fields

The **magnetic field** of a magnet is the region in which its magnetic effect can be felt. You can see the shape of a magnetic field by using iron filings. When iron filings are sprinkled over a magnet, they arrange themselves along the lines of magnetic force. The pattern that is made by the iron filings represents the shape of the magnetic field. The pull of the magnet is strongest where the lines of force are most closely crowded together. See Figure 14.8.

The lines of magnetic force also have a direction. They start at the N-pole and travel toward the S-pole. A compass can be used to determine the direction of the magnetic lines of force.

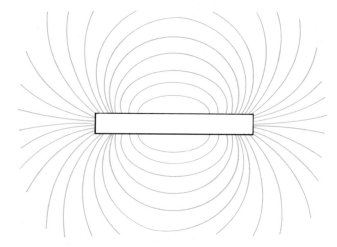

Figure 14.8 *The diagram shows magnetic lines of force drawn to indicate the shapes of the magnetic field near a bar magnet. The poles of the magnet and the directions of the lines of force are not shown.*

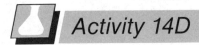

Activity 14D

Problem

What happens to the magnetic field when another magnet is placed near it?

Materials

2 bar magnets
iron filings in shaker
piece of clear acetate

Procedure

1. Place a sheet of acetate over a bar magnet.
2. Sprinkle iron filings from a shaker onto the acetate sheet so that they are over and around the magnet.
3. Tap the sheet lightly to help the filings spread themselves out along the lines of force.
4. Draw the pattern formed by the filings. Show just enough detail to indicate the general shape of the field. Indicate the N-pole and S-pole of the magnet.
5. Lift up the acetate sheet and pour the filings back into the shaker.
6. Arrange 2 magnets as shown in Figure 14.9 (a).
7. Repeat steps 1–5 for each of the arrangements shown in Figure 14.9 (b) and (c).

(a)

| N | S | | N | S |

(b)

| N | S | | S | N |

(c)

| S | N | | N | S |

Figure 14.9 *Arrangement of magnets for Activity 14D, step 7*

8. Repeat steps 1–5 for each of the arrangements shown in Figure 14.10.

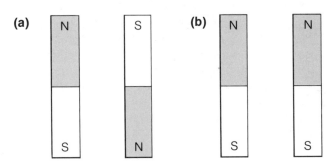

Figure 14.10 *Other magnetic arrangements for Activity 14D, step 8*

Observations

1. Make a drawing of the magnetic field for each arrangement tested. Be sure to indicate the N-pole and S-pole of each magnet.

Questions

1. Compare the magnetic fields shown by the arrangements in Figure 14.9 (a) with those shown by the arrangements in Figure 14.10. Are there any similarities? If so, describe them.
2. Compare the magnetic fields shown by the arrangements in Figure 14.9 (b) with those shown by the arrangements in Figure 14.10. Are there any similarities? If so, describe them.
3. Compare the magnetic fields shown by the arrangements in Figure 14.9 (c) with those shown by the arrangements in Figure 14.10. Are there any similarities? If so, describe them.
4. What statement can you make regarding the magnetic field around two magnets when similar poles are placed near each other?
5. What statement can you make regarding the magnetic field around two magnets when opposite poles are placed near each other?

Challenge

Self-check

1. What are the two characteristics used to describe a magnetic field?
2. What is the polarity (N-pole or S-pole) of each of the numbered poles shown in Figure 14.11?

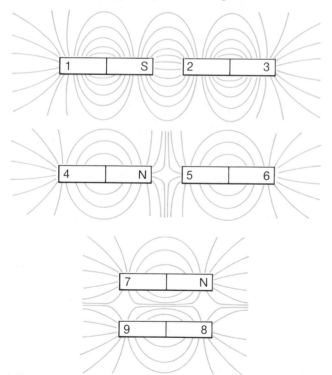

Figure 14.11 *In your notebook, identify the numbered poles as N-poles or S-poles.*

The Earth Is a Giant Magnet

In 1660, Dr. William Gilbert suggested that the earth was one big magnet. He did not know why the earth was magnetic. He believed, however, that the earth had a magnetic field around it as if there was a large bar magnet inside it. The "poles" of the earth's magnetic field, however, did not appear in exactly the same places as the earth's geographic North and South Poles. See Figure 14.12. The magnetic North Pole is actually more than 1500 km away from the point known as the **geographical North Pole**. The **magnetic North Pole** apparently changes location due to movement in the earth's outer crust. At present, it is located in northern Canada on Prince of Wales Island.

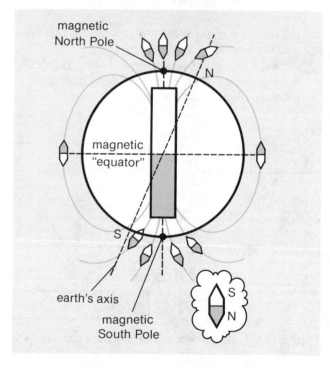

Figure 14.12 *The earth's magnetic North and South Poles in relation to the geographical North and South Poles*

"North" on a compass points to the magnetic North Pole. Navigators must be aware of the angle between the magnetic North Pole and the geographic North Pole in order to plot their courses accurately.

Challenge

Make your own compass. Run the north pole of a strong magnet down the length of a sewing needle that is at least 6 cm long. Make a small boat out of the bottom of a styrofoam coffee cup. Push the needle through the cup as shown below. Float the cup on water in a container.

A homemade compass

Challenge

The magnetic North Pole is actually a south-seeking pole, or S-pole. Explain why this is true.

What Causes the Earth's Magnetism?

No one knows the whole story behind the earth's magnetism. Scientists think that the earth's core contains molten (liquid) metals such as iron and nickel. These hot liquids are thought to be in constant motion. The movement of charged atoms within them would produce a current, which in turn would produce a magnetic field. It is impossible to test this theory since no one has yet reached the earth's core.

One thing scientists do know is that the earth's magnetic field is slowly changing. The iron atoms found in lava from ancient volcanoes have been carefully studied. These iron atoms seem to be aligned in the direction of the magnetic field that existed at the time the volcano erupted. This is quite different from the present day direction. There is evidence that the earth's magnetic field has reversed itself many times in the past. Scientists think that eventually the magnetic field may reverse itself again. If this happens, the needle on the compass that now points north would then point south, and vice versa.

Self-check

1. What is the difference between the magnetic North pole and the geographical North Pole?
2. Where is the magnetic North Pole currently located?
3. What activity is thought to cause the earth's magnetic field?
4. What do scientists predict will eventually happen to the earth's magnetic field?

Using Electricity to Produce Magnetism

In Activity 14A, you discovered that some substances are magnetic while others are not. It is possible to make a temporary magnet out of some of these magnetic substances. Is it possible to make a magnetic field using substances that are not normally magnetic? In 1819, the Danish scientist Hans Christian Oersted (Figure 14.13) was able to do just that. In the next activity, you will try to perform an experiment similar to the one that Oersted performed over 160 years ago.

Figure 14.13 *Hans Christian Oersted*

Activity 14E

Problem

How can a magnetic field be made using the non-magnetic substance copper?

Materials

copper wire (50 cm long)
compass
dry cell
push-button switch

Procedure

1. Set up the equipment as shown in Figure 14.14.
2. Line up the long segment of copper wire in a north-south direction as shown.
3. Place a compass under the north-south segment of wire so that the needle points in the same direction as this section of wire.

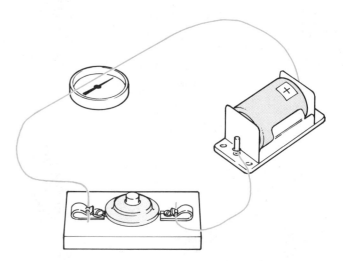

Figure 14.14 *Set-up for Activity 14E. The long section of wire should be arranged in a north-south direction.*

4. Draw three diagrams in your notebook similar to the one shown in Figure 14.15 (a). Draw in the needle on the first diagram to show which way the compass needle is pointing when no current is flowing. Give this diagram an appropriate title.
5. Push the button for an instant and observe the compass needle's direction. Record your results on the second diagram of Figure 14.15 (a) in your notebook. Include a title.
6. Reverse the connections to the cell.
7. Push the button for a brief instant and observe the compass needle's direction. Record your results on the third diagram of Figure 14.15 (a) in your notebook. Include a title. Remember to switch the + and - symbols on your diagram.
8. Place the compass above the wire.
9. Draw three diagrams in your notebook similar to the one shown in Figure 14.15 (b).
10. Draw in the needle on the first diagram to show which way the compass needle is pointing when no current is flowing.
11. Repeat steps 5–7 for this set up. Make sure that each diagram is given an appropriate title.

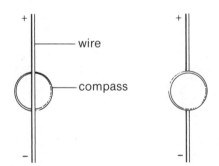

(a) *compass under wire*   **(b)** *compass over wire*

Figure 14.15 *Make three diagrams similar to (a) to record the results when the compass is under the wire. Make three diagrams similar to (b) to record the results when the compass is over the wire. Note: The "+" represents the end of the wire that is connected to the positive terminal of the dry cell.*

Observations

You should have made one diagram for each of the following conditions:
(a) Compass is placed under the wire and current is not flowing.
(b) Compass is placed under the wire and current is flowing.
(c) Compass is placed under the wire and current is flowing (connections reversed).
(d) Compass is placed over the wire and current is not flowing.
(e) Compass is placed over the wire and current is flowing.
(f) Compass is placed over the wire and current is flowing (connections reversed).

Questions

1. How did you show that a magnetic field was produced by an electrical current?
2. What effect did the direction of current flow have on the magnetic field?
3. How does the magnetic field above the electrical current compare with the magnetic field below the electrical current when the current is flowing in the same direction?

Challenge

Set up the equipment from Activity 14E with the long straight part of the copper wire coming vertically upward through a horizontal piece of cardboard. Sprinkle iron filings on the cardboard. Close the switch and gently tap the cardboard. Observe the magnetic field shown by the iron filings. Use a compass to determine the direction of the lines of force. What would happen if the direction of the current flow was reversed?

Magnetic Fields around a Wire

When an electrical current flows through a conductor, a magnetic field is formed. This field consists of a number of circles surrounding the conductor. The direction of the lines of force depends on the direction of the current in the conductor. Look at the diagrams in Figure 14.16. Imagine that you are holding the wire in your left hand with your thumb pointing in the direction of current flow. Notice that your fingers would curl so that they point in the direction of the magnetic lines of force. This is known as the **left-hand rule**. If you know which direction the electrical current is flowing, you can use the left-hand rule to determine the direction of the magnetic lines of force (Figure 14.17).

Refer to your results from Activity 14E. Do your results agree with the left-hand rule?

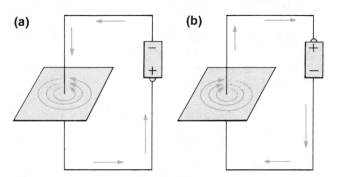

Figure 14.16 *The direction of the magnetic lines of force depends on the direction of the current flow.*

Magnetic Fields around A Solenoid

The left-hand rule allows you to determine the direction of the magnetic lines of force around a straight length of wire. You can also use this rule to predict the direction of the magnetic field when the wire is bent to form a loop. See Figure 14.18.

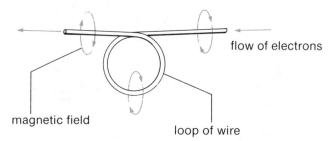

Figure 14.18 *The magnetic field around a loop of wire*

A **solenoid** is formed when a conducting wire is looped several times around a cylinder to form a coil. A simple solenoid is shown in Figure 14.19. Predict what the magnetic field around the solenoid will look like.

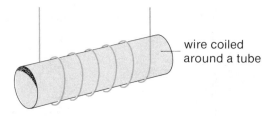

Figure 14.19 *A simple solenoid*

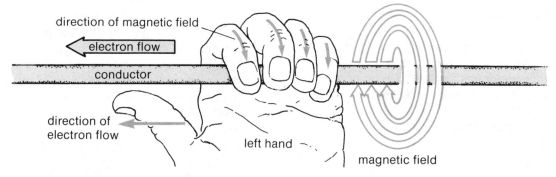

Figure 14.17 *Use the left-hand rule to determine the direction of the magnetic lines of force.*

Problem

What is the shape and direction of the magnetic field around a solenoid?

Materials

pill vial
insulated copper wire
compass
dry cell
alligator connectors
push-button switch
masking tape

Procedure

1. Make a simple solenoid by winding a length of copper wire about 20 times around a pill vial. Make sure that the vial is large enough to hold the compass inside it. Hold the ends of the wire in place with masking tape.
2. Set up the equipment as shown in Figure 14.20.
3. Make a diagram in your notebook similar to the one shown in Figure 14.21.
4. Place the compass inside the solenoid.

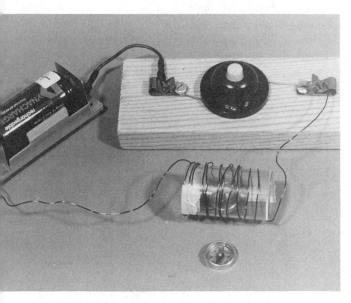

Figure 14.20 *Set-up for Activity 14F*

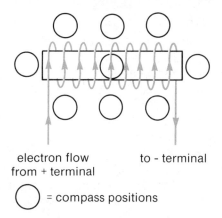

electron flow   to - terminal
from + terminal

= compass positions

Figure 14.21 *Record your results in your notebook in a diagram similar to this one.*

5. Push the switch and watch the direction of the compass needle. Record your results on the diagram in your notebook by drawing in the compass needle.
6. Place the compass at one of the locations shown in Figure 14.21.
7. Push the button and observe the behaviour of the compass needle.
8. Record your results on the diagram in your notebook.
9. Repeat steps 6–8 for all the other compass positions indicated in Figure 14.21.
10. Choose any single turn of wire on your solenoid and test the left-hand rule on this turn.
11. Reverse the cell connections.
12. Repeat steps 3–10. Remember to change the direction of the current in your diagram.

Observations

Your should have made a diagram similar to that shown in Figure 14.21 for each of the following conditions:

(a) compass needle directions for original set-up
(b) compass needle directions for set-up with reversed connections

Questions

1. Did the left-hand rule work for a single turn of the solenoid? Explain.
2. Compare the direction of the compass needle at all locations shown in Figure 14.21. What patterns did you discover?
3. What effect did reversing the connections have on your results?
4. Compare the drawings you made of the magnetic field directions around a solenoid with the ones you made of the field around a bar magnet (Activity 14D). Are there any similarities? If so, describe them.
5. Figure 14.22 shows the behaviour of iron filings when scattered around a solenoid carrying a very strong current. Where is the magnetic field strongest—inside or outside the solenoid? How can you tell?

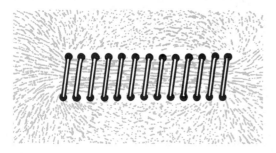

Figure 14.22 *Iron filings scattered around a solenoid indicate the magnetic field.*

Activity 14G

In Activity 14F, you built a solenoid and found that it can become a magnet when current flows in it. **Electromagnets** are magnets that are only magnetic when current flows in them.

If a bar of soft iron is placed inside a solenoid, the current will cause the domains of the iron to line up in one direction. As a result, the iron itself becomes magnetized. This increases the strength of the magnetic field of the electromagnet.

Problem

How can the strength of an electromagnet be changed?

Materials

iron nail	push-button switch
insulated copper wire	alligator connectors
2 dry cells	paper clips

Procedure

1. Make a table in your notebook similar to Table 14.1.
2. Make a solenoid by wrapping 10 turns of wire around the iron nail.
3. Remove the iron nail.
4. Connect the wire to the push-button switch and dry cell as shown in Figure 14.23.
5. Push the button. Attempt to pick up some paper clips with the wire coil.

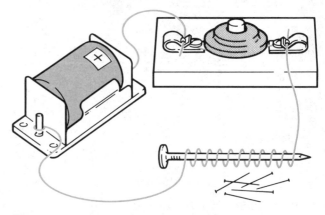

Figure 14.23 *Set-up for Activity 14G*

Table 14.1 *Comparison of Electromagnets*

NUMBER OF DRY CELLS	NUMBER OF TURNS OF WIRE	NAIL INSERTED (YES/NO)	NUMBER OF PAPER CLIPS PICKED UP
1	10	no	
1	10	yes	
1	20	no	
1	20	yes	
2	20	no	
2	20	yes	

6. In the table in your notebook, record the number of paper clips that were picked up.
7. Release the button.
8. Insert the nail into the wire coil.
9. Repeat steps 5–7.
10. Continue coiling the wire so that there are now 20 turns of wire around the nail. Remove the nail.
11. Repeat steps 5–7.
12. Insert the nail into the wire coil.
13. Repeat steps 5–7.
14. Attach a second dry cell in series with the first one as shown in Figure 14.24. Remove the nail.
15. Repeat steps 5–7.
16. Insert the nail into the wire coil.
17. Repeat steps 5–7.

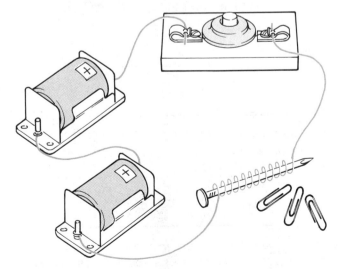

Figure 14.24 *Connect two cells in series.*

Observations

(see Table 14.1)

Questions

1. How was the strength of the electromagnet measured in this activity?
2. What effect did the presence of the iron nail in the core of the electromagnet have on its strength?
3. What effect did increasing the number of coils have on the strength of the electromagnet?
4. What effect did increasing the number of dry cells have on the strength of the electromagnet?
5. What conditions will result in the strongest electromagnet?

Self-check

1. What is the difference between an ordinary magnet and an electromagnet?
2. (a) Describe the magnetic field around a wire in which a current is flowing.
   (b) What happens to the magnetic field if the direction of current flow is reversed?
3. What is meant by the left-hand rule?
4. What is a solenoid?
5. Describe three ways to increase the strength of an electromagnet.

Uses of Magnets

Magnets can be used in many different ways. Magnets in the refrigerator door help keep it closed. Many cabinet doors have magnets in the latch for the same reason. Screwdriver bits are often magnetized. The screws are attracted to the bit and do not slip out of place as they are being installed. Electric can openers have small magnets to hold the lid in place after the can has been opened. What other simple devices rely on magnets in order to function?

Magnets (and electromagnets) are an important part of many complex pieces of equipment. Some of these are described below.

Electric Bell

When the schoolbell rings to begin class, magnets are working. Look at Figure 14.25 to see what the inside of a bell looks like. When the switch is closed, current flows through the wire coil, creating an electromagnet. The electromagnet attracts the arm of the bell and

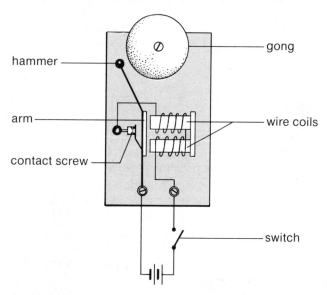

Figure 14.25 *How are magnets used to make an electric bell work?*

the hammer strikes the gong. However, the movement of the arm creates a gap between the arm and the contact screw, and the circuit is broken. Current no longer flows, so there is no magnetic field. As a result, the arm is no longer attracted and goes back to its resting position. Now the circuit is once again complete so that the process is repeated as long as the switch remains closed.

Magnetic Tapes

Tape recorders and tape players rely on magnets in order to work. The actual tape on which a recording is made is a thin piece of plastic on which tiny magnetic particles are randomly scattered. See Figure 14.26 (a). When you speak into the microphone, your voice is changed into electrical signals. Because your voice consists of sound waves that vary in frequency, intensity, and pitch, the electrical signals also vary. These signals produce a variable current that is sent to an electromagnet in the recording head of the tape recorder. Since the current going through the magnet varies, the magnetic field that is produced also varies. As a result, the tiny magnetic particles on the tape are rearranged in

Figure 14.26

(a) *The magnetic particles on a blank tape are scattered at random.*

(b) *The magnetic particles in a recorded tape are arranged in various patterns, depending on the input from the microphone.*

specific patterns. These patterns depend on the strength of the magnetic field at the time the tape passes by the recording head. The tape is then reorganized in a way similar to that shown in Figure 14.26 (b).

The same principle applies to videotapes. They are much larger than audio tapes, since visual as well as audio information must be recorded.

The floppy disks used in computers are also made of plastic with a magnetic coating. The magnetic patterns set up are arranged in circles instead of in a straight line (as in an audio tape). The disk drive is able to "read" these patterns quickly to bring back the information stored on them.

Loudspeakers

Loudspeakers are able to convert electrical current from a microphone or amplifier into sound. This is only possible because of the magnets found inside a loudspeaker.

Take a look at Figure 14.27. A loudspeaker contains a permanent magnet and a hollow tube that is surrounded by coils of wire and attached to a paper cone. When current flows through the wire, a magnetic field is produced. This attracts the cone to the magnet. If the current is strong, the magnetic field will be strong and the cone is attracted by a large amount. If the current is weak, the attraction is much smaller. The variation in movement of the cone causes the air in front of the speaker to be squeezed in and out, reproducing sound waves which you can hear.

The radio waves that reach your radio generate a variable electrical current. This current travels to the speaker and results in a certain variation in magnetic fields. This causes a certain pattern in the movement of the cone which in fact results in a reproduction of the original sound waves—sound waves that may have originated many kilometres away.

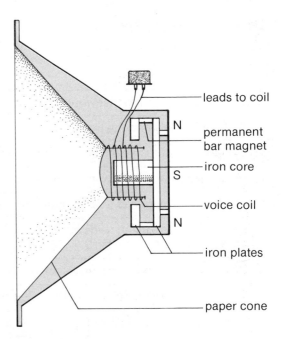

Figure 14.27 *Loudspeakers require magnets in order to work.*

Self-check

1. Why do most trains and planes have magnetic latches on cupboard doors?
2. In what two places can the circuit in an electric bell be broken?
3. What are the similarities between the operation of a tape recorder and the operation of a loudspeaker?

Chapter Objectives

NOW THAT YOU HAVE COMPLETED THIS CHAPTER, CAN YOU DO THE FOLLOWING?	FOR REVIEW, TURN TO SECTION
1. List three substances that would make good magnets.	14.1, 14.2
2. Distinguish between the N-pole and the S-pole of a bar magnet.	14.2
3. Explain how domains affect the magnetic properties of a substance.	14.3
4. Magnetize a substance with a magnet.	14.3
5. Describe the magnetic field surrounding a bar magnet.	14.4
6. Describe the magnetic fields surrounding two bar magnets placed with like and with unlike poles close together.	14.4
7. Distinguish between the magnetic North Pole and the geographical North Pole.	14.5
8. Make an electromagnet and state the left-hand rule of magnetic fields.	14.6
9. Draw the magnetic lines of force around a wire.	14.6
10. Make a solenoid and draw the lines of force surrounding a solenoid.	14.6
11. List two ways to increase the strength of an electromagnet.	14.6
12. Explain how magnets are used in various devices.	14.7

Words To Know

magnet
lodestone
temporary magnet
permanent magnet
pole
north-seeking pole (N-pole)
south-seeking pole (S-pole)

domain
magnetic field
magnetic North Pole
geographical North Pole
left-hand rule
solenoid
electromagnet

Tying It Together

1. List three substances that can be magnetized.
2. What are the differences between a temporary magnet, a permanent magnet, and an electromagnet?
3. Where on a bar magnet is the magnetic field strongest?
4. List three materials that are not magnetic.
5. Figure 14.28 shows the domains of three different objects. Identify each of the objects as

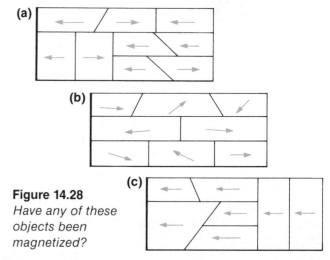

Figure 14.28
Have any of these objects been magnetized?

either magnetized, demagnetized, or partially magnetized.

6. What are the two characteristics of magnetic fields?
7. How can you locate the strongest part of a magnetic field?
8. Draw the magnetic lines of force surrounding
   (a) a bar magnet
   (b) two bar magnets placed end to end with N-poles closest together
   (c) two bar magnets placed side by side with opposite poles closest together.
9. Distinguish between the magnetic North Pole and the geographical North Pole.
10. Figure 14.29 shows two wires carrying a current. The arrows indicate the direction of the magnetic lines of force. State whether the current in the wire is flowing out of the page or into the page.
11. List two ways to increase the strength of an electromagnet.

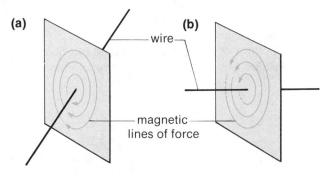

Figure 14.29 *Which way must the current in the wire be flowing to produce these lines of force?*

Applying Your Knowledge

1. You have been given two different materials. One is a magnet and one is a magnetic substance. How could you use a compass to tell the difference?
2. A horseshoe magnet is formed by bending a bar magnet into a "U" shape. Draw a horseshoe magnet in your notebook. Draw in the lines of magnetic force surrounding the magnet.

3. A "dipping needle," like the one shown in Figure 14.30, is like a compass needle that is being held in a vertical position. It consists of a needle that is pivoted so that it can swing back and forth like a pendulum. A protractor is attached to the dipping needle so that the angle between the horizon and the dipping needle can be measured. This angle is known as the angle of inclination. What would be the angle of inclination if you were standing
   (a) at the magnetic North Pole?
   (b) at the magnetic South Pole?
   (c) at the magnetic equator?

Figure 14.30 *A dipping needle measures the angle of inclination.*

Projects for Investigation

1. Scientists suspect that tuna have a magnetic sense because they often migrate across the ocean without the sight of land or stars. Scientists at the National Marine Fisheries Service in Honolulu discovered magnetite in the skull of the tuna. Read the report entitled "Magnetic Tuna" on page 10 in the April 1982 issue of *Science 82* to find out how these scientists intend to conduct experiments to determine whether or not the presence of the magnetite is linked to the magnetic sense in tuna.
2. Electromagnets can be used as switches. If the current going through an electromagnet is greater than a certain amount, the switch is pulled open and the current is turned on or off in the circuit. Design, on paper, a possible set-up for this type of switch.

Unit 4: Magnetism and Electricity

MATCH

In your notebook, write the letters (a) to (f). Beside each letter, write the number of the word in the right column that corresponds to each description in the left column.

(a) an object that gains electrons

(b) electrical current resulting from water flow

(c) two or more cells connected together

(d) current that changes direction

(e) one coulomb per second

(f) path of an electrical current

1. battery
2. circuit
3. negatively charged
4. ampere
5. positively charged
6. hydro-electricity
7. parallel
8. AC
9. DC

MULTIPLE CHOICE

In your notebook, write the numbers 1 to 10. Beside each number, write the letter of the best choice.

1. Which of the following will most likely occur when a negatively charged object is brought close to (but not touching) a positively charged object?
   (a) There will be no effect on the positively charged object.
   (b) They will attract one another.
   (c) They will repel one another.
   (d) They will swing back and forth.

2. Which statement correctly describes an atom?
   (a) Electrons orbit around the protons and neutrons.
   (b) Neutrons orbit around the protons and electrons.
   (c) Protons orbit around the electrons and neutrons.
   (d) None of the above is correct.

3. If a neutral object becomes positively charged, it must have
   (a) gained electrons   (c) lost electrons
   (b) gained protons   (d) lost protons.

4. What do all generators need to function?
   (a) thermocouple
   (b) solar cell
   (c) battery
   (d) magnet

5. Which statement describes the circuit below?
   (a) 3 cells in parallel and 2 lamps
   (b) 3 lamps in series and a closed switch
   (c) 2 lamps in parallel and an open switch
   (d) 2 lamps in series and 3 cells

6. What would happen in the circuit below if bulb 3 burnt out?
   (a) All the bulbs would go out.
   (b) Bulbs 1, 2, and 4 would remain on with no change in brightness.
   (c) Bulbs 1, 2, and 4 would become brighter.
   (d) Bulbs 1, 2, and 4 would become dimmer.

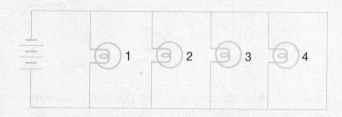

7. What could happen if you put in a fuse that carries a larger current than the correct one you're replacing?
   (a) The wires in the circuit could overheat.
   (b) There might not be enough current for appliances in the circuit.
   (c) There could be a short circuit.
   (d) The fuse could blow.

8. Which substance is *least* magnetic?
   (a) iron   (c) copper
   (b) nickel   (d) cobalt

9. What properties describe a magnetic field?
   (a) type and shape
   (b) direction and size
   (c) size and shape
   (d) shape and direction
10. Which of these would produce the largest magnetic force?

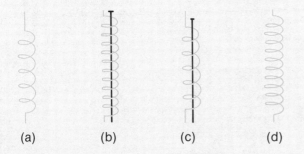

(a)　　　(b)　　　(c)　　　(d)

TRUE/FALSE

Write the numbers 1 to 10 in your notebook. Beside each number, write T if the statement is true and F if the statement is false. For each false statement, rewrite it as a true statement.

1. Like charges repel one another.
2. An electroscope detects static charge.
3. Contact isn't needed when charging an object by induction.
4. A thermocouple needs a moving magnet.
5. A flashlight cell is made of a zinc case, a carbon rod, and a conducting paste.
6. In a circuit where 3 lamps are connected in parallel, the current is the same everywhere in the circuit.
7. The grounding wire carries current to the ground when an appliance in good repair is turned on.
8. The strongest part of a magnet is the pole.
9. The strength of the magnetic force is greatest when most of the atoms are spinning the same way.
10. The magnetic North Pole is the same as the geographical North Pole.

FOR DISCUSSION

Read the paragraphs below and answer the questions that follow.

Potentially harmful radiation from space is continually showering down on the earth. Without protection from it, much damage would occur to life on earth. Luckily, earth's magnetic field offers some defence. Radiation contains very tiny charged particles. The magnetic field deflects many of these particles back into space. Other particles are bounced back between the magnetic North and South Poles along the lines of the magnetic field. Thus, most particles never reach the earth's surface.

Sometimes, when these tiny particles approach the poles of the earth, they collide with oxygen and nitrogen atoms in the air. When this happens, the oxygen and nitrogen atoms give off coloured light. This is called the *aurora borealis* (or northern lights) when it occurs at the North Pole. This display can appear as great bands of colour across the night sky.

An aurora borealis was created artificially by humans by exploding an atomic bomb high above the earth on July 8, 1962. The explosion caused many tiny particles to collide with the atoms in air, producing a wide range of coloured light similar to the aurora borealis.

1. Why is radiation harmful to life on earth?
2. How does the earth's magnetic field affect radiation from space?
3. How is the aurora borealis created?
4. How was an artificial aurora borealis created?

The Wise Use of Resources

For many hundreds of years, people have harnessed the wind to operate sailboats, to pump water, and to grind grain. Now this free resource is being harnessed for other purposes. The photograph shows a windmill "orchard" being used to change wind energy into electrical energy. This is one of many examples of ways in which humans are changing their habits by using different energy resources.

Some of the earth's natural resources are being used up at an alarming rate. Alternative resources are now being developed. This unit deals with the wise use of energy resources. You will learn about many forms of energy and how to measure energy in homes and industries. And you will learn how important it is for everyone in our society to try to conserve energy.

Energy Forms, Resources, and Systems

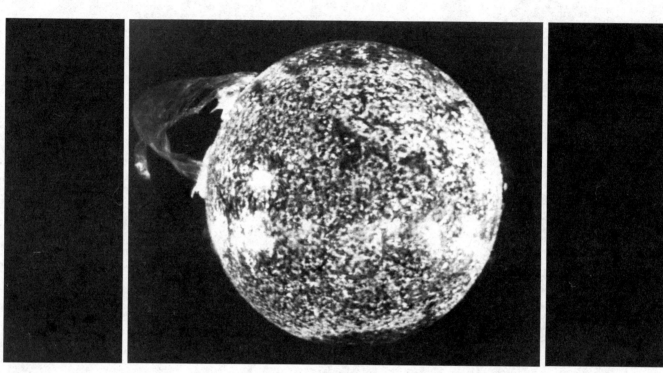

Key Ideas

- Energy is important and useful.
- Energy can take different forms, and these forms may be converted into other forms.
- Some energy resources are renewable, while others are non-renewable.
- The efficiency of an energy system may be calculated if you know the input and output energies of the system.

This photograph of the sun shows some of the violent activity at the sun's surface. The sun gives off more energy in one second than humans have used in their entire history. But only a small amount of the sun's energy reaches the earth. Even so, this small amount is our earth's most important source of energy.

In this chapter, you will learn about various sources of energy, including the sun. Some of these sources we are using up rapidly, while we are just learning how to use others. You will also study how energy can change from one form to another. Finally, you will discover what energy systems are and why they are important.

Energy and Forms of Energy

What does the word "energy" mean? In order to think of a definition for energy, let us first look at some of the things energy can do for us. We use energy to cook our food, keep us warm in the winter, light our streets and buildings, transport us from place to place, operate countless electrical appliances and gadgets, and obtain raw materials to manufacture almost everything we use. In all these cases, and many others you might think of, the energy does some work for us. Thus, a simple but common definition is that **energy** is the ability to do work.

Why is it important to study energy? One reason is that we use energy almost all the time, so our daily lives are affected by it. Another is that our usual supplies of energy, such as crude oil, are being used up and we must learn how to cope with this situation. What other reasons are there for you to study energy?

Energy has many forms, some of which may be familiar to you. Table 15.1 lists the most common forms of energy and gives a simple definition and example of each form. Study this list carefully.

Table 15.1 *Forms of Energy*

FORM OF ENERGY	BASIC DEFINITION	EXAMPLES
1. Radiant energy	Energy that travels in the form of high-speed waves	Visible light, microwaves, X rays, heat from the sun
2. Thermal energy	Internal energy of an object (possessed by molecules)	Hot frying pan
3. Sound energy	Energy produced by vibrating objects	Musical sounds
4. Elastic potential energy	Energy stored in stretched or compressed objects	Archer's bow
5. Chemical potential energy	Energy stored in molecules of matter	Food we eat
6. Gravitational potential energy	Energy stored in raised objects	Waterfall
7. Kinetic energy	Energy of moving objects	Moving truck
8. Electrical energy	Energy of charged particles such as electrons and protons	Balloon rubbed on a sweater
9. Nuclear potential energy	Energy stored in the central part (nucleus) of an atom	Nuclear fission (in nuclear reactors)

Figure 15.1 *Examples of potential (stored) energy*

Notice in Table 15.1 that the potential energies are "stored" energies. Figure 15.1 shows three examples of potential energy changing to other forms of energy. In Figure 15.1 (a), the **chemical potential energy** in the fireworks is changing to **sound energy** and **radiant energy** (light). The water at the top of the falls in Figure 15.1 (b) has **gravitational potential energy** due to its raised position. As the force of gravity causes the falling water to move faster, this potential energy changes to **kinetic energy**. Figure 15.1 (c) shows the explosion of a nuclear testing device. Here, **nuclear potential energy** is changing to sound energy, radiant energy, and vast amounts of **thermal energy** (heat).

(a) *Chemical potential energy is released as light and sound when fireworks explode.*

(b) *Water at the top of a waterfall has gravitational potential energy. This view is of Victoria Falls in Zimbabwe, Africa.*

(c) *Nuclear potential energy is released as light, sound, heat, and wind when a nuclear test bomb explodes. Controlled amounts of this type of energy can be used to run submarines, spacecraft, and electric generating stations.*

Challenge

Choose a typical day in your life and list at least 20 activities in which you are involved. The list should include such activities as brushing your teeth, making toast, riding a bus, etc. Beside each activity, write the form or forms of energy that are used to perform it. Discuss your list in class.

Self-check

1. What is a definition of energy?
2. State what form (or forms) of energy is associated with each of the following examples.
   (a) A person walks across a rug in the winter, then touches a metal doorknob and receives a shock.
   (b) A quantity of dynamite explodes.
   (c) A bird chirps.
   (d) Ultraviolet radiation reaches us from the sun.
   (e) A baseball accidentally smashes through a window.
   (f) A metal soup spoon becomes warm soon after being placed into hot soup.
   (g) The spring of a wind-up toy is fully wound.
   (h) Nuclear fusion produces energy on the sun.
   (i) An axe is raised above a block of wood.
3. Give another example for each of the nine forms of energy listed in Table 15.1. Use an example that has not been given in this section.

Energy Conversions

Some of the forms of energy (Table 15.1) can be used directly. For example, visible light is radiant energy that allows us to see. But several forms cannot be used directly for many of our needs. For example, it would be difficult to cook a meal directly using elastic potential energy. Thus, if we want to have energy do useful work for us, we have to convert (change) the energy into at least one other form. An **energy conversion** is the changing of energy from one form to another form.

There are numerous examples of energy conversions. In Activity 15A, you will be asked to design ways of demonstrating such conversions in class. But before you start that activity, you should read the following examples of energy conversions.

Converting Elastic Potential Energy to Kinetic Energy

A simple example of this type of energy conversion is the use of a bow and arrow. An archer places an arrow onto a bow and stretches the bowstring. The stretched bowstring has elastic potential energy. When the string is released, most of this elastic potential energy is given to the arrow, causing the arrow to move forward at a high speed. Thus, the arrow has kinetic energy (energy of motion). This can be summarized with the following word equation:

$$\text{elastic potential energy} \rightarrow \text{kinetic energy}$$

Converting Radiant Energy to Sound Energy

You are sitting in a room and you turn on a portable radio or a personal stereo with headphones. You tune in to your favourite AM or FM radio station. How is the sound from the radio produced?

The radio station emits radiant energy from an antenna on top of a tower. The radiant energy is in the form of radio waves that travel at the speed of light (3.0×10^8 m/s). These waves can travel through the walls of a building and get picked up by the antenna in the radio. In the antenna are electrons that move according to the information carried by the radio waves. Thus, electrical energy is produced. This energy is amplified and causes the speakers to vibrate. The vibrating speakers then produce sound energy which you can hear.

Thus, there are three energy conversions in this example. Radiant energy (radio waves) is converted to electrical energy. This energy is converted to kinetic energy of the vibrating speakers. Finally, the kinetic energy is converted to sound energy. The word equation for this set of conversions is

$$\text{radiant energy} \rightarrow \text{electrical energy} \rightarrow$$
$$\text{kinetic energy} \rightarrow \text{sound energy}$$

Problem

How can you demonstrate examples of energy conversions?

CAUTION Use only materials that are safe and approved by your teacher. Safety goggles must be used if you are using the Bunsen burner for heating.

Materials

The materials you use will depend on which demonstration(s) you choose. Examples of some of the apparatus and materials are

chemical batteries
toys
solar cells
light bulbs or floodlights
Bunsen burners or other sources of heat
water and running water
elastics
springs
metal masses
safety goggles
electrical outlets

Procedure

1. Think of at least one way to demonstrate in class each of the following energy conversions. Try to think of interesting demonstrations.
    (a) chemical potential energy to radiant energy
    (b) chemical potential energy to kinetic energy
    (c) radiant energy to electrical energy
    (d) radiant energy to kinetic energy
    (e) electrical energy to kinetic energy
    (f) gravitational potential energy to kinetic energy
    (g) elastic potential energy to kinetic energy
    (h) thermal energy to kinetic energy
    (i) radiant energy to thermal energy
    (j) one other appropriate energy conversion you can think of

2. Choose your most interesting and appropriate demonstration idea. Discuss with your teacher whether it is safe and easy enough to set up. If it is approved, write a report using the following titles:
>   Problem
>   Materials
>   Safety Precautions
>   Procedure (Include diagrams if they will help.)
3. When your teacher has approved your demonstration ideas, set up the apparatus and demonstrate the energy conversion to the rest of the class.

Observations

Set up an observation table to summarize the energy conversions demonstrated by your classmates (and/or your teacher). The table can have three columns with the following titles:

>   Name of Demonstration
>   Word Equation
>   Description of the Energy Conversion

The third column should be quite detailed.

Questions

1. State two examples of a direct energy conversion (that is, from initial to final without any middle steps).
2. State two examples of an indirect energy conversion in which some energy forms(s) occurred between the initial and final forms.
3. Which energy conversion method would be most useful in the future to help save our energy supplies? Explain your answer.

Self-check

1. Define energy conversion.
2. State which forms of energy are involved in the energy conversions listed below.
   (a) A rechargeable battery is used to set off a camera's flashbulb.
   (b) Gasoline is used to operate a motorcycle.
   (c) Light strikes a solar-powered calculator.
   (d) An electric toaster toasts some bread.
   (e) An alarm bell rings on a wind-up travel alarm clock.
   (f) Some vegetables are cooked in a microwave oven.
   (g) A magnifying glass focusses sunlight to start a campfire.
   (h) An electric motor is used to operate a sewing machine.
   (i) An athlete attains a high speed before jumping over a pole-vault bar.
   (j) A toy steam engine moves along a track.

Energy Resources

We use energy for many purposes. Probably the most important uses are to provide heat for cooking our food and keeping us warm, to provide energy for all our electrical devices (including lighting), and to provide transportation. What are the main energy resources needed for these purposes? What resources will be used in the future when our current resources are used up? These and other questions are answered in this section.

An **energy resource** is a raw material from nature that can be converted to useful energy. A **renewable resource** renews itself within a normal human life span (about 75 years). A **non-renewable resource** takes so long to renew that once it is used it is gone forever. The main types of non-renewable resources are fossil fuels and uranium. A **fossil fuel** is an energy resource formed from plants and animals that died millions of years ago. Table 15.2 gives a detailed comparison of fossil fuels and uranium.

Table 15.2 *Non-renewable Energy Resources*

RESOURCE	COMPOSITION	AGE
Coal	mainly carbon (from plants)	About 400 million yea
Crude oil	Hydrocarbons (from plants and animals)	About 500 million yea
Natural gas	Hydrocarbons (from plants and animals)	About 500 million yea
Uranium	Uranium	As old as the earth (billions of years)

Figure 15.2

(a) *This fossil imprint was left by a fern about 300 million years ago.*

(b) *Open-pit mining is used to extract coal that is near the surface. Canada has about one percent of the earth's supply of coal.*

(c) *The drilling shown here is carried out on an artificial island in the Arctic called Kugmallit. Canada has about one percent of the earth's supply of oil.*

ORIGIN	HOW IT IS OBTAINED	USES	COMMENTS
Plants died and decayed, forming peat. The high pressure of several layers of peat forced out hydrogen and oxygen, leaving a hard form of carbon. See Figure 15.2 (a).	Underground mining and open-pit mining. See Figure 15.2 (b).	• Heating • Industrial applications • Producing electricity (Figure 15.3)	Three main types of coal are lignite (70% carbon) which has a smoky flame, bituminous coal (80% carbon) which has a slightly smoky flame, and anthracite (95% carbon) which has a hot flame and little smoke.
Tiny plants and animals in oceans died and decayed. High pressure forced out the oxygen, leaving hydrogen and carbon (hydrocarbons).	Drilling and pumping. See Figure 15.2 (c).	• Transportation • Industrial operations • Heating • Producing electricity (Figure 15.3)	The production of hydrocarbons from dead organisms continues to this day. Methane is produced by decaying matter at the bottoms of swamps and bubbles to the surface. Sometimes it is ignited by lightning.
The origin is the same as for crude oil, but the hydrocarbon molecules are smaller.	Drilling and pumping	• Industrial applications • Heating • Producing electricity (Figure 15.3)	Canada has about 3% of the earth's supply of natural gas. Scientists estimate this supply will be used up in less than 200 years.
Energy is stored in the nucleus of the atom. Some of this energy is released when a large nucleus undergoes fission, forming smaller nuclei.	Underground mining	• Producing electricity at nuclear generating stations • Operating some satellites and submarines	Canada has a rich supply of uranium —about 20% of the earth's supply. This supply may last for more than 1000 years.

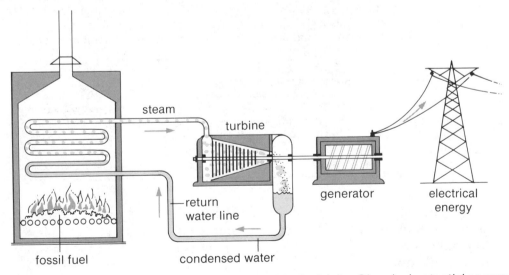

Figure 15.3 *Fossil fuels can be used to generate electricity. Chemical potential energy in the fuel changes to thermal energy. This thermal energy heats water to boiling, producing steam. The steam forces turbines to spin. The turbines are connected to generators that change the mechanical energy of spinning into electrical energy.*

Table 15.3 *Renewable Energy Resources*

RESOURCE	DEFINITION	ORIGIN OF ENERGY	METHOD(S) OF USING ENERGY
Biomass energy	Chemical potential energy stored in plants and animal wastes	This energy comes indirectly from the sun. Solar energy combines with carbon dioxide from the air to help plants grow.	• Burning wood in homes and industries • Burning trash to produce heat • Fermenting plant materials or garbage
Wind energy	Kinetic energy of moving air	Solar energy strikes the earth, causing different air masses to warm up at different rates. This causes the wind to blow.	• Pumping water or producing electricity • Using wind generators (Figure 15.4)
Geothermal energy	Energy available beneath the earth's surface	Nuclear fission of elements in rocks inside the earth produces heat.	• Heating • Producing electricity
Solar energy	Radiant energy from the sun	Nuclear fusion of elements on the sun produces vast amounts of heat and light.	• Heating • Producing electricity using solar cells (Figure 15.6)
Tidal energy	Kinetic energy of water moving in and out of coastal regions	Tides result from the pull of gravity of the moon and sun on ocean water.	• Producing electricity by building a dam and forcing the water to flow through turbines connected to generators
Hydraulic energy	Kinetic energy of falling water	Solar energy strikes water on earth, causing evaporation. The water rises, condenses, then falls as rain or snow. It gathers in lakes and rivers where it has gravitational potential energy.	• Producing electricity by allowing water to rush through turbines and cause generators to spin (Figure 15.8)
Nuclear fusion	The joining together of one small nucleus with another, releasing energy	When two small nuclei fuse together, a small amount of mass changes into energy (Figure 15.9).	• Producing electricity by using heat to boil water and operate electric generators

Table 15.3 describes seven different types of renewable energy resources. These are **biomass energy**, **wind energy**, **geothermal energy**, **solar energy**, **tidal energy**, **hydraulic energy**, and **nuclear fusion**. Study carefully these two tables and Figures 15.2 to 15.9 on pages 284-289 so you can answer questions about them.

LOCATION (S) FOR USE	ADVANTAGES	DISADVANTAGES	COMMENTS
• Homes • Industries that burn leftover products of forestry industry	• Can be available continuously • Can be used in a variety of ways	• Produces large amounts of polluting particles and gases, and waste heat	This resource is only renewable if forests are properly managed (reforestation).
• Windy regions (for example, parts of the east and west coasts of Canada)	• Non-polluting	• Noisy • Not continuously available	Some Canadian fishing boats are saving fuel by using sails to assist the engines whenever the wind is suitable.
• Iceland, parts of the U.S., New Zealand, Italy, British Columbia, and the Yukon Territory	• Non-polluting • Can be available continuously	• Can corrode pipes • Often far from location where needed	Evidence of this energy is seen in hot springs and geysers (Figure 15.5).
• Anywhere that the sun shines	• Large amounts available • Non-polluting	• Non-continuous	Both *passive solar heating* and *active solar heating* can be used to heat buildings.
• Coastal regions where the tide is high (Figure 15.7)	• Produces little pollution	• Non-continuous • Can affect the ecology of the entire area • Few locations available	Some of the biggest tides on earth occur on the Bay of Fundy. The tidal difference there is up to 15 m.
• Along rivers (near dams and falls)	• Least expensive way to produce large amounts of electricity • Produces little pollution	• Not available everywhere • Building a dam can affect the ecology of the area	Most available sites near populated areas in Canada have already been developed.
• Wherever a nuclear fusion reactor can be built and maintained	• Very plentiful resource using hydrogen from ocean water • Radiation is less harmful than from nuclear fission	• Not available yet • Expensive to set up	The amount of energy produced by fusion reactions is $E = mc^2$, where m is the mass lost and c is the speed of light.

Figure 15.4 *This vertical axis wind generator was designed by Canada's National Research Council. It can rotate no matter which way the wind is blowing.*

Figure 15.5 *Geysers and hot springs are found near sources of geothermal energy.*

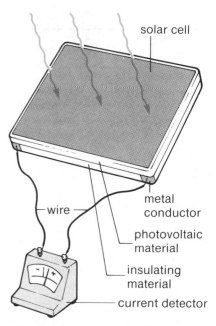

Figure 15.6 *Solar cells depend on the properties of special materials called photovoltaic materials. When radiant energy strikes such a material, tiny particles inside start to move in one direction. This produces an electrical current that passes out through metal conductors into the wires.*

Figure 15.7 *Canada's first tidal generating station is located in the Bay of Fundy, between New Brunswick and Nova Scotia. Tides here are among the highest in the world.*

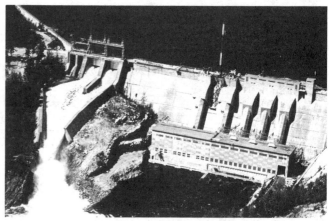

Figure 15.8 *This hydro-electric generating station is located on the Madawaska River in northeastern Ontario. The dam is 400 m long and over 60 m high.*

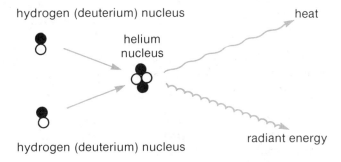

hydrogen (deuterium) nucleus

helium nucleus

heat

radiant energy

hydrogen (deuterium) nucleus

Figure 15.9 *A simplified view of a fusion reaction. Two hydrogen nuclei (called deuterium nuclei) fuse together at a very high temperature to produce a helium nucleus. Much energy is released in this reaction.*

Self-check

1. Explain why fossil fuels are called non-renewable resources.
2. (a) How did coal originate?
   (b) What is the main element found in coal?
3. Based on the information in Table 15.2, which type of coal would produce the least pollution. Explain your answer.
4. (a) How did crude oil and natural gas originate?
   (b) What are the two main elements found in these resources?
5. Write the word equation for the energy conversions shown in Figure 15.4.
6. Explain why nuclear fission is called non-renewable, but nuclear fusion is called renewable.
7. There are seven renewable energy resources described in Table 15.3.
   (a) Name those that originate with the sun's energy.
   (b) Which one is caused by gravitational forces?
   (c) Which one is caused by nuclear fission reactions in rock?
   (d) Which resources could be harnessed all day, every day?

Challenge

Design and build a solar cooker such as the one shown here. How does it work? Why is the angle at which the sun hits the aluminum surface important?

This solar cooker is made from wood and lined with aluminum foil.

Energy Systems

You have studied several forms of energy and how energy can be converted from one form to another. When scientists discuss these energy conversions, they often speak of energy systems. An **energy system** is a device that converts one form of energy into one or more other forms of energy. The device can be as simple as an electric kettle or as complex as a nuclear generating station. What other examples of energy systems have you seen earlier in this chapter?

Energy Input, Energy Output, and Waste

In an energy system, it is useful to compare input and output energies. **Energy input** is the amount of energy used to operate the system. **Energy output** is the useful energy obtained from the system. The SI unit of energy is the joule, so energy input and output can be measured in joules (J), kilojoules (kJ), megajoules (MJ), or larger units.

Consider, for example, an electric kettle. A certain amount of water is put into the kettle and the kettle is plugged in. Assume that while the kettle is plugged in 500 000 J of energy are used. This is the energy input. Assume also that 490 000 J go to heating the water in the kettle. This energy is useful, and it is called the energy output. Where did the other 10 000 J of energy go? This energy went to heating some parts of the kettle and producing some sound. This is the waste energy. Refer to Figure 15.10.

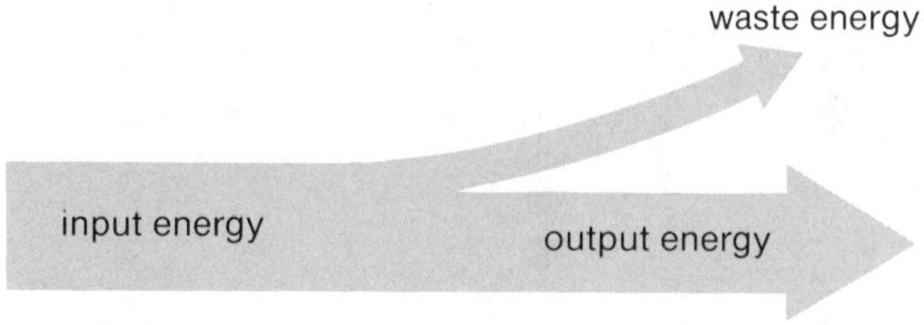

Figure 15.10 *Input energy is always greater than output energy. The energy that is not useful is called waste energy.*

Calculating the Efficiency of Energy Systems

It is important to study energy systems to be able to compare which systems are best to use. One way of comparing energy systems is to calculate their efficiencies. The **efficiency** of a system is a measure of the energy output compared to the energy input. It is usually expressed as a percentage. This definition can be written in equation form:

$$\text{efficiency} = \frac{\text{energy output}}{\text{energy input}} \times 100\%$$

or

$$\text{efficiency} = \frac{E_{\text{out}}}{E_{\text{in}}} \times 100\%$$

For the example of the electric kettle given above,

$$\text{efficiency} = \frac{E_{\text{out}}}{E_{\text{in}}} \times 100\%$$

$$= \frac{490\ 000\ \text{J}}{500\ 000\ \text{J}} \times 100\%$$

$$= 98\%$$

Thus, the electric kettle has an efficiency of 98%, and it wastes only 2% of the input energy.

In Activity 15B you will determine the efficiency and waste of several energy systems.

Activity 15B

Problem

How efficient are various energy systems?

Materials

Procedure

1. Copy Table 15.4 into your notebook.
2. Determine the information needed to complete the table. Show the calculations you made to get your answer. The first energy system has the columns completed.
3. For the last row(s) of the table, complete the information obtained during a class demonstration or discussion for at least one more energy system.

Observations

1. (a) List the three most efficient energy systems in this activity.
   (b) What do these systems have in common (besides high efficiency)?
2. (a) List the three least efficient energy systems.
   (b) Explain why these systems are likely to have low efficiencies.
3. What difficulties did you experience when trying to determine the efficiency of a particular energy system in class?

Questions

1. Two neighbours are mowing their lawns with two different lawn mowers, one with an electric motor and one with a gasoline motor. How would you expect the sounds and temperatures of the two motors to be different? Compare your answer with the efficiency of electric and gasoline motors you calculated in this activity.
2. Suggest reasons why the efficiency of energy systems would be of interest to
   (a) scientists
   (b) the general public (including you).

Table 15.4 *Data for Activity 15B*

SYSTEM	INTENDED TYPE OF OUTPUT ENERGY	EXAMPLE OF ENERGY OUTPUT	CORRESPONDING EXAMPLE OF ENERGY INPUT	EFFICIENCY OF SYSTEM	TYPE(S) OF WASTE ENERGY	PERCENTAGE WASTE (%)
Fluorescent lamp	Light	100 000J	500 000 J	20%	Heat, sound	80%
Incandescent light bulb		2 000 J	100 000 J			
Oil furnace		660 kJ	1 000 kJ			
Jet plane		500 MJ	2 000 MJ			
Gasoline lawn mower		6 MJ	24 MJ			
Steam locomotive		18 MJ	200 MJ			
Diesel engine (automobile)		48 MJ	120 MJ			
Gasoline engine (automobile)		30 MJ	120 MJ			
Other (Explain)						

SAMPLE ONLY

Comparing the Efficiencies of Energy Systems

When engineers understand the efficiencies of various energy systems, they can try to improve the ones with low efficiency. When people in the general public understand efficiency, they can make wiser decisions about which device to buy to save money on energy consumption. In both cases, the final result is the reduction of waste of our energy resources.

Table 15.5 lists the average efficiencies of devices that are in good condition. Notice that electric motors and heaters have a high efficiency, whereas devices that produce much waste heat have a low efficiency.

Table 15.5 *Efficiency of Energy Systems in Good Condition*

ENERGY SYSTEM	EFFICIENCY
Electric generator	99%
Electric oven	99%
Large electric motor	95%
Dry cell	90%
Home gas furnace	90%
Home oil furnace	70%
Small electric motor	65%
Steam turbine	50%
Diesel engine	40%
Aircraft gas turbine	35%
Gasoline engine	25%
Fluorescent lamp	20%
Solar cell	10%
Incandescent lamp	5%

Self-check

1. Predict an *approximate* efficiency for each of the energy systems listed below. Give reasons for your predictions. Hint: Use Table 15.5 as a reference.
   (a) electric can opener
   (b) farm tractor
   (c) electric hair dryer
   (d) headlight of a car
   (e) burglar alarm
2. In general, what clues are there that a particular energy system has low efficiency? Use two examples to illustrate your answer.
3. Explain how a dimmer switch might increase the efficiency of home lighting.

Chapter Objectives

NOW THAT YOU HAVE COMPLETED THIS CHAPTER, CAN YOU DO THE FOLLOWING?	FOR REVIEW, TURN TO SECTION
1. Define energy.	15.1
2. Explain why energy is important.	15.1
3. List the various forms of energy and state at least one example of each form.	15.1
4. Explain the meaning of energy conversion.	15.2
5. Write word equations summarizing the changes of form during an energy conversion.	15.2
6. Explain the differences between non-renewable and renewable energy resources, and give examples of each.	15.3
7. Define energy system and give examples of such systems.	15.4
8. Calculate the efficiency of an energy system given its energy output and input.	15.4

Words to Know

energy
chemical potential energy
sound energy
radiant energy
gravitational potential energy
kinetic energy
nuclear potential energy
thermal energy
electrical energy
elastic potential energy
energy conversion
energy resource
renewable resource
non-renewable resource
fossil fuel
biomass energy
wind energy
geothermal energy
solar energy
tidal energy
hydraulic energy

nuclear fusion
nuclear fission
energy system
energy input
energy output
efficiency

Tying It Together

1. What is the function of energy?
2. What must most forms of energy undergo before they can be of use to us?
3. List all the forms of energy that you have used or observed within the last 24 hours. State what you used or observed the energy for.
4. Give an example of each of the following energy conversions:
   (a) chemical potential energy to kinetic energy
   (b) kinetic energy to thermal energy
   (c) electrical energy to radiant energy
   (d) kinetic energy to elastic potential energy
   (e) kinetic energy to electrical energy
5. Write the word equation for each energy conversion listed below. If more than one change is involved, be sure to include all steps.
   (a) A hamburger is cooked on a natural gas barbecue.
   (b) Eggs are cooked in a metal frying pan on a burner of an electric stove.
   (c) A car horn is blown.

(d) Energy from the sun is stored in plants.
(e) An electric pump is used to force water up to an elevated storage tank (Figure 15.11).

6. Explain the differences between non-renewable and renewable energy resources. Give two examples of each type of resource.

7. State which energy resource (or resources) from Tables 15.2 and 15.3 corresponds to each description below:
(a) provided by ancient life forms
(b) provided by the rise and fall of oceans
(c) provided by the earth's internal heat
(d) provided by moving water
(e) provided when small nuclei join together
(f) provided by living organisms or their wastes
(g) provided when large nuclei split apart
(h) provided directly by the sun

8. What substance in coal makes it a useful energy resource?

9. Describe how coal and crude oil are
(a) different
(b) similar.

Figure 15.11 *This tank is used to store water at a level high above the ground.*

10. (a) What does an energy system do?
(b) Why is it important to study energy systems?

11. Explain how the automobile can be considered an energy system. For an automobile, state what form of energy provides the following:
(a) input
(b) desired output
(c) waste (More than one form should be listed here.)

12. What is the SI unit of energy?

13. Determine the efficiency and percentage of input energy wasted in each case:
(a) A chemical storage battery uses 20 MJ of input energy in operating the electric motor of a small motor boat. The output is 14 MJ.
(b) The same output as in (a) is obtained when a gasoline engine supplies 50 MJ of energy in operating the boat.

Applying Your Knowledge

1. What form of energy is the end product of most waste energy? Give three examples to support your answer.

2. Assume you are in charge of designing wood-burning stoves for use in small cottages. What features would you give a wood-burning stove to help it achieve a high efficiency?

3. According to Table 15.2, which type of coal would provide
(a) the highest efficiency
(b) the lowest efficiency.

4. What renewable energy resource would be most appropriate for development in your region? Explain why.

5. An electric washing machine has an efficiency of 48%. Explain what this statement means.

6. Describe ways of improving the efficiency of
(a) a car engine
(b) an incandescent lamp.

7. What resource(s) do you think will provide energy for transportation once fossil fuels are used up? Explain.

Projects for Investigation

1. A "whatsit machine" is a device that uses several energy conversions to perform a fairly simple task. An example of such a device is shown in Figure 15.12. On paper, design a "whatsit machine" that you think you could use to perform some interesting little job. If time permits, your class may try to build such a machine.

2. Set up a class discussion or a debate to consider one or more of the statements given below. Research can provide you with the needed background information.
   (a) It is wise to increase the rate of removal of fossil fuels from the ground to provide cheaper energy for the world's population.
   (b) The tar sands of western Canada should not be mined until a more efficient way of mining is found.
   (c) Canada should export its natural resources to any country willing to pay for them.

3. Research an energy system and produce a poster to represent it. Include the type of input energy, the type(s) of output energy, and the type(s) of waste energy involved in the system. Use the poster to help you present your findings to the class. Some suggested energy systems that you might investigate are a chocolate bar manufacturing system, an electric can opener system, a food processor system, a bicycle system, or a computer system.

4. Choose the energy resource that interests you most. Choose either a renewable resource or a non-renewable resource. Research information about the resource in the school library. Look for information in books, encyclopedias, magazines, newspaper articles, and other references. Write a report on your research, considering the following:
   (a) Your report should include an introductory paragraph, a main body, a concluding paragraph, and a bibliography.
   (b) The main body of the report should contain information about
      (i) the origin of the resource
      (ii) how to obtain the resource
      (iii) how to convert the resource into a useful form of energy
      (iv) advantages of the resource
      (v) disadvantages of the resource
      (vi) any other related information you find interesting.

Figure 15.12 *What energy conversions occur in this "whatsit machine"?*

Energy Consumption and Industrial Processes

Key Ideas

- Technology has affected the way people use energy.
- Problems will occur if energy consumption continues to increase and if non-renewable energy resources continue to be depleted.
- A dial electric meter tells how much electricity is being used in the home.
- Energy is needed to manufacture different kinds of products.

Have you used and thrown out any plastic glasses in the past year? People seldom think about where those plastic glasses came from or how much energy was used to manufacture them. The same applies to the dozens of other plastic products we use. Plastic materials are just one example of products made from petroleum. Other examples include food preservatives, pain killers, fabrics for clothing and upholstery, and rubber for tires. We are using this non-renewable resource to manufacture products. We are also using much energy in the manufacturing process.

Using energy in this way is a recent development in world history. We use far more energy now than was ever used before. And our energy use continues to increase. In this chapter, you will find out several reasons why our energy use is growing and how to measure your own family's energy use. Then you will discover how to make at least one product with petroleum ingredients and how to relate what you make to the manufacture of similar products. Finally, you will evaluate consumer products from an energy point of view.

Our Growing Use of Energy

Until about 500 000 years ago, food and sunlight were the only energy resources that people were able to use. Then people learned to make fires, so they were able to use the chemical energy stored in wood to provide heat and light.

Making fires is an example of technology. **Technology** is the development of tools, machines, or processes that help people make use of resources. Water wheels and windmills are examples of technology that enabled people to use running water and wind as energy resources (Figure 16.1). As technology continued to develop, other energy resources came into use.

Figure 16.1 *Windmills were invented around A.D. 1000. They were common in areas where there was a need to pump water from the ground.*

To see how patterns of energy use have changed during world history, study Table 16.1. Notice that the right-hand column gives the dates of some of the inventions that changed the way people used energy. In Activity 16A you will study the amounts of energy used by an average member of each kind of society. You may have to refer to Table 16.1 to answer some of the questions in this activity.

Table 16.1 *Patterns of Energy Use of the Past and Present*

TYPE OF SOCIETY AND DATE	ENERGY RESOURCES USED BY THE SOCIETY	TECHNOLOGY AVAILABLE	DATE OF INVENTION
Primitive society (1 000 000 B.C.)	Food and sunlight	Stones and sticks	1 750 000 B.C.
Hunting and gathering society (100 000 B.C.)	Wood and both resources listed above	Fire-making Scraping and cutting tools Blade tools	500 000 B.C. 100 000 B.C. 40 000 B.C.
Primitive agricultural society (5000 B.C.)	Water, domestic animals, and all the resources listed above	Wooden plough Wheel Water pump Water wheel	5000 B.C. 3500 B.C. 200 B.C. 100 B.C.
Advanced agricultural society (A.D. 1400)	Wind and all the resources listed above	Rigid horse collar Windmill Compass Gunpowder Printing	A.D. 800 1000 1100 1300 1440
Industrial society (A.D. 1800)	Coal, oil, natural gas, and all the resources listed above	Steam engine Steam-driven loom Electric battery Steam locomotive Match Tractor and automobile Telephone	1698 1780 1800 1804 1844 1870 1876
Technological society (at present)	Uranium and all the resources listed above	Radio Television Computer Jet airplane Nuclear reactor Artificial satellite	1910 1928 1930 1939 1942 1957

Problem

How has energy use changed as societies have changed?

Materials

Procedure

Study Figure 16.2 which shows the average amount of energy used each day by a member of each kind of society. The energy is given in **megajoules** (MJ). One megajoule is equal to one million joules, or 1.0 MJ = 1 000 000 J. After studying the bar graph, answer the questions. In some cases, you will have to refer to the information in Table 16.1.

Observations

1. According to Figure 16.2, approximately what percentage of your daily energy use serves each of the following purposes?
   (a) energy from food for use in the body
   (b) heating and cooking
   (c) industry and agriculture
   (d) transportation

A ruler may help you calculate the answers. For example, if the "use" is 7 mm long and the entire bar is 94 mm long, then the percentage is

$$\frac{7 \text{ mm}}{94 \text{ mm}} \times 100\% = 7.4\% \text{ or about } 7\%$$

2. (a) If you had lived in a primitive society, what percentage of your daily energy use would have come from food?
   (b) Describe how the percentage of energy from food changes as a society develops from a primitive stage to a technological stage.
   (c) What reasons might there be for such a change?

3. (a) At what stage did energy obtained from food drop to much less than 50% of an average person's daily energy use?
   (b) What new energy resources had people learned how to use by this time? (Refer to Table 16.1.)

4. (a) At what stage did the energy used for industry and agriculture begin to exceed the energy obtained from food?
   (b) Which fossil fuel had people begun to use extensively by this time?
   (c) What inventions enabled people to use this fossil fuel? Explain.

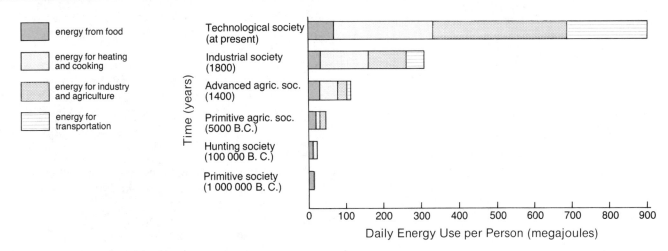

Figure 16.2 *This bar graph shows how the use of energy has changed throughout history. Notice that the uppermost bar represents energy use in today's technological society.*

5. (a) In what stage did energy use for transportation become very large?
   (b) What new (non-fossil) energy resource did people learn how to use at this stage?
   (c) Which invention enabled people to make peaceful use of the energy resource?

Questions

1. Describe how total energy use changes as a society develops from primitive to technological. For example, a hunting society consumes about twice as much energy per person as a primitive society.
2. Assume that the pattern shown in Figure 16.2 continues to develop as it has to date. Predict the total daily energy consumption in a society 100 years from now. Note: The scale on the time axis is not evenly spaced.

Scientists and other groups of people study the effects of various types of growth. Some people study the growth of disease. Others are concerned about increased wages and the costs of consumer goods. Still others are concerned about the growth of population and energy use. In all these areas, the effect of growth is often surprising.

Problem

How can water be used to study growth patterns?

Materials

large bucket with a capacity of about 15 L
at least one eyedropper
two or three graduated cylinders (small and medium sizes)
two or three beakers (medium and large sizes)
stopwatch
graph paper
Note: Procedure step 3 is best done in groups of four or five students.

Procedure

1. Predict an answer to the following question: How long will it take to fill the bucket with water if you add one drop of water to the empty bucket, and then *double* the amount of water added every 10 s?
2. Discuss the predictions in class. Also discuss how you will perform the experiment using the apparatus available.
3. Perform an experiment to determine an answer to the question in step 1. If you have trouble completing the experiment properly, repeat it until you get a consistent result. See Figure 16.3.

Observations

1. How did your actual time to fill the bucket compare with your predicted time? If there was a difference, explain why.
2. Set up a table of calculations based on Table 16.2. The table should record the times until the experiment ended. Complete the calculations for the table.

Figure 16.3 *Good organization and careful measurements are needed for this activity to be successful.*

Table 16.2 *Data Calculations for Activity 16B*

TIME (s)	NUMBER OF DROPS ADDED
0	1
10	2
20	4
30	8
40	16
Etc.	Etc.

3. Based on your data calculations, about how many drops of water does the bucket hold?
4. Plot a graph using the data calculations, placing time along the horizontal axis and number of drops added along the vertical axis.

Questions

1. What is the general shape of a graph which shows the growth of a quantity that keeps on doubling?
2. Describe any difficulties you had in this activity.
3. Why do you think scientists and other people worry when energy use keeps on doubling?

Continued Growth of Energy Use

Anyone who performs an experiment on the effects of growth, such as Activity 16B, knows how rapidly a quantity grows when it keeps doubling. A useful way to study such growth patterns is to use data tables and graphs. Consider, for example, the data in Table 16.3. These data show how much natural gas will be consumed worldwide if the amount doubles every 20 years. A graph of these data is shown in Figure 16.4 on page 302. The graph ends when the estimated available natural gas is used up. Thus, if the amount of natural gas we use doubles every 20 years, all the natural gas in the world (240×10^9 m^3) will be gone by the year 2070. To prevent this from happening, we must reduce the growth of our use of this resource.

Table 16.3 *Estimated Worldwide Consumption of Natural Gas*

YEAR	1990	2010	2030	2050	2070
Consumption of natural gas ($\times 10^9$ m^3)	15	30	60	120	240

Note: The data shown here are based on the assumption that the consumption of natural gas will double every 20 years.

We have seen one important reason why our energy use has grown—each person is consuming more energy now than ever before. A second important factor that has caused increased energy use is the increase in the world's population. If both of these factors continue to increase, our supplies of all fossil fuels will decrease rapidly, and we will have to use alternative sources of energy.

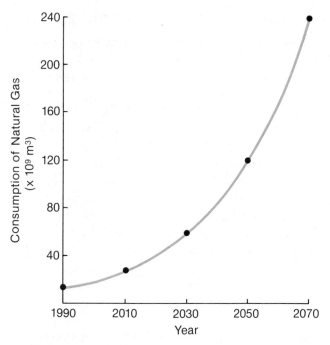

Figure 16.4 *Graph of the consumption of natural gas. This graph is drawn with the assumption that the quantity consumed doubles every 20 years. The shape of the line on the graph can be called a "growth pattern."*

Ideas and Applications

Often the amount of energy available from a resource is stated in terms of its "oil equivalent," which is usually given in barrels. A barrel contains 150 L of oil, enough to provide 5900 MJ of energy (or 5.9×10^9 J). With this much energy, a runner could run about 200 marathons, each 40 km long.

Self-check

1. What has always been the main energy source for humans?
2. (a) What is technology?
   (b) State three examples of technology developed during the centuries before Christ (B.C.).
   (c) State three examples of technology developed in the last 2000 years.
3. In a technological society, where are the greatest amounts of energy used?
4. (a) Name three electrical devices that were not available 50 years ago.
   (b) How do these devices change our energy use?
5. The "doubling time" in Activity 16B was 10 seconds. Explain what you think this statement means.
6. The "doubling" time in Figure 16.4 is 20 years. Explain how the general shape of the line on the graph would change if the doubling time were
   (a) 15 years
   (b) 40 years.
7. Describe two main reasons why the *total* energy consumed by humans has increased to its highest amount ever.

Measuring Energy Consumption

Much of the energy we consume is difficult to measure because it is actually consumed by all of society. For example, grapes, bananas, or watermelons found in Canadian stores in the winter were brought here in a temperature-controlled truck from some southern region, such as Mexico. The transportation and refrigeration use a lot of energy. Energy is also consumed in other processes such as the harvesting and packaging of fruit. The total amount of energy required to get the fruit from the farm to the consumer is difficult to calculate. This is just one of many examples of the indirect use of energy. See Figure 16.5.

Direct uses of energy are much easier to measure. For example, it is possible to find the amount of natural gas, home heating oil, or electrical energy used in a home in one year. It is also possible to calculate the amount of gasoline a car uses in a year. In this section, we will look closely at two of these calculations.

Figure 16.5 *Many of the products available in our fruit markets and grocery stores are imported from other countries. Much energy is needed to transport these products.*

Gasoline Consumption

An example can be used to calculate the average gasoline consumption of a car for one year. Assume that the average distance travelled each month by the car is 2000 km, and that the car has a consumption rate of 10 L/100 km. The quantity of gasoline used per month is

$$2000 \text{ km} \times \frac{10 \text{ L}}{100 \text{ km}} = 200 \text{ L}$$

Thus, in 12 months, the total gasoline consumption is

$$12 \text{ months} \times \frac{200 \text{ L}}{\text{month}} = 2400 \text{ L}$$

Electrical Energy in the Home

There are two basic ways of calculating how much electrical energy is used in the home. One way is to use tables of data, and the other way is to read the electric meter where the electricity enters the home. In both cases, the energy consumed is usually stated in **kilowatt hours** (kW·h), rather than joules or megajoules.

To calculate the electrical energy used by one appliance, express the power of the appliance in kilowatts and the time the appliance is used in hours. Then simply multiply the two values. The following equation can be used: energy = power x time.

SAMPLE PROBLEM

Calculate the energy (in kilowatt hours) used by a 100 W light bulb in half a day.

SOLUTION

The time is 12 h, and the power is 0.10 kW (because 1000 W = 1.0 kW).

energy = power x time
= 0.10 kW x 12 h
= 1.2 kW·h

Thus, the bulb uses 1.2 kW·h of electrical energy.

Every appliance has a label that indicates its power rating in watts or kilowatts. You can refer to that label when you need to calculate the energy consumed. If the label is hard to find, you might choose to refer to the data given in Table 16.4. This table indicates the average power rating of some common appliances.

Table 16.4 *Average Power Rating of Common Electric Appliances*

APPLIANCE	AVERAGE POWER RATING (W)
Stove	12000
Clothes dryer	5000
Air conditioner (window)	2000
Microwave oven	1500
Dishwasher	1200
Frying pan	1200
Toaster	1200
Hair dryer	1000
Iron	1000
Coffee maker	900
Vacuum cleaner	600
Food freezer (frost-free)	500
Washing machine	500
Refrigerator (frost-free)	350
Blanket	200
Fan (window)	200
Humidifier	200
Colour television	200
Radio	80
Black-and-white television	50
Clock	2

To determine the *total* electrical energy consumed for a period of time, the energy used by all appliances must be added together.

The second way to determine the total energy consumed for a period of time is to read the electric meter at the beginning and end of the time period. Digital meters are easy to read, so they will not be discussed here. Dial meters, like the one shown in Figure 16.6, are more difficult to read, but a little practice will help you understand them.

Figure 16.6 *A typical dial electric meter*

Figure 16.7 shows a typical set of readings on a five-dial electric meter. Notice that the dial on the left moves counterclockwise, the next one moves clockwise, and so on. When reading each dial, consider which number the arrow has passed. Do you see that the reading in Figure 16.7 is 73 054 kW·h?

Figure 16.7 *If an electric meter has five dials, the amount of energy in kilowatt hours is read directly. In this case, the reading is 73 054 kW·h.*

Some dial meters have five dials, but many have only four dials. In this case, the reading must be multiplied by 10. The reason will become clear in the next sample problem.

SAMPLE PROBLEM

Figure 16.8 shows the dial readings of a home on July 1 and on September 1. Calculate the energy consumed during the two months.

SOLUTION

The July 1 reading is 58 320 kW·h.
The September 1 reading is 58 460 kW·h.
The energy consumed is
  58 460 kW·h – 58 320 kW·h = 140 kW·h.

These two methods of determining electrical energy will be applied in the following activity. To distinguish between the two methods, let us call the meter readings the *measurement method*, and the use of the data table the *calculation method*.

July 1

x 10 kW·h

September 1

x 10 kW·h

Figure 16.8 *If the electric meter has only four dials, the reading must be multiplied by 10 to obtain the number of kilowatt hours. These diagrams are used in the sample problem.*

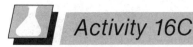

Activity 16C

Problem

How closely does the measurement method compare to the calculated method when determining electrical energy consumption?

Procedure

1. Determine the electric meter readings for your home or a friend's home at least twice. Take the readings a pre-determined time apart (for example, exactly one week). Record the date, time, and value of each reading. Also, to help your teacher check each reading, draw a diagram in each case showing all the dials and the arrows on the dials. Be sure you don't read the natural gas meter or water meter.

2. Set up a table of data based on Table 16.5. The first row in Table 16.5 shows an example of five clocks that operate continuously for one week (168 h). On your table, give the names and data of all the appliances in your home. Complete the table for a time period equal to the total time period used in step 1 (for example, exactly one week). To determine the power rating, either read the label on the appliance or use the information found in Table 16.4.

Table 16.5 *Data Table For the Calculation Method in Activity 16C*

APPLIANCE	POWER (W)	POWER (kW)	TIME USED (h)	ENERGY (kW·h)
5 clocks	10	0.01	168	1.68

Observations

1. Use subtraction to find the total electrical energy used during the time period chosen in Procedure step 1.

2. Use addition to find the total electrical energy used during the time period chosen in Procedure step 2.

3. Compare the measured energy with the calculated energy. If there is any difference, explain it.

Questions

1. Did most students in your class tend to have higher measured values than calculated values, or the reverse? Explain why this is likely to happen.
2. Which appliances tend to consume the most electrical energy? Why?
3. What can be done in your home to reduce the electrical energy consumption?

Challenge

Have your family practise energy conservation for the same amount of time you used in this activity. Determine the amount of electrical energy used during this conservation period. What do you conclude?

Challenge

If your home uses another energy resource besides electricity, determine the amount of energy that resource consumed for a period of time such as one week or one month. Report on all measurements and calculations involved. For example, if your home uses natural gas, you could either read the dials one month apart or use the monthly statement sent by the supplier.

Self-check

1. A person receives a postcard from a friend travelling in Europe. What uses of energy are involved in getting that card from Europe to its destination? Explain why it would be difficult to calculate the amount of energy involved.
2. A car pulling a trailer has an average consumption rate of 40 L/100 km. On a four-week vacation, the car and trailer travel a total distance of 6000 km. What quantity of gasoline is used during the vacation?
3. Determine the average monthly gasoline consumption of the main car used by your family (or a friend's family). Show all your calculations.
4. An 80 W stereo system is left running for 16 h.
   (a) What is the power of the stereo in kilowatts?
   (b) How much energy is consumed in the 16 h?
5. Four outdoor lights, each 150 W, are operated 8 h each night for one week. Determine the total electrical energy consumed by these lights in kilowatt hours.
6. Figure 16.9 shows the meter readings for a household on two different dates. Determine the electrical energy consumed during the elapsed time.
7. List ways you can conserve energy
   (a) in the home
   (b) for transportation.

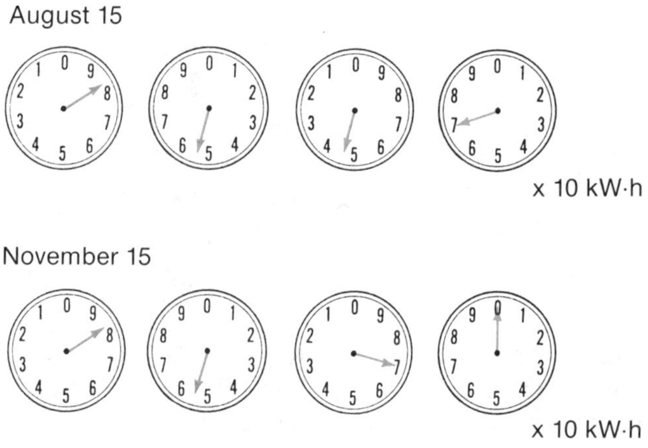

August 15

x 10 kW·h

November 15

x 10 kW·h

Figure 16.9 *What is the electrical energy consumed in the elapsed time?*

16.3

Using Energy in Industry

As you learned in the previous section, you can determine the energy consumed for such purposes as car travel and the use of home appliances. Similar calculations can be made in industries. In the activity that follows, you will focus on the energy consumed in the manufacture of one ballpoint pen. Energy is consumed to make the parts of the pen and to assemble those parts into the final product. A diagram of the parts of the pen is shown in Figure 16.10.

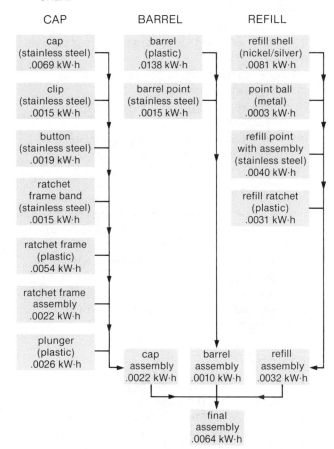

Figure 16.10 *The parts of the Jotter ballpoint pen manufactured by the Parker Pen Company*

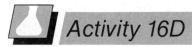

Activity 16D

Problem

How much energy is required to manufacture a typical ballpoint pen?

Procedure

1. Study the flow chart shown in Figure 16.11. If necessary, refer to Figure 16.10 to see the components of the pen referred to in the flow chart.

Figure 16.11 *Study this flow chart carefully before you begin the calculations in Activity 16D. The flow chart shows the components used to make the cap, barrel, and refill of each Parker ballpoint pen. The type of material used to make each component is shown in brackets. The amount of energy needed to make or assemble each part is indicated in kilowatt hours.*

2. Determine the energy (in kilowatt hours) used to make and assemble the
   (a) cap   (c) refill.
   (b) barrel
3. Find the sum of the energies in Procedure step 2.
4. Determine the total energy required to manufacture the ballpoint pen. Include the ballpoint pen final assembly.
5. There are six assembly steps shown in the flow chart. What total energy is consumed by those steps?
6. There are eleven fabrication steps shown in the flow chart. Seven involve metals and four involve plastic.
   (a) How much energy is consumed by the fabrication of metals?
   (b) How much energy is consumed by the fabrication of plastics?
   (c) Find the total energy consumed by all the fabrications steps.

Observations

1. Which process requires a greater amount of energy, the fabrication process or the assembly? Try to give reasons for this.
2. Which type of material requires more energy for fabrication, plastic or metal? Explain why this might be so. Hint: Consider both the size of the parts and the heat needed to melt the material before it is moulded.

Questions

1. Parker Pen Limited, the company that manufactures the pens described in this activity, produces 3000 of these pens each hour.
   (a) Calculate the total energy consumption per hour for this manufacturing process.
   (b) Calculate the total energy consumed during an eight-hour shift at the factory where this process is carried out.
2. What parts of the manufacturing process do you think have not been taken into consideration in making the pens described in this activity?
3. What is likely the greatest source of waste energy in the manufacturing of ballpoint pens? Explain.

Home-Made Manufacturing

You have learned about the industrial manufacturing of ballpoint pens, just one of thousands of products made in our modern society. Many of these products contain **natural materials**. These are materials found in nature, such as iron, wool, and cotton. However, numerous products contain materials made by chemical processes. These materials are called **synthetic materials**. Many of them are produced at oil refineries where crude oil (petroleum) is refined. See Figure 16.12. Others are produced at later stages of the oil refining process, in petrochemical plants. Refer to Figure 16.13.

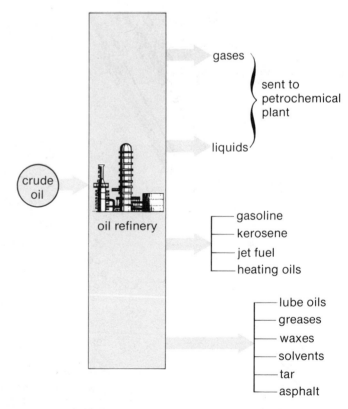

Figure 16.12 *Petroleum (crude oil) enters an oil refinery where various gases, liquids, lubricants, and other products are made. Only a small number of the products are shown here.*

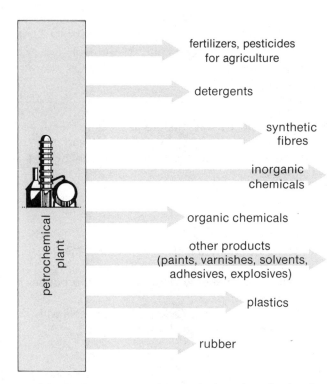

Figure 16.13 *At a petrochemical plant, hundreds of products are made from the hydrocarbons obtained from fossil fuels.*

As you can see in Figures 16.12 and 16.13, many materials are produced from non-renewable resources, such as petroleum. Numerous products that we use daily are made from those materials. Examples are rubber for tires, plastics, fibres, explosives, home insulation, and pain killers. In Activity 16E, you will manufacture one product, a protective sunscreen, which contains mostly synthetic materials produced from petroleum. A sunscreen offers protection from the sun's ultraviolet rays and allows people to enjoy outdoor sports and relaxation more safely. Making your own sunscreen helps save money and shows how easily products can be made at home. After performing this activity, you may become interested in jobs related to the cosmetic or chemical industries.

Challenge

Make a list of jobs which you think are related to the cosmetic or petrochemical industries. Discuss your list in class.

Ideas and Applications

Synthetic polymer raw materials can be formed into many different types of plastics. Thermoplastic plastics, such as those used for plastic spoons, may be remelted with heat and reshaped. Thermosetting plastics become hard when they are formed, and cannot be softened again easily. They are baked in moulds to produce such items as car battery and telephone casings, and electrical switches and fittings.

Activity 16E

Problem

What can be learned by using a "recipe" to produce a protective sunscreen?

Note: This activity can be performed at home using chemicals available at local stores and from your teacher. If you do perform it at home, be sure to follow the instructions carefully, considering safety first. Also, try to involve your family in this activity.

Materials

6 mL petroleum jelly (available in drugstores and most food stores)

6 mL beeswax (available from scientific supply companies)

4 mL mineral oil (liquid petroleum, available at drugstores and most food stores)

1 mL zinc oxide (available from scientific supply companies)

double boiler (or any metal container which can be steam heated)

measuring devices (for example, measuring spoons)

laboratory or candy thermometer

mortar and pestle

clean jar with lid (you can recycle a jam jar)

stirring rod

water

Procedure

1. Be sure that all the apparatus to be used is clean and dry.
2. Place the mineral oil and zinc oxide in the mortar and grind the mixture well using the pestle.
3. Add about a half litre of water to the bottom of the double boiler and heat the water to boiling. As the water is being heated, place the beeswax and petroleum jelly in the top of the double boiler, and heat this mixture until the temperature reaches 75° C. Stir the mixture well once it has melted.

4. Add the melted wax mixture to the zinc oxide mixture in the mortar. Mix thoroughly and place the resulting product into the jar for cooling and storage.
5. Clean and dry all the apparatus.

Observations

1. List the raw materials used to produce the sunscreen.
2. What forms of energy were required to produce the sunscreen?
3. Compare how homemade sunscreen feels with how manufactured sunscreen feels.

Questions

1. Which materials used to produce the sunscreen were probably made originally from petroleum? Which were natural materials? Explain.
2. Where and when would people be likely to use the product made in this activity?
3. What part of the homemade production of sunscreen involves the greatest waste of energy? Explain.
4. Describe how you think the process you used in this activity would be changed in order to produce sunscreen in a big factory.

Energy and Consumer Products

At all stages of manufacturing consumer products, energy is required. It takes energy to mine and purify the raw materials. It takes energy to fabricate the purified materials into the components of a product, then to assemble and package the product. Furthermore, it takes energy to transport the raw materials and final products.

For our purposes here, it is useful to compare at least a few products from the viewpoint of the energy used to produce them. Table 16.6 compares containers made of plastic with containers made of other materials, such as glass, paper, and metal. The energy values stated include both the energy used to produce the ingredient materials and the energy used in the fabrication process.

When manufacturers consider which types of containers to use for packaging, energy is only one problem they think about. Other concerns include ease of transportation, handling and storage, recycling possibilities, and the environmental impact of discarding the product, to name just a few. Some of these factors will be considered in the next chapter where you will learn how recycling helps to conserve both raw materials and energy.

Table 16.6 *Input Energies to Produce Plastic and Other Products*

CONTAINER	ENERGY TO PRODUCE PLASTIC CONTAINER		ALTERNATIVE MATERIAL	ENERGY TO PRODUCE ALTERNATIVE	
	(MJ)	(kW·h)		(MJ)	(kW·h)
2 L bottle	12.9	3.6	Glass	27.1	7.6
4 L produce bag	0.5	0.14	Paper	0.6	0.17
4 L oblong container	17.0	4.8	Steel	21.4	5.9
4 L milk container	7.9	3.5	Paper	7.6	2.1
225 mL dairy tub	2.0	0.56	Aluminum	6.1	1.7
250 mL vending cup	0.6	0.17	Paper	0.3	0.08

Self-check

1. Listed below are eight general steps of the manufacturing process. Rewrite the steps in the order they would occur.

   packaging of product
   fabrication of substances into component parts
   delivery of chemical substances to the manufacturer
   mining of raw materials
   refining of raw materials
   delivery of product to retail outlets
   delivery of raw materials to the refinery
   assembly of component parts into the final product

2. In most of the steps in Self-check question 1, much of the input energy becomes wasted. Explain why this waste occurs.

3. (a) List three natural materials.
   (b) Name three common products made from natural materials.

4. (a) List three synthetic materials.
   (b) Name three common products made from synthetic materials.

5. Compare the total energy needed to make one ballpoint pen with the energy needed to make one vending cup. Refer to your calculations in Activity 16D and to Table 16.6.

6. Refer to Table 16.6 to answer the following questions:
   (a) In which cases is the energy required to make the plastic container greater than the energy required to make the other containers?
   (b) How does the energy needed to make glass or metal containers compare to the energy needed to make plastic containers? Explain reasons for this.

7. Based on your own experience and the information in Table 16.6, state the advantages that plastic has over
   (a) glass   (c) steel
   (b) paper   (d) aluminum.

8. State the advantages that the materials listed in Self-check question 7 have over plastic.

Chapter Objectives

NOW THAT YOU HAVE COMPLETED THIS CHAPTER, CAN YOU DO THE FOLLOWING?	FOR REVIEW, TURN TO SECTION
1. Define and give examples of technology.	16.1
2. Describe why the energy used per person each day is greater now than in the past.	16.1
3. Explain patterns of energy use by referring to tables.	16.1, 16.2 16.3
4. Understand why continual growth can be a problem, especially for energy consumption.	16.2
5. Calculate the gasoline consumption of an automobile knowing the consumption rate and the distance travelled.	16.2
6. Read a dial electric meter.	16.2
7. Calculate the energy consumed (in kilowatt hours) given the power and the time.	16.2
8. Know that joules and kilowatt hours are common units of energy.	16.2
9. Understand why energy is needed in the manufacturing of products.	16.3
10. Distinguish between synthetic and natural materials, and give examples of each.	16.3

Words to Know

technology
megajoule
kilowatt hour
natural material
synthetic material

Tying It Together

1. In your notebook, write the headings Discovery and Invention. Then list the words from the sets below in the correct column.

   light bulbs, electricity
   laser printers, laser light
   solid state physics, computers
   convection current, convection ovens
   magnetic tapes, laws of magnetism

2. In your answer to Tying It Together question 1, one list represents "technology" and the other "science." Which list is which? Explain.

3. Draw an energy-time graph showing the general growth of energy consumption throughout human history. Place "time" on the horizontal axis. Numbers are not required. Simply show the general shape of the line on the graph.

4. How would each factor listed below affect the consumption of energy in Canada?
   (a) Our country's population is growing.
   (b) Automobiles are being made smaller and lighter.
   (c) Public transportation is becoming more common.
   (d) Fresh produce is trucked to supermarkets daily, even in the winter.

5. The number of vehicles owned by a certain trucking company is shown in the table below.

YEAR	1935	1945	1955	1965	1975	1985
Number of Trucks	10	20	40	80	160	320

   (a) What is the doubling time of the number of trucks?
   (b) If the growth pattern continues, how many trucks will the company own in 1995? 2005?
   (c) Plot a graph showing the growth pattern from 1935 to 1985.

6. What gasoline consumption rate (in litres per 100 km) would you expect for
   (a) an efficient compact car?
   (b) a motorbike?
   (c) a stretch limousine?

7. Calculate the amount of gasoline used in one year by a car that travels 3000 km per month. Assume the average consumption rate is 8 L/100 km.

8. In each case, calculate the electrical energy used in kilowatt hours.
   (a) A 1500 W microwave oven is operated for 12 h in one month.
   (b) A 200 W colour television is left on for 60 h in one month.

9. Figure 16.14 shows electric meter dials that were read six months apart. What is the electrical energy consumed during the six months?

10. You learned about two methods of determining electrical energy consumption—the calculation method using power ratings and time, and the measurement method using electric meter readings. Which method do you think is more accurate? Explain why.

11. Throughout Chapters 15 and 16, you have seen several examples of energy being wasted. Which form of energy tends to be the end result of waste energy?

12. State what manufacturing processes require input energy.

13. (a) Explain the difference between synthetic and natural materials.
    (b) Give two examples of each type of material.

January 1

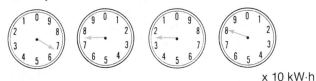

x 10 kW·h

July 1

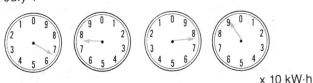

x 10 kW·h

Figure 16.14 *What is the electrical energy consumed during the six months?*

313

Applying Your Knowledge

1. In your opinion, which solution listed below would be better in solving the world's energy problems? Explain your choice.
   - (a) Prevent the world's population from growing.
   - (b) Be sure that the amount of energy used per person does not grow.
2. If the solutions in the previous question are not possible, what other solution(s) would you suggest?
3. Some home appliances use the 240 V electric circuits, while many appliances use the 120 V electric circuits.
   - (a) Name two appliances which use 240 V.
   - (b) Name four appliances which use 120 V.
   - (c) Which appliances tend to use more electrical energy? Why?
4. In manufacturing cars, the recent trend has been to use more plastic parts and fewer metal parts.
   - (a) State the advantages of this trend.
   - (b) State the disadvantages of this trend. Consider energy input and output in your answers.
5. Assume you have a job in which you must choose between plastic and paper disposable vending cups. State which you would choose for each job listed below, and explain each choice. Consider several factors, including the energy information given in Table 16.6.
   - (a) You own a company that operates coffee-vending machines.
   - (b) You operate a day-care nursery.
   - (c) You are a salesperson for a petrochemical company.
   - (d) You are an environmental scientist concerned about pollution.
6. Some consumers are in the habit of wasting energy and natural resources. List three common ways in which this waste occurs in your own family.
7. Because of a major technological improvement, imagine that all vehicles on the highways in the world are converted to running on batteries instead of gasoline. Describe the changes that would occur in the need for the various sources of energy used in (a) making a car and (b) operating a car.

Projects for Investigation

1. Investigate the difference in energy use patterns between the different generations in your family. Interview a parent, uncle, aunt, or grandparent, for example, and find out what tools and machines did not exist during their childhood. Draw some conclusions about which invention(s), since their childhood, have most dramatically changed people's lives.
2. Visit a local industry or write a letter to discover information about manufacturing some product. Use photographs, brochures, and samples to make a display of the manufacturing process. Include information about energy input, output, and waste.
3. Obtain a reference book that contains recipes for homemade products. Choose a product that interests you and that is made of materials you can obtain. Make the product and bring it to class. Make sure you follow all the safety rules.
4. Choose a consumer product and answer the questions listed below about that product. Some suggested products are a bicycle, a hair dryer, a calculator, or a musical instrument.
   - (a) What materials were used to manufacture the product?
   - (b) At what stages of the manufacturing process would energy input be required?
   - (c) What energy is required to use or maintain the product?

Conserving Our Energy Resources

Key Ideas

- Society and industry can help conserve energy.
- Individuals can reduce their energy consumption in many different ways.
- Governments and industries can reduce energy consumption.
- There are advantages to using energy resources that do not depend on fossil fuels.

The aircraft shown in the photograph, called the *Gossamer Penguin*, was the world's first piloted solar aircraft. It is one example of ways

people are using to take advantage of energy resources that are renewable. In this case, the resource is the sun's energy. As our non-renewable resources quickly run out, we must find other ways of obtaining energy. Furthermore, we must learn not to waste the resources we have. In this chapter, you will learn about ways to conserve energy. You will study what is meant by a "conserver society" and discover how governments and industries are recycling waste materials and developing new sources of energy.

Our Individual Roles in Conserving Energy

Every time you turn on a radio or TV, ride a bus, get a cold drink from the refrigerator, or eat a hot meal, you are taking advantage of energy. What would happen if the sources of that energy, such as electricity, gasoline, and natural gas, were no longer available? Or course, your lifestyle would be very different. In order to maintain and improve our lifestyle, we, as individuals, should learn how we can contribute to the conservation of energy.

Many people do not care about how much energy they use because the energy is still fairly cheap. They are not aware that we will have to face major problems in the future. Individuals must become aware that energy is an important concern in our society. Refer to Figure 17.1 which shows the titles of several recent magazine articles. Read the titles, and determine how many of them indicate problems associated with energy. One way to become aware of the energy situation is to read articles published by the news media.

Besides becoming aware of our energy needs and problems, what can an individual do to help reduce the problems? On an individual basis, one person will not change the energy needs of the future. However, if all individuals learn how to conserve energy, the future will be much brighter. For example, if our energy needs increase by about 6% each year, in only 12 years our energy needs will be double what they are today! However, if everyone tries to conserve energy so that the increase in needs is only 2%, it will take about 36 years to double our needs.

"Cry Havoc" or "Cry Wolf"— The Nature of the Energy Crisis

Why America Must End Its Wasteful Ways

Nuclear Reactors: How Safe Is Safe? LIVING WITHOUT ELECTRICITY

WHAT PRICE "FREE" ENERGY?

THE "OIL GLUT": DON'T BE FOOLED **Hard Times for Nuclear Power**

Nuclear Reactor Research Unaffected by Chernobyl *An Oil-Short World: The Coming Crunch*

What's in a Glut? The High Cost of Low Oil Prices

Figure 17.1 *These headlines were found in magazines in recent years.*

Challenge

Using magazines and newspaper articles published within the last one or two years, make two lists of energy-related articles. In one list, name the titles that describe problems. In the other list, name the titles that describe solutions to problems. Which list is longer? What can you conclude about coverage in the news media? Note: An excellent source of information for these articles is the vertical file in the school's resource centre. The librarian can suggest additional related titles that you can research.

Activity 17A

Problem

What are the ten most important ways in which I can conserve energy?

Materials

Procedure

Listed below are 16 statements regarding energy-related activities performed by most people. For each statement, state whether you consider it to be *true* or *false*. For each *true statement*, state its importance or value in your own life or the lives of future Canadians. For each *false statement*, state why it is false and rewrite the statement so it becomes true.

1. In the winter, it is possible to keep my home fairly cool and wear a sweater to keep warm.
2. Energy can be conserved by turning off lights and electrical appliances when they are not in use.
3. Incandescent lights consume less electrical energy than fluorescent lights.
4. Dimmer switches on incandescent lights help conserve energy and extend the life of the lights.
5. Toasting one piece of bread at a time in a toaster does not waste energy.
6. Washing dishes consumes more energy than using throw-away containers, plates, and cutlery.
7. When travelling a short distance, it is better to take a car than walk or ride a bicycle.
8. There are entertainment and sport activities that consume very little of our energy resources, yet they are as good for us as large energy consumers such as water skiing, motorboating, and snowmobiling.
9. An individual can do absolutely nothing about the insulation in his or her own home or apartment.
10. Leaving the refrigerator door open while deciding what to eat makes no difference to the energy consumed because the refrigerator motor runs constantly anyhow.
11. People who put glass jars and bottles out for recycling should first wash them in their electric dishwasher.
12. The best fireplace to choose is one with a heat circulator that sends warm air to the room rather than letting all the hot air rise up the chimney.
13. People who roll plastic covers over their swimming pools to keep the heat in at night need not bother to do so during July, the hottest month of the year.
14. Having regular tune-ups for a car ensures that the car starts well. It has nothing to do with the efficiency of energy consumption.
15. A shower consumes less hot water than a hot bath.
16. Heating a full kettle of water to make one cup of a hot drink is an obvious waste of energy.

Observations

1. List which statements were considered *true* by all students in the class.
2. List which statements were considered *false* by all students in the class.
3. Choose 10 of the 16 statements (either true or rewritten as true) that you consider to be the most important ways in which you can help conserve energy. List these 10 statements in order of most important to least important.
4. List any statements regarding energy conservation that have not been included here but are important to you.

Questions

Based on your observations in Observations questions 3 and 4, prepare a report entitled "Ten Ways I Can Conserve Energy." Include more than just electrical energy. For each of the 10 ways, describe how you, personally, could reduce the consumption of energy.

Society's Role in Conserving Energy

Figure 17.2 shows three vehicles that operate at different levels of energy consumption. The big car in Figure 17.2 (a) was built in the 1950s. At that time, gasoline cost about 7¢/L or 8¢/L and people were not greatly concerned that the car consumed about 40 L of gasoline for every 100 km. The more modern family car in Figure 17.2 (b) is streamlined, lighter, and much more efficient than the older car. It consumes perhaps 8–10 L of gasoline for every 100 km. The vehicle in Figure 17.2 (c) is an experimental "efficiency" car called the "Canadian Challenge X." It was designed at the University of Saskatchewan. In 1986 it set a world fuel economy record by using only 50 mL (0.050 L) of gasoline to travel 100 km. At that rate, this vehicle would require only 3.0 L of gasoline to travel across Canada!

Unfortunately, the efficiency car would not be practical in traffic and it could not carry passengers and luggage. However, it does represent an advancement in our ability to produce energy-efficient devices. In many instances, universities and private companies are designing devices that consume much less energy than similar devices built years ago. In other instances, governments had to bring in laws to force manufacturers to increase efficiency. The automobile industry is a good example of this.

The concerns about energy resources, energy conservation, and efficiency have led to what is

Figure 17.2 *Comparing the energy consumption of three types of cars*

(a) *In the 1940s and 1950s, the average car in North America was large and heavy. The rate of gasoline consumption for a car like this one was about 40 L/100 km.*

(b) *Modern cars have features that allow more efficient rates of gasoline consumption.*

called a conserver society. A **conserver society** is one in which all parts of the society, from individuals to industries and public institutions (schools, universities, hospitals, governments, etc.) are concerned about the use of energy today and the availability of energy in the future.

Consider the importance of heating and cooling our homes, offices, and other buildings. Our climate has extreme temperatures, from very hot to bitterly cold. We spend large amounts of effort and money to keep cool in the summer and warm in the winter. Maintaining a comfortable year-round temperature consumes a lot of energy.

The most important feature of an energy-efficient home is its insulation. In Activity 17B you will discover how to compare the insulating properties of various materials.

(c) *The* Canadian Challenge X *has a very low rate of gasoline consumption mainly because of its low mass (about 38 kg). This type of vehicle is experimental and can't be used for practical purposes.*

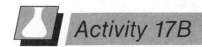

Activity 17B

Problem

What common materials provide the best resistance to the transfer of heat?

Materials

various insulating materials (pieces of fabric, styrofoam chips, glass wool, vermiculite, fibreglass, rubber foams, sheets of newspaper, etc.)
2 equal-size plastic coffee cups with plastic lids
other containers (2 large glass beakers, 2 large plastic beakers, or large metal cans)
2 thermometers
graduated cylinder (100 mL)
source of hot water

Note: An alternate method to the one described here is to build a cardboard house and test various insulating materials in the walls of the house. Ask your teacher for more details.

CAUTION Be careful when handling hot water and the hot water source.

Procedure

1. Predict which of the various materials available for this activity will act as the best insulator. Explain your choice.
2. To compare the insulating abilities of various materials, place the two plastic coffee cups inside two identical larger containers. Surround one coffee cup with the first material to be tested, and surround the other coffee cup with the second material to be tested. See Figure 17.3 on page 320. When the apparatus is ready, add an equal amount of hot water from the graduated cylinder to each coffee cup, put on the lids, and insert the thermometers into the hot water. Take temperature readings every minute for 10–15 min, or until a noticeable pattern is seen. Record the data in a table.

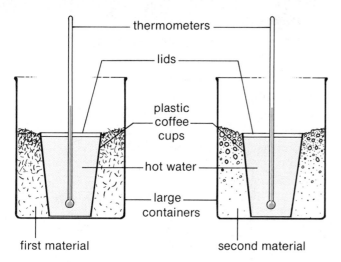

thermometers

lids

plastic coffee cups

hot water

large containers

first material

second material

Figure 17.3 *Set-up for Activity 17B*

3. Repeat step 2 for the other available insulating materials. You can also use air as one of the insulating materials.

Observations

1. On a single graph, which should be drawn as large as possible, plot all the data from Procedure steps 2 and 3. Place temperature on the vertical axis and time on the horizontal axis. Label each line on the graph. Which material was the best insulator?
2. Compare your results with the results of other groups in the class.

Questions

1. List the insulating materials tested from the best insulator to the poorest.
2. What factors other than the insulating ability would have to be considered when buying insulation for a home?

Challenge

Set up and perform an experiment to determine whether a dark, dull metal surface acts as a better insulator than a shiny metal surface. Begin by predicting an answer to the problem. Then place hot water in two equal-size metal containers, one painted dull black and the other bright and shiny. Place a lid on each container and insert a thermometer in each lid. Take temperature-time readings as you did in Activity 17B. Plot the readings on a graph and describe your conclusions.

Challenge

In the metric system, the resistance to heat transfer is stated in RSI values, where the "R" represents resistance and the "SI" represents the Système International (International System of Units). A higher RSI value means a greater resistance to heat transfer, and thus a better insulator. The RSI values are listed in Table 17.1. Compare your lists from Activity 17B with the list in Table 17.1.

Table 17.1 *RSI Values of 10 cm of Insulating Materials*

MATERIAL	RSI VALUE
Brick	0.08
Gypsum board	0.46
Plywood	0.88
Vermiculite	1.6
Glass fibre (poured)	2.1
Mineral wool (poured)	2.2
Cellulose fibre (poured)	2.4
Polystyrene (expanded)	2.8
Styrofoam	3.5
Polyurethane foam	4.1

Other Methods of Conserving Energy

In this section we have seen two ways in which our society has attempted to conserve energy. Our society has tried to (1) develop more efficient automobiles and (2) improve the insulation of buildings. What other ways are being studied and used?

Governments have provided money for people who replaced old, inefficient furnaces with new ones. The new furnaces use cleaner, more plentiful sources of energy. Governments also promote the use of alternative energy sources.

In transportation, governments support reduced speed limits and the use of car pools, both of which reduce energy consumption. Governments also promote public transportation, especially in cities. Some lanes on city roads are available for buses only. This restriction adds to the efficiency of public transportation.

Government agencies also sponsor tests on electrical appliances to see how energy efficient they are. A booklet containing the test results is available to the consumer from Consumer and Corporate Affairs Canada in Ottawa. Every appliance sold in Canada must have an energy guide ("Energuide") label indicating its rate of energy consumption. See Figure 17.4.

Some of the other ways in which governments and individuals are working together to conserve energy are discussed in the remainder of this chapter.

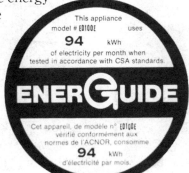

Figure 17.4 *A typical "Energuide" label*

Self-check

1. State whether each factor listed below has caused an *increase* or a *decrease* in the total amount of energy consumed for automobile transportation during the past 30 years in Canada.
   (a) the average size of cars
   (b) streamlining
   (c) engine efficiency
   (d) the number of cars per family
   (e) the cost of gasoline
   (f) the average distance each car is driven per year
2. Figure 17.5 shows five common ways of making windows for houses. They are arranged in order of how efficient they are in preventing heat transfer.
   (a) Which type do you think provides the best heat insulation?
   (b) Give possible reasons why some designs are better than others for preventing heat loss from a house.
3. A builder uses 10 cm of poured cellulose fibre, 10 cm of styrofoam, and 10 cm of brick to make a wall. Calculate the total RSI value of the wall. RSI values are found in Table 17.1.
4. Some people think that highway express lanes in and near large cities should be reserved during rush hour for cars with two or more people. Discuss what this has to do with topics in this section.

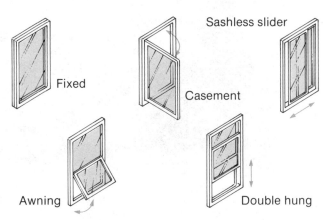

Figure 17.5 *Five possible designs for windows*

The R-2000 Home

What are governments and other groups doing to reduce the energy consumed to heat or cool our buildings? One important program undertaken by the federal government is the improvement of insulation in homes and other buildings. The Canadian government wants to be sure that, by the year 2000, all buildings being constructed have the best insulation possible. The program is called R-2000, where R refers to the resistance of heat transfer and 2000 represents the target year.

The R-2000 program is the biggest of its kind in the world. The program began when Canada's first super energy-efficient house was completed in 1977. This house was located in Regina, Saskatchewan, where the winters tend to be long and cold.

In the first year of operation, the entire space-heating bill for the house was only $50.00.

Following the success of the Saskatchewan house, several other energy-efficient houses in other provinces were designed and built. The energy consumed per home was about 70% lower than the energy consumed by other homes without the R-2000 technology. The extra cost needed to improve the homes was soon paid for by the savings in energy costs. Thus, the research and efforts paid off. As the end of the 1980s approached, the R-2000 program was fully in place in all provinces.

There are six main features of an R-2000 home. These features promote the efficient use of energy and the availability of clean, fresh air in the home.

1. Insulation and Wall Construction. R-2000 homes use two to three times more insulation than conventional homes in the exterior walls, roofs, and basements.
2. Reduced Air Leakage. R-2000 homes have a sealed air-vapour barrier to reduce air leakage as much as possible. This prevents winter drafts and summer dust from entering. The barrier is made of a plastic (such as polyethylene) and is placed on the inside of the wall.

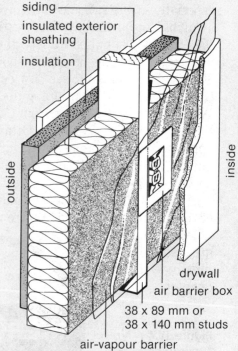

The walls of R-2000 homes have excellent insulating properties. Notice that even the electric outlet is well insulated.

The Saskatchewan Conservation House was the first super energy-efficient house built in Canada.

3. Ventilation and Heat Recovery. R-2000 homes are designed to provide healthy indoor air every day, all day long. Each house is equipped with a continuous ventilation system to bring in fresh air from outdoors. Some homes also have a method of transferring heat from the outgoing air to the incoming fresh air. The moisture content of the air is also controlled.

4. Windows and Doors. Windows are either double-glazed or triple-glazed. Doors are made from good insulating materials, or else a double-door system is used. All windows and doors have tight weather seals.

5. Direction of Construction. Whenever possible, an R-2000 home faces toward the sun (east-west with southern exposure) and uses a special design to take advantage of solar energy. The process of using the sun's energy in the winter is called *passive solar heating*.

6. Appliances. Each R-2000 home has energy-efficient appliances and lighting. Water heaters have extra insulation to prevent heat loss.

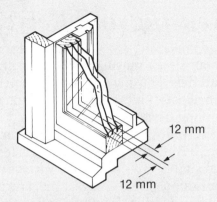

12 mm
12 mm

Triple-glazed windows provide excellent insulation because of tight seals along the edges and the "dead air" spaces between the panes of glass. This diagram shows a cut-away view of a triple-glazed window.

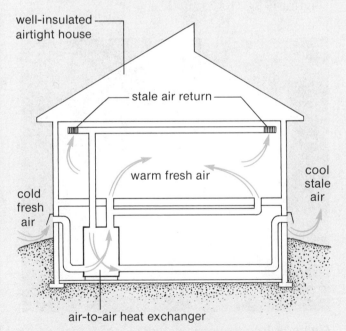

well-insulated airtight house

stale air return

warm fresh air

cold fresh air

cool stale air

air-to-air heat exchanger

In the winter cool, fresh air is pumped continuously from outdoors to replace the stale air indoors. In the R-2000 home shown here, the outgoing warm air gives some of its thermal energy to the incoming cool air in a device called a heat exchanger. This feature helps reduce the heating bill.

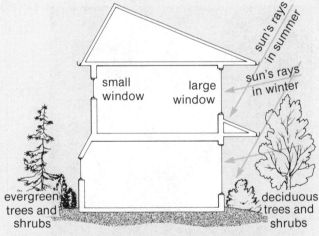

small window

large window

sun's rays in summer

sun's rays in winter

evergreen trees and shrubs

deciduous trees and shrubs

The basic features of a home with passive solar heating. Notice the large sizes of the windows and overhangs on the south side of the house. Notice also that deciduous trees are placed on the south side to provide shade in the summer. These trees lose their leaves in winter and allow the sun's rays to enter the house. Other features not shown here include carpets that absorb radiant energy in winter and window shutters that are closed at night to prevent heat loss.

Reusing and Recycling

Two important ways of conserving our energy resources are reusing products and recycling materials. Reusing and recycling involve individuals, industries, and governments all working together.

Reusing means using an item more than once before throwing it out as waste. We can all find simple ways of reusing various products. For example, boxes, bags, cans, and glass jars can be reused in and around the home. Old rubber tires can be used for something as simple as the swing shown in Figure 17.6. They have also been used as a base for a successful highway constructed as an experiment near Brockville, Ontario. In this case, the old tires were cut into pieces and placed in layers to make the base.

Recycling is the collection of waste material in order to make more of the same product. Recycling obviously saves on materials. But it also saves energy because recycled materials do not need as much processing as the original raw material. Some materials that can be successfully recycled are paper, glass, metals, oil, and parts of storage batteries.

Recycling programs require the co-operation of a large portion of the local population who help by separating the useful products from other waste. An example of a successful recycling program is found in Mississauga, Ontario, where recyclable materials are collected weekly on garbage collection day. Each home owner separates newspapers, glass products, and metal cans and places them into a special box (Figure 17.7).

Figure 17.6 *An example of reusing a common product*

Figure 17.7 *An important part of the recycling program in Mississauga, Ontario, is the recycling box provided by the recycling company. Homeowners put newsprint, glass, and metal cans into the boxes for collection on garbage-collection day.*

These products are collected in specially designed trucks and delivered to a central depot. After each truck weighs in, the load is dumped in three separate areas, one for newspapers, one for glass, and the third for metal cans (Figure 17.8).

Figure 17.8 *The central depot for recyclable materials*

(a) *The back portion of the truck contains newspapers that are dumped into a covered hanger.*

(b) *A tractor makes room for more newspapers about to be delivered.*

(c) *The newspapers are compressed and wrapped for delivery to the paper-recycling plant.*

(e) *The front part of the truck contains the metal cans that are last to be dumped from the truck. After this, the truck is washed by a portable cleaning service.*

(d) *The central part of the truck holds the glass containers that are piled outdoors.*

At the central depot, the piles of waste are checked for unwanted materials. Then the recyclable materials are sent to three different companies. There, the actual recycling processes are carried out. Refer to Figure 17.9.

The recycling program in Mississauga has been highly successful. About 90% of all homeowners in the city take part in the program by placing their "blue box" out for collection on average once every three weeks. The city's Public Affairs Department publishes a brochure titled *Recycling News* which goes to all households. In the first seven months of operation, the program saved about 90 000 trees and 12 million kilowatt hours of energy. It is estimated that the program will reduce the land needed for garbage dumps by more than 20%.

Challenge

Recycling programs such as the one in Mississauga, Ontario, are organized mainly for houses. This means that people who live in apartment buildings can only contribute by personally taking their recyclable wastes to specified recycling depots. Your class (and other classes in your school and perhaps other schools) could design and implement a recycling program that includes apartment buildings as well as houses. Such a program will require a lot of work and commitment, but the benefits to you, your community, and your province will more than make up for it. Ask your teacher for more details on how you can become an active part of a conserver society.

Figure 17.9 *Recycling glass*

(a) *As partially crushed glass passes along conveyor belts, unwanted materials such as metal caps are removed.*

(b) *Crushed glass is stockpiled and ready to be used.*

(c) *Bottles made of recycled glass mixed with raw materials are ready for shipping from the plant.*

Self-check

1. Describe the difference between reusing and recycling.
2. State at least two specific ways in which you could reuse each of the following products:
   (a) cardboard boxes
   (b) paper bags
   (c) plastic bags
   (d) metal cans
   (e) glass jars
3. List several reusable products in addition to those named in Self-check question 2.
4. Public education and co-operation are needed to make a recycling program successful. Explain why this is true.
5. Explain why recycling helps to conserve
   (a) raw materials
   (b) energy.
6. Choose *one* of the following products and describe how various parts of it might be reused and/or recycled. Each product is assumed to be old.
   (a) car
   (b) house
   (c) bicycle
   (d) refrigerator
   (e) sofa

New Uses for Waste

Figure 17.10 shows what one community has done with some of its waste. This artificial hill was made by piling solid waste materials layer upon layer and covering it with sod and trees. The hill and its surrounding park are now used for skiing and tobogganing in the winter and for hiking, hang-gliding, and other sports in the summer. Energy was saved in making the hill because the waste did not have to be transported far.

Figure 17.10 *These hills and the surrounding parkland are built from solid waste materials. As the waste was delivered, it was packed down, then later covered with sod and trees. In the winter, the slopes are used for skiing and toboganning.*

Another use for waste is to produce energy from biomass. Recall from Chapter 15 that biomass is the fuel that comes from living organisms, such as plants. Ways of using waste biomass and other waste materials to help conserve energy are described on the next page.

Waste Wood

People who live near wooded areas often use dead and dying trees as a source of heat in wood-burning stoves. Lumbermills and pulpmills produce sawdust and other wood by-products called "hog fuel." The hog fuel can be burned to heat buildings and produce electricity. A newer use of waste wood is to heat it without any oxygen present in a special process. This process, commonly called *destructive distillation*, produces liquid and gaseous fuels that are much easier to transport than wood.

Garbage

If you could measure the amount of garbage you throw out that is made of plant or animal material, you would discover that the amount is quite high. Although most people don't realize it, this type of biomass garbage can be burned to produce heat. It can also be heated in the absence of oxygen (destructive distillation) to produce non-solid fuels, such as methane gas. Fermentation is another process of producing methane gas fuel from garbage. Fermentation occurs when tiny organisms, such as yeast or bacteria, act on plant and animal material in the absence of oxygen. Refer to Figure 17.11.

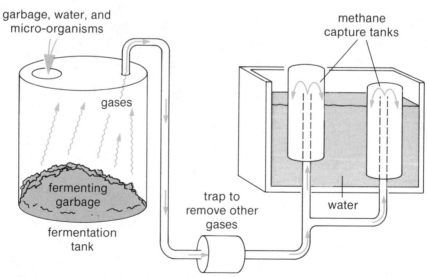

Figure 17.11 *The fermentation of biomass garbage produces methane gas that can be used as a fuel.*

Incinerators

An **incinerator** is a device that burns solid waste at a high temperature. Incineration is the most common means of waste disposal in Canadian cities. Refer to Figure 17.12. The heat given off by this burning can be used to heat buildings or generate electricity. In this way, all the heat is not wasted. A disadvantage of burning waste is that it produces pollution. But the high-temperature burning produces less pollution than low-temperature burning.

Self-check

1. Make a list of six ways of using waste to conserve energy.
2. Describe what the energy is used for when wood or garbage is heated
   (a) in the presence of oxygen
   (b) in the absence of oxygen.
3. What types of fuel are produced when wood undergoes destructive distillation? Why are these fuels more convenient than the original wood?
4. Besides conserving energy, what advantages can you think of for some of the uses of waste materials described in this section?

Figure 17.12 *This incinerator receives solid wastes from both domestic and industrial sources. It burns these wastes at very high temperatures.*

Choosing Alternative Energy Resources

In this chapter, you have learned how energy can be conserved and produced from waste materials. Earlier in this unit (Chapter 15), you studied sources of energy, including fossil fuels and alternative resources. Some new, alternative resources are still in the research and planning stages so their importance may not be known for several years. To complete this unit, you will be asked in Activity 17C to consider which resources provide the greatest advantages for the future.

In order to answer the questions in Activity 17C, you will have to review the features of various energy resources. To do this, refer to Table 15.2 (Non-renewable Energy Resources) and Table 15.3 (Renewable Energy Resources). You will also have to consider the energy situation in your local area. For example, one of the questions asks whether or not the resource is convenient. Be sure to consider your own location and situation when you answer this question. Refer also to Figure 17.13.

Figure 17.13 *Some of the biggest electric generating stations in the world use nuclear fission as the source of energy. The station shown here has eight nuclear reactor buildings. It is located on the north shore of Lake Ontario. Producing electricity this way has some disadvantages, including the problem of nuclear waste. Photographs of other energy resources were shown in Chapter 15.*

Problem

Which alternative energy resources are best for the future?

Materials

Procedure

1. Set up a table based on Table 17.2. If possible, add more non-fossil energy resources to the vertical list.
2. Rate each resource (using + or -) by considering each of the questions from (a) to (h). Add one or two of your own questions.
    (a) Is it renewable?
    (b) Is it plentiful?
    (c) Is it continuous?
    (d) Is it clean and convenient?
    (e) Is the technology needed currently available?
    (f) Is it inexpensive to use?
    (g) Is it safe for the environment?
    (h) Can it be used to operate automobiles?

3. Add up the total (+) and (-) scores for each resource, and place the totals in the table.

Observations

1. Which of the questions asked in Procedure step 2 do you think is the most important? Why?
2. Which question do you think is the least important? Why?
3. Do you think this rating system is fair? Explain your answer.
4. List the resources in order of most acceptable to least acceptable. Is one resource clearly superior to the others? Explain.

Questions

1. Do you think we should research only the top-ranked resources listed in this activity? Explain.
2. Which resources do you think will be most important in the future of the world? of your province? Explain.
3. Which resources might provide most of the energy for transportation in the future? Explain.

Table 17.2 *Summary Table for Activity 17C*

NON-FOSSIL ENERGY RESOURCES	QUESTIONS ABOUT QUALITY										TOTAL	
	a	b	c	d	e	f	g	h	i	j	(+)	(-)
Biomass fuel												
Wind												
Running water												
Solar energy												
Tidal energy												
Geothermal energy												
Nuclear fission												
Nuclear fusion												

Chapter Objectives

NOW THAT YOU HAVE COMPLETED THIS CHAPTER, CAN YOU DO THE FOLLOWING?	FOR REVIEW, TURN TO SECTION
1. Describe at least ten ways in which individuals can reduce the consumption of energy and resources.	17.1
2. Explain what is meant by a conserver society.	17.2
3. List ways in which governments and industries are helping conserve energy in transportation, housing, and electric appliances.	17.2
4. Describe how to experimentally compare the insulating qualities of various materials.	17.2
5. Describe how reusing and recycling help conserve both natural resources and energy.	17.3
6. Describe ways of using wastes to help conserve energy.	17.4
7. Compare the advantages of various non-fossil energy resources.	17.5

Words to Know

conserver society
reusing
recycling
incinerator

Tying It Together

1. Describe one important way of conserving energy for each of the following:
   (a) personal washing
   (b) using a refrigerator
   (c) washing dishes
   (d) washing clothes
   (e) transportation
   (f) home heating
   (g) home air conditioning
   (h) cooking food
2. What are the main concerns of a conserver society?
3. (a) What is the function of home insulation?
   (b) List examples of materials that are good insulators.
4. What is meant by the term "an energy-efficient house"?
5. An experiment is performed to compare the insulating qualities of three different materials, A, B, and C. It is discovered that B is the best insulator and C is the poorest. Assuming the experiment is performed in a similar way to Activity 17B, sketch a graph of what the results of this experiment would look like.
6. Reusing, recycling, and producing energy from waste are three methods of energy conservation. Explain your choices.
   (a) Which one requires the greatest co-operation of all members of a conserver society (individuals, industries, and governments)?
   (b) Which one is easiest for individuals to do on a daily basis?
   (c) Which one is mostly the responsibility of industries and governments?
7. Describe how liquid or gaseous fuels can be made from wood or garbage.
8. How can the heat produced by incineration help conserve energy?

Applying Your Knowledge

1. If you were buying a car, what gasoline consumption rate would you consider to be good from the viewpoint of a conserver society? Explain your answer. (The units for this answer are litres per 100 kilometres.)
2. An R-2000 house has an air ventilation system to provide fresh air for the occupants. It also has separate air supplies for such devices as a furnace and fireplace. Explain why these separate air supplies would be very important.
3. How could your knowledge of insulation be applied to determining the insulating qualities of various clothing materials?
4. Describe ways in which your school could and/or should contribute to the concept of a conserver society.
5. In Activity 17C you compared non-fossil energy resources in terms of the world's future. Of the resources named in that activity, which one would likely be best in your area? Why?

Projects for Investigation

1. Describe an experiment you could perform to compare the amount of hot water you need for a bath with the amount you need for a shower. Discuss your ideas with your teacher. Then carry out and report on the experiment.
2. Various countries, such as Ireland and the U.S.S.R., have used peat as a heating fuel for many years. An excellent source of information on this topic is the article entitled "Mysteries of the Bog" by Louise E. Levathes. It appears in the March 1987 issue of *National Geographic Magazine*. Another source is entitled "Peat in Ontario." It is available from the Ontario Ministry of Energy. Explain what peat is, how it was formed, its possible energy uses, and the advantages and disadvantages of its widespread use.

3. Write a letter to the Manager, Canadian Waste Materials Exchange, Ontario Research Foundation, Sheridan Park Research Community, Mississauga, Ontario, L5K 9Z9. Request information on this program, including the categories of waste that are handled, some of the most difficult wastes to handle, the success of the program, and the problems of the program. Request a recent copy of their bulletin. Organize a class discussion about their program.
4. Part of the R-2000 program is testing the air quality in homes. The testing covers three main items: the rate of air exchange, the capability of the ventilation system, and the levels of three indoor air pollutants—formaldehyde, nitrogen dioxide, and radon gas. Research and report on how the R-2000 homes compare with conventional homes in these items.
5. It is possible to recycle your own paper from old newsprint. Obtain the instructions from your teacher. Set up the procedure carefully and have it checked with your teacher before beginning. What recycled paper have you used?

Unit 5: The Wise Use of Resources

MATCH

In your notebook, write the letters (a) to (i). Beside each letter, write the number of the word in the right column that corresponds to each description in the left column.

(a) energy possessed by water at the top of a falls
(b) SI unit of energy
(c) energy available from ancient life forms
(d) earth's most important energy resource
(e) using the same item more than once
(f) SI unit of power
(g) using waste to make new material
(h) measure of output energy/input energy
(i) change of energy from one form to another

1. nuclear potential energy
2. incinerator
3. geothermal energy
4. watt
5. conversion
6. fossil fuels
7. recycling
8. solar energy
9. joule
10. efficiency
11. reusing
12. gravitational potential energy

MULTIPLE CHOICE

In your notebook, write the numbers 1 to 10. Beside each number, write the letter of the best choice.

1. In almost all processes and devices, the greatest amount of waste energy becomes
   (a) radiant energy
   (b) chemical potential energy
   (c) thermal energy
   (d) electrical energy.
2. Which of the following is *not* a property of an R-2000 home?
   (a) It has good insulation.
   (b) It costs less to build than a conventional home.
   (c) Whenever possible, it faces south.
   (d) It has good air quality.

3. Allowing radiant energy from the sun to heat water in a swimming pool is an example of
   (a) passive solar heating
   (b) using synthetics
   (c) incineration
   (d) recycling.
4. An electric device operates with an efficiency of 85%. This means that the percentage of waste energy is
   (a) 85%
   (b) 0%
   (c) 100%
   (d) 15%.
5. Which of the following energy resources is obtained directly from solar energy?
   (a) wind energy
   (b) biomass energy
   (c) hydraulic energy
   (d) tidal energy
6. Incineration is an example of the use of
   (a) nuclear potential energy
   (b) chemical potential energy
   (c) geothermal energy
   (d) hydraulic energy.
7. An old motorcycle consumes 100 MJ of energy for every 20 MJ of output energy it provides. What is the efficiency of the motorcycle?
   (a) 80%
   (b) 20%
   (c) 100 MJ
   (d) 20 MJ
8. The consumption of a certain energy resource doubles every 10 years. After 30 years, the consumption has increased by
   (a) 2 times
   (b) 4 times
   (c) 6 times
   (d) 8 times.
9. Which of the following is considered to be a renewable energy resource?
   (a) nuclear fusion
   (b) coal
   (c) natural gas
   (d) petroleum

10. A 100 W light bulb is operated for 24 h. How much electrical energy is consumed?
    (a) 2400 kW·h
    (b) 240 kW·h
    (c) 24 kW·h
    (d) 2.4 kW·h

TRUE/FALSE

Write the numbers 1 to 10 in your notebook. Beside each number, write T if the statement is true and F if the statement is false. For each false statement, rewrite it as a true statement.

1. The discovery of X rays is an example of technology.
2. A conserver society uses both energy and natural resources wisely.
3. A gasoline consumption rate of 22 L/100 km is poor for an average family car.
4. Uranium will be the first non-renewable resource to be used up.
5. Wool is an example of a synthetic material.
6. Burning garbage is an example of the use of biomass energy.
7. Styrofoam provides better insulation than an equal thickness of plywood.
8. Gasoline engines have a higher efficiency than electric motors.
9. Coal, biomass, natural gas, and wind energy are all examples of renewable energy resources.
10. Discoveries are examples of science, whereas inventions are examples of technology.

FOR DISCUSSION

Read the paragraph below and answer the questions that follow.

Ontario consumes more energy than any other province in Canada. Much of Ontario's consumption goes to industrial use. The following table indicates the portion of industrial energy consumption in Ontario used for various purposes.

INDUSTRIAL USE OF ENERGY	PORTION OF TOTAL INDUSTRIAL ENERGY INPUT
Direct or indirect heat for such purposes as melting metals or producing steam in boilers	55%
Driving motors	17%
Producing petrochemicals such as plastics and ammonia for fertilizer	13%
Producing lubricants, waxes, asphalt, etc.	8%
For utilities such as lighting and space heating	7%

1. (a) According to the table, which form of energy requires by far the greatest amount of input energy?
   (b) How does this fact relate to energy consumption discussed throughout this unit?
2. Give an example of one industry that
   (a) uses heat directly
   (b) uses heat indirectly
   (c) requires motors to be driven.
3. Describe ways in which Ontario's industries could waste less heat and thus use the energy to produce greater amounts of useful products.

Environmental Chemistry: Chemicals, Air, and Water

The products of industrial plants such as the one shown on page 336 make it possible for you to read a newspaper, a magazine, or even a book such as this one. Many of the products of industry improve our quality of living. But such gains are not without cost. Every day, chemical pollutants affect the air we breathe, the water we drink, and the earth we live on.

Who is responsible for these pollutants? How do they affect the biosphere? Are there ways to control them? These important questions are the focus of this unit.

The Air We Breathe

Key Ideas

- A supply of clean air is essential to most living things.
- Many different kinds of pollutants affect the air we breathe.
- Air pollution is a product of our society, its industries, and transportation methods.
- There are ways to control and/or reduce air pollution.

O ne of the bad things was that you could be standing right by your house and not know it, for you could hardly see your hand in front of you."

The person who said this was speaking about the smog that settled over London, England, on December 5, 1952. This thick, dense smog lasted for four days. During this time, over 4000 people died as a result of the smog.

Smog is an example of air pollution. Air pollution isn't always as visible as the smog that took so many lives in England. But it can be just as damaging and deadly. In this chapter, you will investigate some of the air pollutants that affect our environment. You will find out where they come from, what their effects are, and some methods for controlling them.

The Air around Us

Air is a mixture of different gases. Table 18.1 shows several of the gases contained in clean, dry air.

Table 18.1 *Average Composition of Clean, Dry Air*

GAS	PERCENTAGE BY VOLUME
Nitrogen	78.09
Oxygen	20.94
Argon	0.9
Carbon dioxide	0.03
Hydrogen	0.01
Neon	0.001

The different components of air—especially carbon dioxide, oxygen, and nitrogen—have many important uses. For example,

- **Carbon dioxide** is used by plants in photosynthesis.
- **Oxygen** and carbon dioxide dissolve in water for use by both aquatic plants and animals. Oxygen is essential for most living things. It is also needed for the *combustion* (burning) of the fuels that drive our vehicles and heat our homes.
- **Nitrogen** is an important nutrient for plants.

In Unit One, you learned about cycles in nature such as the water cycle and the carbon cycle. These natural cycles help make substances such as carbon dioxide and nitrogen available to living things. But a problem occurs when *too much* of these substances is contained in the air.

Table 18.1 shows you the most common components of clean air. Clean air is hard to find, especially in our cities. Air is usually contaminated with a variety of other substances or *pollutants*. You will find out about these in the next section.

Self-check

1. List four major components of clean air in order from the most plentiful to the least plentiful.
2. Draw either a bar graph or a pie chart showing the components of air as listed in Table 18.1.
3. State the importance of the following components of air:
   (a) carbon dioxide
   (b) oxygen
   (c) nitrogen

Air Pollution

Anything that is added to the environment and that causes harm to living things is **pollution**. Pollution can be too much of an otherwise harmless substance, or it can be a small amount of a harmful one. See Figure 18.1.

In Canada, an **air pollutant** is defined as something that has one or all of these effects:

1. It endangers the health, safety, or welfare of people.
2. It interferes with the normal enjoyment of life or property.
3. It endangers the health of other animals.
4. It causes damage to plant life.

Air pollutants may be found in every region of the world today. Many of these substances were once thought to be harmless. People assumed they were conveniently "blown away" by the wind. In fact, it is the major wind systems circling the earth that spread these pollutants throughout the atmosphere. See Figure 18.2 (a).

Figure 18.1 *Name the source and kind of pollution in each of these photographs.*

Figure 18.2 *A simplified view of global wind patterns. Winds are the result of three factors: the amount of solar radiation striking the earth, the distribution of oceans and continents, and the rotation of the earth.*

(a) *The major winds on earth are the trade winds, which blow toward the tropics, and the westerlies, which blow in high latitudes (except near the poles). There are also local winds caused by heating differences due to land, sea, or mountains.*

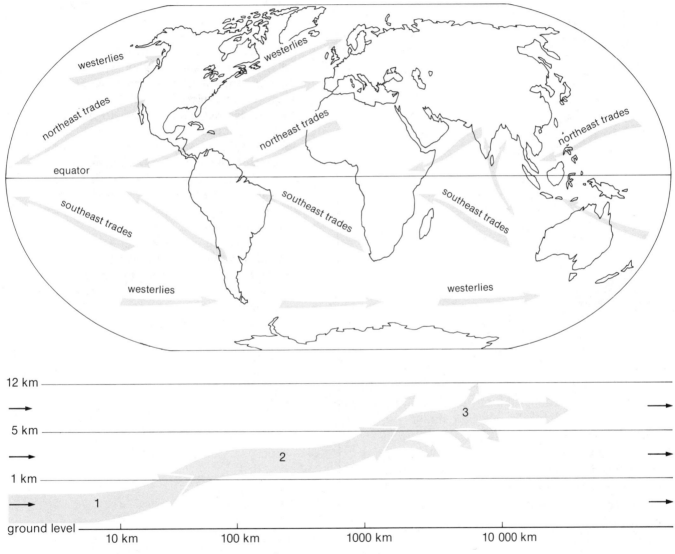

1. Heavier pollutant particles settle due to gravity.

2. Higher in the atmosphere, precipitation removes some pollutants, which fall back to earth dissolved in rain or snow.

3. Much higher in the atmosphere, pollutants may spread for hundreds or thousands of kilometres.

Most of the sources of air pollution are in urban (city) areas of the world. Figure 18.2 (b) shows the activities that commonly result in air pollution.

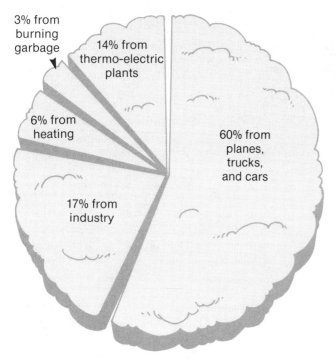

3% from burning garbage

14% from thermo-electric plants

6% from heating

60% from planes, trucks, and cars

17% from industry

Figure 18.2 (b) *Air pollution results from these activities.*

There are two general kinds of air pollutants: gases and particulates. Some of the major polluting gases are carbon monoxide, nitrogen oxides, hydrocarbons, and sulphur oxides. You will be learning more about these. **Particulates** are tiny particles in the air. They include such substances as soot and fly ash, lead, zinc, arsenic, dust, pollen, and fine mists of suspended liquid aerosols.

Challenge

Predict areas near or in your school where you might expect to find the greatest pollution due to particles settling from the air. Particles, as well as gases, result from the burning of many substances. Now, to test your prediction, collect particulate pollution from several different locations. One way is to lay cellophane tape with the sticky side up at each location. Another is to spread a thin coat of oil or grease on a microscope slide. In either case, the particles will cling to the material you use. Be certain you label each particle collector that you decide to use.

Decide how long you want to leave the materials that you wish to compare. After bringing the pieces of tape or microscope slides back to your classroom, observe each with a hand lens or a microscope.

Determine a system of comparison. For example, you might devise a three-point scale showing heavy to moderate to light pollution. If your class decides to *quantify* the results, you will have to find a way to count a random sample of the particles on your particle collectors.

You saw in Figure 18.2 that 60% of air pollution comes from automobiles. The exhaust pipes release gases produced by the incomplete combustion of fuel. In this activity, you will discover how these gases affect some life forms.

Problem

What is the effect of automobile exhaust on plants?

Materials

plants in small flower pots (suggested: 2 each of weeds, chrysanthemums, geraniums, ivy, begonia, radish seedlings)
wide mouth jars with lids large enough to fit over the plants
car or truck (preferably one *without* a catalytic converter)

CAUTION This activity involves collecting vehicle exhaust fumes. It is vital that extreme care be taken both outside and inside the classroom. If you suffer from any kind of respiratory problem, make sure you inform your teacher.

Procedure

1. Design a table to record your observations.
2. Select two of the same kind of plants. Examine the plants carefully. Mark in your notebook any sign of disfiguration or dead leaves on either plant.
3. *A teacher must be present for steps 3, 4, and 5.* Your teacher will start up a vehicle engine in the parking lot (Figure 18.3). One student in each pair will hold one of the open jars *above* the exhaust. Be sure not to cover the opening. After 10 s of collecting the exhaust fumes, quickly put the lid on the jar. After each student's jar has been filled, your teacher will turn off the engine. Return, with your jars, to the classroom.

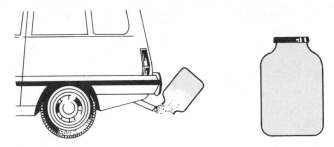

Figure 18.3 *The jar should be filled carefully with exhaust fumes.*

4. Place one air-filled jar and one exhaust-filled jar upside down on the counter. Holding the lid flat on the counter, unscrew one of the jars and set it *mouth down* nearby. Put the potted plant on the lid and quickly replace the jar. Then screw the jar tightly onto the lid. Label the jar with your initials, the date, and the contents. See Figure 18.4. Repeat the procedure for the other jar.

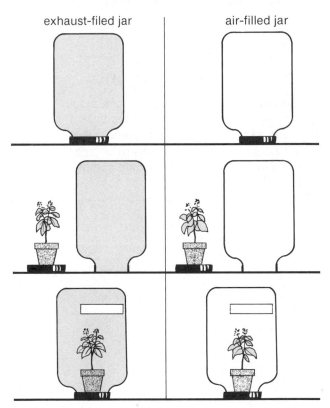

exhaust-filed jar   air-filled jar

Figure 18.4 *Set-up for Activity 18A*

5. Repeat steps 2–4 for each type of plant to be tested.
6. Leave the jars in place over the plants for at least one day.
7. When the time is up, open the jars and examine the plants. Note any new details about their conditions and record them in your table.

Observations

1. (a) In what ways were the plants affected?
   (b) What caused these effects?
2. Which plants were most affected by the exhaust fumes and which were least affected?

Questions

1. What was the purpose of putting one of each pair of plants in the jar containing air only?
2. Do you think this activity proves that exhaust fumes affect plants? Explain your answer.

Ideas and Applications

Laws differ, but in some provinces, black smoke densities are illegal at *any* time. They are used by the Waste Management Branches in various provinces to measure degrees of pollution. Inspectors investigate complaints from the public.

Sources of Air Pollution

Where do polluting gases and particulates come from? Figure 18.5 and the text that follows show the main sources of air pollution in Canada.

CARBON MONOXIDE

Carbon monoxide gas is odourless, invisible, and poisonous. It is produced by the incomplete combustion of fuels.

NITROGEN OXIDES

Nitrogen oxides are formed when fuels are burned at high temperatures in engines and furnaces. They are a mixture of various compounds of nitrogen and oxygen. Nitrogen oxides react chemically with sunlight to produce ozone. Ozone is a deadly gas.

HYDROCARBONS

Hydrocarbons are compounds made up of hydrogen and carbon. These compounds are released when fuels such as gasoline are burned and when products such as paint or varnish evaporate.

SULPHUR DIOXIDE

Sulphur dioxide and other sulphur oxide gases are formed when oxygen and sulphur combine during a chemical change. Sulphur dioxide is a clear, colourless gas with a pungent, suffocating odour that is detectable only in high concentrations. It is highly corrosive and is one of the major causes of acid precipitation.

Self-check

1. What is pollution?
2. What is the definition of an air pollutant?
3. Name the two general kinds of air pollutants, and give three examples of each.
4. Name the four sources of air pollution, and give two examples of each.

Figure 18.5 *Main sources of air pollution in Canada*

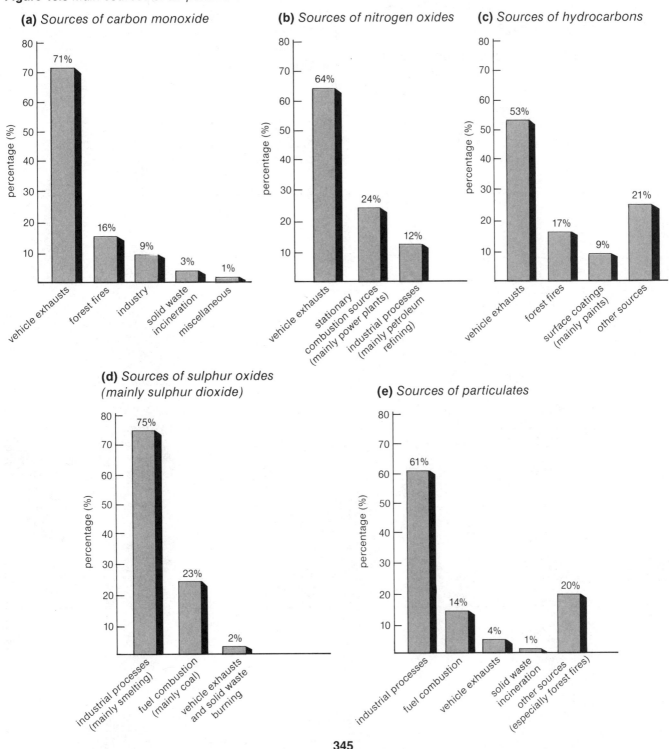

(a) *Sources of carbon monoxide*

(b) *Sources of nitrogen oxides*

(c) *Sources of hydrocarbons*

(d) *Sources of sulphur oxides (mainly sulphur dioxide)*

(e) *Sources of particulates*

Air Pollution and Acid Precipitation

Acid precipitation is a problem that you have no doubt heard about in previous studies or through the news media. This particular form of air pollution causes changes in fresh water rivers and lakes. It kills fish and other animals in the water. It also changes the way plant life grows both in water and on land. See Figure 18.6.

As well as threatening living things, acid precipitation causes severe damage to stone buildings and exposed metal surfaces. It can also release toxic substances such as mercury into the soil and water.

Figure 18.6 *Winds carry the pollutants that cause acid precipitation over long distances.*

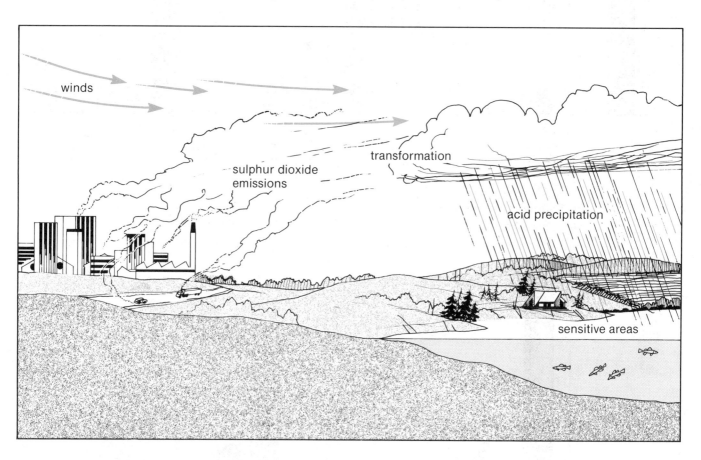

What Is Acid Precipitation?

All the processes shown in Figure 18.7 produce large quantities of sulphur dioxide gas and mixtures of several nitrogen oxide gases. When these gases enter the atmosphere and dissolve in water vapour, they change into products that produce acids. These acids fall to the earth in the form of precipitation—rain or snow.

In the rest of this section, you will investigate the properties and effects of acid precipitation. But first, you need to know more about acids and their chemical opposites, bases. You also need to know how these substances can be identified.

Figure 18.7 *How do these processes help cause acid precipitation?*

Acids and Bases

Whether you know it or not, many of the substances you use every day are acids or bases. What are these important compounds?

Acids are sour-tasting substances that always dissolve in water. They are used everywhere from cooking to industry to cleaning. Common examples are the acetic acid in vinegar, the citric acid in lemons, the sulphuric acid in automobile storage batteries, and the hydrochloric acid in some industrial cleaners. See Figure 18.8. *Never taste an unknown substance.*

Figure 18.8 *Common products that contain acids*

Bases also dissolve in water. Common examples of bases include the ammonia and sodium hydroxide (lye) found in household cleaners, the lime used to make white lines on playing fields, and sodium hydrogen carbonate (baking soda). See Figure 18.9. When bases are combined with acids, the bases *neutralize*, or cancel, the properties of both the acid and the base.

We can describe how acidic or basic a substance is using the **pH scale**. See Figure 18.10. For example, normal rain has a pH of about 5.6, while acid rain has a pH lower than 5.6. The *lower* the pH, the more *acidic* the rain. A drop in pH of one pH unit means that the acid content has *increased* ten times.

Figure 18.9 *Common products that contain bases*

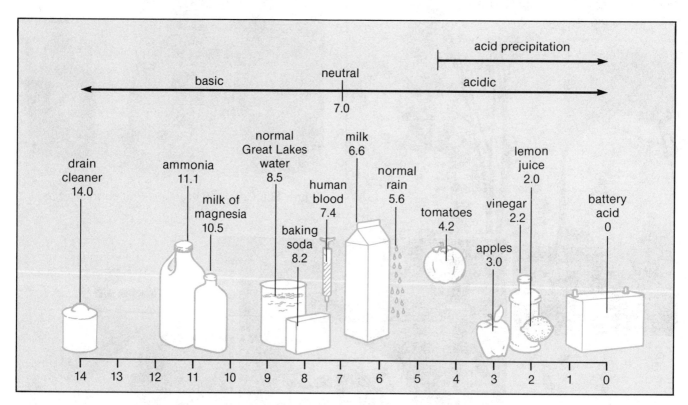

Figure 18.10 *The pH scale. A lower pH reading indicates a more acidic solution. A higher pH reading indicates a more basic solution.*

348

Figure 18.11 (a) *Sources of acid precipitation in North America* **(b)** *Areas in North America that are especially sensitive to acid precipitation. How can areas of northern Canada be sensitive if there are no industries there that produce sulphur oxides and nitrogen oxides?* **(c)** *Sources of acid precipitation that affect Norway and other parts of Europe. What does this tell you about the role of the wind in transporting pollutants?*

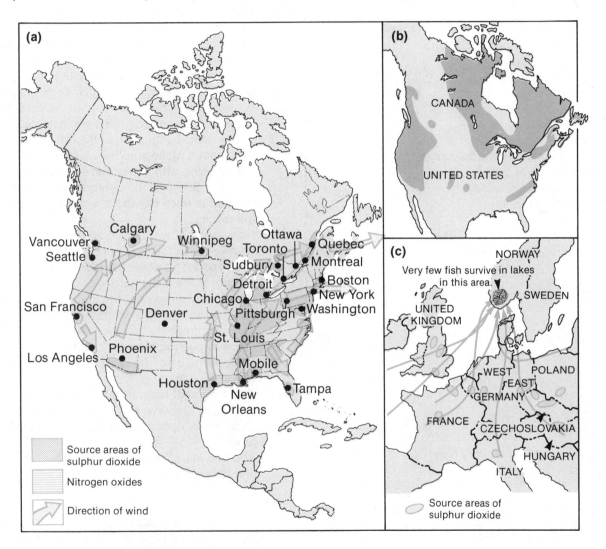

Chemical indicators can be used to detect the presence of acids and bases. The indicators change colour in response to the acidity of the substance. In the next activity, you will practise using chemical indicators. You will also find out about other properties of acids and bases. Then, in Activity 18C, you will investigate the properties of sulphur dioxide gas. Finally, in Activity 18D, you will determine the effects of acid precipitation on soil. See Figure 18.11.

Activity 18B

Problem

How can acids and bases be identified?

Materials

red and blue litmus paper (or pH paper if available)
bromthymol blue indicator solution
phenolphthalein solution
magnesium ribbon
marble chips
6 test tubes
glass rod
watch glass
test solutions including the following:
    dilute hydrochloric acid
    dilute sodium hydroxide
    household ammonia
    vinegar
    baking soda
    clear carbonated beverage

> **CAUTION** Acids and bases can cause damage to the eyes, skin, and clothing. Handle these substances with care as directed by your teacher. Clean up spills immediately with lots of clean water. Do not mix the test solutions.

Procedure

1. Copy Table 18.2 into your notebook to record your observations.

2. In one test tube, place about 1 cm of distilled water. Dissolve a small amount of baking soda into the water.
3. In the remaining test tubes, place about 1 cm of each of the other substances to be tested.
4. Place pieces of blue and red litmus paper on a watch glass. Dip the glass rod into one of the test solutions. Then touch the glass rod to each of the pieces of litmus paper. Note: If pH paper is used instead of litmus paper, compare the colours produced with the chart on the side of the package and record the pH indicated.
5. Repeat step 4 with each of the other test substances. Make sure the glass rod is cleaned before using with a new test substance.
6. Add one or two drops of bromthymol blue solution to each of the test solutions and record the results.
7. Rinse out the test tubes carefully with water (distilled, if possible). Don't let the pieces of litmus paper go down the drain. Capture them and put them in the garbage.
8. Place fresh samples of the materials in the test tubes as described in steps 2 and 3.
9. Test each fresh test solution with one or two drops of phenolphthalein indicator.
10. Once more, carefully rinse and refill the test tubes.
11. Add 1–2 cm of magnesium ribbon to each of the test tubes. Observe and record the results.
12. Once more, rinse the test tubes. Refill the test tubes.
13. Add one marble chip to each test tube. Observe and record the results.

Table 18.2 *Reactions of Acids and Bases for Activity 18B*

SUBSTANCE	BLUE LITMUS	RED LITMUS	BROMTHYMOL BLUE	PHENOLPHTHALEIN	MAGNESIUM	MARBLE CHIP
Vinegar						
Sodium hydroxide						
Etc.						

SAMPLE ONLY

Observations

(see Table 18.2)

1. Sort the substances into two groups based on their reactions with litmus paper.
2. Is the reaction of each group with magnesium similar?
3. Is the reaction of each group with a marble chip similar?

Questions

1. Which of the two groups are acids and which are bases? Explain.
2. If pH paper was available, how do the pH values for each group compare?
3. What class of materials is represented by magnesium?
4. Which types of building materials do marble chips represent?
5. List the properties of acids and bases as found in this activity.
6. If you are handed a sample of a clear liquid, describe how you would safely tell if it is an acid or a base.
7. Prepare a chart that compares the colours of the three indicators in acids, bases, and water.

You have learned that some of the main causes of acid precipitation are the burning of coal and the smelting of sulphur-containing ores. The main acid-causing product of each of these processes is sulphur dioxide gas. In this activity, your teacher will produce a small amount of this gas and you will observe its acidic properties.

Problem

What are the properties of sulphur dioxide gas?

Materials

small pieces of sulphur
distilled water
Bunsen burner
gas bottle
beaker, 250 mL
indicator (litmus, pH paper, or bromthymol blue)
oxygen (if available)
deflagrating spoon
glass cover plate
calcium carbonate (as powdered chalk or marble chips)
fume hood
safety goggles

CAUTION Adequate ventilation is essential for this activity. Sulphur dioxide gas irritates the lungs and will cause breathing problems for people with respiratory problems. It is therefore most important to carefully limit the amount of gas released. Although a fume hood is recommended, this activity can be done safely without a fume hood if the room is *very well* ventilated. Safety goggles must be worn for this activity.

Procedure

1. Your teacher will place about 1 cm of water in the bottom of a clean gas bottle.
2. If oxygen is available, your teacher will fill the gas bottle with oxygen and cover it with a glass plate. If oxygen is not available, the air in the bottle will provide enough oxygen for the burning of sulphur.
3. Your teacher will fill a 250 mL beaker halfway with water.
4. Your teacher will place a small amount of sulphur (about the size of a pea) in a deflagrating spoon. The sulphur will be heated with a Bunsen burner until it ignites. The glass plate of the gas bottle will be slid partly aside and *immediately* the spoon will be lowered about halfway into the gas bottle. See Figure 18.12. Then the glass plate will be replaced quickly to let as little gas escape into the room as possible.

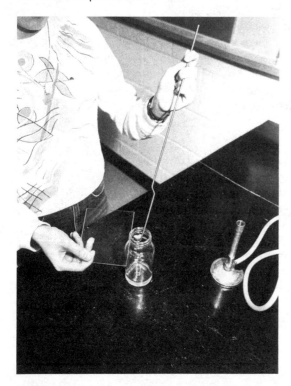

Figure 18.12 *Heating sulphur in a deflagrating spoon. What is the gas produced when sulphur is burned?*

5. When the reaction has stopped, your teacher will quickly slide the glass plate aside, remove the spoon, and replace the plate. Then the spoon will be plunged into the beaker of water to cool it and to stop the burning of sulphur.
6. Keeping the glass plate tightly over the bottle, your teacher will shake the water and gas together. Observe the colour change when an indicator is added.
7. Your teacher will add a small amount of calcium carbonate to the solution and shake the bottle again. Observe any change in the colour of the indicator.

Observations

1. Describe the appearance of the sulphur before heating.
2. If oxygen was used, what change took place in the burning when the spoon was lowered into the bottle?
3. Describe the properties of the gas produced.
4. Describe the colour of the indicator before and after the addition of the calcium carbonate.

Questions

1. Why was the gas shaken with the water before testing with the indicator?
2. This activity is very similar to one method by which acid precipitation is formed.
   (a) In the environment, where does the sulphur dioxide come from?
   (b) Where does the water come from?
   (c) How does the acid solution enter the water and soil of the environment?
3. What was the effect of the calcium carbonate on the sulphur dioxide solution?
4. (a) Where do you think calcium carbonate is found in large quantities in the environment?
   (b) What effect would it have on acid precipitation?

When acid precipitation comes in contact with soils, several things may happen. In some cases, substances in the soil—called *buffers*—can neutralize the effect of the acid. (Which natural substance has already been used in an earlier activity to neutralize an acid?) In other cases, the acid removes important nutrients from the soil by a process called *leaching*. Soil lacking these nutrients cannot support healthy plant life.

Problem

What are the effects of acid precipitation on soil?

Materials

acid precipitation solution (either sulphurous acid solution or vinegar solution with pH of about 4)
potting soil
radish or bean seeds
soil testing kit (to test for pH, phosphorus, nitrogen, and potassium)
paper cups
pH paper
tray

 **CAUTION** Wash your hands after handling the soil and chemicals.

Procedure

1. Copy Table 18.3 in your notebook to record your observations on soil testing.
2. Following the instructions that come with the soil-testing kit, test samples of the potting soil for pH, phosphorus, nitrogen, and potassium.
3. Fill two paper cups to within 2 cm of the top with potting soil. Poke a small hole (for drainage) in the bottom of each cup. Put your name clearly on each cup. Label one cup A and the other cup B.
4. Plant several seeds in each cup. Place both cups in the same location, preferably a sunny window sill, on the tray provided.

5. Water cup A with clean tap water and cup B with the acid precipitation solution. Use equal, measured quantities in each case.
6. Observe the growth of the seedlings for at least two weeks. Whenever the soil seems dry, water the cups with the same solutions in similar quantities as you used before. Record your observations on the condition of the seedlings in a table you have designed yourself.
7. At the end of two weeks, test the soil in each cup with the soil-testing kit. Be careful not to mix the soil from the two cups. Make sure you clean the apparatus carefully between tests.

Observations

Table 18.3 *The Effect of Acid Precipitation on Soil*

	NITROGEN	PHOSPHORUS	POTASSIUM	pH
Initial soil test				
After watering with pure water (cup A)				
After watering with acid precipitation solution (cup B)				

Questions

1. Why is the presence of nitrogen, phosphorus, and potassium important for plants?
2. Why was one set of seedlings watered only with water?
3. What was the effect of the acid precipitation solution on (a) the condition of the plants, and (b) the nutrients in the soil?
4. What substance—found in some soils or at the bottom of some lakes and rivers—would make the effects of acid precipitation less severe? Explain your answer.

Self-check

1. List five properties of acids.
2. Name five common acids and give their uses.
3. List three properties of bases.
4. Name three common bases and give their uses.
5. (a) What are two types of gases that cause acid precipitation?
   (b) Name one source from outside the laboratory for each of these gases.
   (c) What happens to these gases in the atmosphere to turn them into acids?
6. (a) How would you chemically test a lake to see if it has been affected by acid precipitation?
   (b) Is there any other way you could tell if the lake had been affected by acid precipitation? Explain.
7. Name a substance that is often found in soil that will neutralize acid precipitation.
8. (a) Name three important nutrients in soil.
   (b) What effect does acid prcipitation have on these nutrients?

Other Forms of Air Pollution

The Products of Combustion

Most of the fuels that we burn to heat our homes, to power our vehicles, and even to barbecue food are fossil fuels. These fossil fuels include gasoline, diesel fuel, natural gas, fuel oil, propane, and butane. They are all products of the petroleum industry. See Chapter 16, Figure 16.12. The molecules of all these fuels consist of strings of different combinations of carbon and hydrogen atoms called hydrocarbons (Figure 18.13).

Hydrocarbon molecules have similar structures. Therefore, when they burn, they combine with the oxygen in air to produce similar products. In the next activity, you will identify some of these products.

Figure 18.13 *You can make models of hydrocarbon molecules using black spheres to represent carbon atoms and white spheres to represent hydrogen atoms. Methane (on the left) is the main substance in natural gas. Butane (centre) is added to gasoline in winter to make it ignite more easily in vehicle engines. Octane (right) is a high-performance fuel. The actual carbon and hydrogen atoms are so small that 100 000 000 side by side would stretch only about 1 cm!*

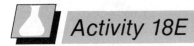

Activity 18E

Problem

What substances are produced when hydrocarbons are burned?

Materials

Bunsen burner
candle
flask, 250 mL
beaker, 250 mL
test tube
watch glass
anhydrous copper(II) sulphate or cobalt chloride
  paper
limewater
glass tube or drinking straw
safety goggles
paper towel
Note: Other hydrocarbon fuels, such as kerosene burned in a kerosene lamp or alcohol lamp, might be added.

CAUTION In steps 4, 8, and 9, do not hold the flask long enough for the outside of the flask to become very warm. Safety goggles must be worn, for this activity.

Procedure

1. Design a table to record your observations.
2. Place either a few crystals of anhydrous copper(II) sulphate or a strip of cobalt chloride paper on a dry watch glass. Add a drop of water and record the changes in colour.
3. Nearly fill the 250 mL flask with cold water and carefully dry the outside surface.
4. Light the Bunsen burner and adjust the flame until no yellow colour is visible. Hold the water-filled flask over the flame for a few seconds.
5. Touch any droplets appearing on the outside of the flask with either a few crystals of anhydrous copper(II) sulphate or a strip of cobalt chloride paper. Record any changes.
6. Place 5 cm of limewater into a test tube and gently "blow bubbles" into it with a glass tube or drinking stop. Stop blowing when a change is visible.
7. Rinse a 250 mL beaker with a few millilitres of limewater. Leave behind enough liquid so that the drops are clearly visible.
8. Turn the beaker upside down and hold it a few centimetres over the Bunsen burner flame to trap any gases produced. Observe and record any changes in the limewater droplets.
9. Adjust the burner flame until its colour becomes quite yellow. Hold the bottom of the beaker a few centimetres over the flame and observe any deposits.
10. Repeat steps 3–9 with a candle or other fossil fuel source.

Observations

1. Describe the colour change that you saw after adding water to the anhydrous copper(II) sulphate or cobalt chloride paper.
2. Describe the droplets that formed on the outside of the cool flask.
3. What change took place when the anhydrous copper(II) sulphate or cobalt chloride paper touched the droplets?
4. Describe the change that took place when you blew through the limewater.
5. What change took place inside the beaker to the droplets of limewater after being exposed to the flame?
6. What deposit did you see forming from the yellow Bunsen burner or candle flame?

1. (a) What is the fuel that is burning in a Bunsen burner?
    (b) Is it a fossil fuel?
    (c) Where does it come from?
2. How can anhydrous copper(II) sulphate or cobalt chloride paper be used to test for the presence of water?
3. (a) What substance was found on the outside of the cold flask after exposing it to the flame?
    (b) Where did the substance come from?
4. (a) What do you do to control the colour of the Bunsen burner flame?
    (b) Why does this affect the flame?
5. What substance did you identify on the outside of the cool flask? How do you know?
6. What substance in your breath caused the change in the limewater?
7. What substance did the limewater detect in the products of burning?
8. (a) What substance was detected in the product of a yellow Bunsen burner or candle flame?
    (b) How can we adjust our fuel burning devices to produce as little of this substance as possible?
    (c) What other advantages are there in carefully adjusting flames?
9. List all the products of burning fossil fuels that you discovered in this activity.

Carbon Dioxide and the Greenhouse Effect

You have probably seen plants growing in a greenhouse. Commercial vegetable growers, for example, use increased temperatures in such buildings to supply lettuce and tomatoes in the middle of a Canadian winter. The warm temperatures inside result from the winter sun. Light energy passes through the glass and is absorbed by the plants. The plants and their surroundings now release heat in the form of infra-red radiation. This type of radiation does not pass through the glass but is reflected by it. Thus, the energy becomes trapped inside the greenhouse, keeping it warm even in winter.

In the atmosphere, carbon dioxide, even though it is a gas, acts in a similar way to the glass of a greenhouse. Light energy passes through the atmosphere and is absorbed by the earth. The earth emits heat in the form of infra-red radiation, which radiates back to the atmosphere. Carbon dioxide in the atmosphere absorbs the infra-red radiation, thus heating up the atmosphere. This is one of the most important functions of carbon dioxide in the atmosphere. Without the assistance of this important gas, our planet would be cooler than it is at present. Scientists estimate that if all the sun's incoming energy were sent back into space, the earth would have an average temperature of about $-24°C$! See Figure 18.14.

Carbon dioxide in the atmosphere is important. But remember that pollution can involve too much of an otherwise harmless substance. After having completed Activity 18E, you know that carbon dioxide is one of the products formed when fossil fuels are burned. So many fossil fuels are being burned at the present time that scientists are worried about the *increasing* amount of carbon dioxide in our atmosphere. They think that increasing amounts of carbon dioxide may act like the glass of a giant, global greenhouse, causing the earth's atmosphere to gradually warm up. This fact is called the **greenhouse effect**. Even a minor increase in worldwide temperatures could have serious effects on the ability of many organisms —plants and animals—to survive.

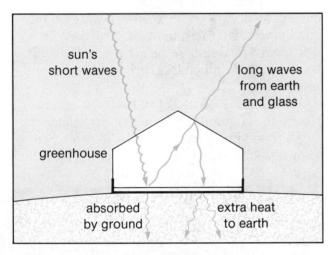

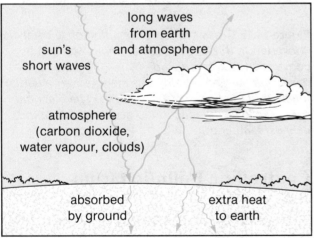

Figure 18.14 *Why is greenhouse effect a good name for the phenomenon shown here?*

Challenge

List as many places as you can where fossil fuels are burned and where carbon dioxide is released into the air. Suggest ways that the amount of carbon dioxide might be reduced.

Air Pollution and the Ozone Layer

Some of the pollutants that we release into the air can have unpredictable indirect effects. Scientists are very concerned about what is happening to the earth's ozone layer.

Ozone is an unstable, toxic form of oxygen. It can be poisonous in large enough concentrations at the earth's surface. But, strangely enough, when ozone lies in the upper atmosphere—about 20 to 50 kilometres above the ground—it provides an essential layer of protection from the sun's damaging ultraviolet radiation. Ultraviolet radiation is the kind of radiation people use to get a suntan. But with prolonged exposure, ultraviolet radiation also causes skin cancer.

There is evidence that the amount of ozone in the atmosphere has been decreasing. Less ozone means more ultraviolet radiation can reach the earth's surface. Many scientists think that the disappearance of this important layer of protection is due to the increasing use of a group of industrial chemicals called *chlorofluorocarbons*. These compounds are found in the propellant gases in some spray cans, in refrigerator cooling systems, and even in the containers in which some fast foods are served. As chlorofluorocarbons break down in the atmosphere, they cause the ozone to change chemically into oxygen. With less protective ozone in the atmosphere, more of the sun's harmful ultraviolet radiation is able to reach the earth's surface.

357

Governments around the world are very concerned about the effects of chlorofluorocarbons in the atmosphere. In 1987, 23 countries endorsed a plan to reduce world consumption of these dangerous compounds by 50% by the year 1999.

Self-check

1. Name two clear, colourless gases that are produced when fossil fuels are burned.
2. Name one solid that is sometimes formed when fossil fuels are burned.
3. How can you test a clear, colourless, odourless liquid to find out if it is water?
4. Describe a chemical test for carbon dioxide.
5. (a) Where is the ozone layer found?
   (b) What does it protect us from?
6. Name two commercial products containing materials that can damage the ozone layer.
7. What potential danger is brought about by the damage to the ozone layer?

Controlling Air Pollution

Pollution from Automobiles

Since the 1970s, automobile manufacturers have been responding to the fact that supplies of fossil fuels are limited and that pollution must be curbed. Most cars on the road today are smaller and lighter than those in use several decades ago. They are also more fuel efficient. Burning less fuel means much less carbon dioxide is produced.

In addition, vehicles now have systems to reduce the amount of carbon monoxide and sulphur and nitrogen oxides they give off. See Figure 18.15.

Figure 18.15 *Cross section of an automobile catalytic converter. In this device, carbon monoxide can be converted to carbon dioxide by mixing the exhaust gases with air and passing this mixture over a bed of finely divided platinum (the catalyst). The platinum catalyst allows the reaction to occur quickly at the exhaust temperature.*

Controlling Pollution from Industry

Early attempts to control emissions from industry included simply building higher smokestacks such as the one shown in Figure 18.16. But a taller smokestack merely puts polluting emissions higher in the atmosphere where prevailing winds may transport them further around the globe. Now, other devices are often installed in smokestacks to reduce the amount of pollution they emit. See Figure 18.17.

Figure 18.16 *Are taller smokestacks the answer to controlling emissions of pollutant gases from industries?*

Figure 18.17 *Two methods for removing pollutants from smokestack emissions*

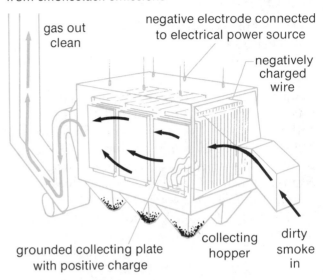

gas out clean

negative electrode connected to electrical power source

negatively charged wire

grounded collecting plate with positive charge

collecting hopper

dirty smoke in

(a) *As exhaust gases pass between the charged plates of an electrostatic precipitator, the tiny solid particles in the gases stick to the plates. They are then collected in the collecting hoppers.*

clean gas out

water spray

dirty smoke in

water and polluting particles out

(b) *As exhaust gases pass through a scrubber, the pollutants dissolve in the water and may be removed.*

Controlling the Effects of Acid Precipitation

Once acid precipitation has fallen, remedies for the damage caused are difficult and expensive. In some cases, if the bedrock surrounding a lake or river contains a great deal of limestone, the effect of the acid is buffered and little harm occurs. Calcium carbonate, which you used in Activity 18B and 18C, is a form of limestone. But if the bedrock is made of granite or similar rock, no buffering takes place and maximum damage occurs. Unfortunately, the Canadian Shield region of Canada rests on bedrock that is primarily granite (Figure 18.18). This region also lies directly in the path of the most severe emissions from the industrialized areas of North America. Recall Figure 18.11 earlier in this chapter.

Once a lake has become acidic, the only remedy is to add a base of some sort to it. Small lakes have been treated with forms of limestone to neutralize the acid. In some very limited cases, liming of lakes has been effective. This is a very expensive process with uncertain long-term effects on the living things in the lake. The only true solution, of course, is to stop the pollution at its source.

Challenge

List as many ways as you can in which burning of fuels is important in industry and in your daily life. For each way, suggest at least one alternative to the burning of the fuel. What effects would each of your suggestions have on the amount and kinds of air pollution produced?

Figure 18.18 *The Canadian Shield region*

The Costs of Controlling Pollution

Once people understand the causes and effects of pollution, many wonder why it is not immediately stopped. For example, why do we still allow industries to release sulphur dioxide into the air? Why do we still burn so many fossil fuels? Do we really need chlorofluorocarbons?

There are no easy answers to these questions. Many considerations must be taken into account. Some deal with our own lifestyle, some with the economy of our country, and some with international politics. On the one hand, governments must consider the health risk posed by poor pollution controls. On the other hand, owners of industry must also be considered. If the government imposes strict pollution controls on industries, industries may choose to leave Canada. This will result in the loss of jobs and will hurt Canada's economy. Figure 18.19 shows the pressures governments must face when considering the issue of pollution control.

Another important factor is the international nature of the problem. For example, the United States produces 25 700 000 tonnes of sulphur dioxide each year. Canada produces about one-fifth this amount—about 5 000 000 tonnes. Scientists estimate that about 50% of Canada's acid precipitation originates in the United States. Once pollution reaches the upper atmosphere, it is affected by the wind and global circulation patterns. Pollution does not respect the boundaries between countries. As a result, when politicians are wrestling with the decisions of how to control air pollution, they must consider the decisions made by their international neighbours. They may even have to consider trying to influence the political decisions on pollution made in other countries.

Everyone can see the need to improve the quality of the air we breathe. The methods used to carry out this improvement and the decisions involved are not simple. There is increasing hope, however, that we will make progress. The future looks much brighter.

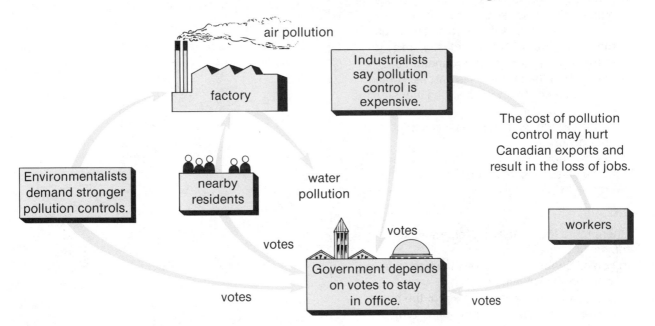

Figure 18.19 *Pressures facing the government*

Air pollution can be controlled by individuals like you and your family, by communities of people and the politicians they elect to represent them, and by industry. You know that the decisions which are made to reduce pollution have many consequences. In this activity, you will work in groups to examine some of these decisions and to look at their consequences for individuals, communities, and industry.

Problem

What are the consequences of some pollution control decisions?

Materials

Procedure

1. Work in groups of three or four.
2. Your teacher will assign each group a source of air pollution. The task of your group is to do the following:
   (a) Propose more than one method to reduce the emissions that cause the problem.
   (b) List some decisions that would have to be made by government, by industry, and by individuals to carry out these methods.
   (c) For each of the above decisions, list some consequences that will affect the industry, the economy, and individuals.
   (d) Decide which method is most acceptable to your group.
   (e) Report your decision and your reasons for it to the class for discussion.

Questions

1. Is there more than one acceptable solution to the problem you investigated?
2. Why do all people not agree on the best solution to air pollution problems?
3. Did the group change its mind about the best solution as the discussion continued? Why or why not?

Self-check

1. How can the amount of pollution released into the air by automobiles be reduced?
2. Why are taller smokestacks not a solution to the acid precipitation problem?
3. Name at least one method of controlling air pollution and describe how it works.
4. Why is the problem of air pollution so difficult to solve easily?

Ideas and Applications

In "brown air" cities, such as Mexico City, Athens, Los Angeles, and Sydney, photochemical smog is a very serious health problem. While ordinary smog is a combination of smoke and fog, *photochemical smog* involves the action of sunlight on suspended chemical pollutants. The combination results in what might be called a photochemical haze. The chemicals that are most susceptible to the action of sunlight are the nitrogen oxides and hydrocarbons.

Chapter Objectives

NOW THAT YOU HAVE COMPLETED THIS CHAPTER, CAN YOU DO THE FOLLOWING?	FOR REVIEW, TURN TO SECTION
1. List the names and proportions of the substances that make up clean, dry air.	18.1
2. State the importance of air to the environment.	18.1
3. Name four common air pollutants and their sources or effects.	18.2
4. Give the properties of acids and bases and perform tests to identify them.	18.3
5. Explain how acid precipitation is formed.	18.3
6. Describe other forms of air pollution.	18.4
7. Explain how each form of air pollution might be controlled.	18.5
8. State at least one consequence of each type of air pollution control.	18.5

Words to Know

carbon dioxide
oxygen
nitrogen
pollution
air pollutant
particulate
carbon monoxide
nitrogen oxides
hydrocarbon

sulphur dioxide
acid precipitation
acid
base
pH scale
acid-base indicator
indicator
greenhouse effect
ozone

Tying It Together

1. (a) List the four most plentiful gases in clean, dry air.
   (b) For each gas listed in (a), briefly state why it is important to us on earth.
2. (a) Name four common air pollutants.
   (b) State at least one source for each pollutant you named in (a).
3. What are the harmful effects of acid precipitation?

4. List four common acids mentioned in this chapter, and add two others not listed in the chapter.
5. List four common bases mentioned in this chapter, and add two others not listed in the chapter.
6. (a) What is the pH scale?
   (b) How is the pH scale used to measure the amount of acid or base present in a solution?
7. List four properties of acids and three properties of bases.
8. Name three important nutrients found in soil.
9. (a) Explain how a greenhouse provides the warmth needed for plants to grow even in winter.
   (b) In what ways is carbon dioxide gas similar to the glass of a greenhouse?
10. Why has the amount of carbon dioxide in the air been increasing?
11. Describe laboratory tests for the following:
    (a) acid
    (b) base
    (c) water
    (d) carbon dioxide

12. Why is the ozone layer important for life on earth?
13. What changes have been made in the design of automobiles to reduce air pollution?
14. How can pollution emitted from smokestacks be controlled and/or reduced?
15. Why does the addition of limestone to acidic lakes reduce the effect of acid precipitation?

Applying Your Knowledge

1. (a) Government agencies spend a great deal of time and resources to monitor air quality on a daily basis. Why is it important for the public to have this information?
   (b) If air pollution is found to be particularly severe on a given day, what actions could be taken by the following: individuals, industry, and government?
2. Many of the lakes that have been killed by acid precipitation look very clear and clean. Why is this not surprising?
3. If the greenhouse effect will raise the temperature on earth a few degrees, is this not a good thing? Will this not simply relieve the unpleasantness of winter weather in countries such as Canada? What harmful effects will this increase in temperature bring?
4. Think of a source of air pollution that is not as severe as it once was. What has happened to cause this change?
5. Based on Unit Five, where you learned about the wise use of resources, do you think that the answer to the air pollution problem lies in the use of renewable energy resources such as wind energy, nuclear energy, and solar energy? Explain your answer.

Projects for Investigation

1. There are many other sources of air pollution besides those discussed in this chapter. These include cigarette smoke, lead, radon gas, cadmium, mercury, and asbestos. Select one of these (or another air pollutant of your choice) and find answers to the following:
   (a) What are the sources of this form of pollution?
   (b) What are its effect on the biotic and abiotic components of the environment?
   (c) How is this form of pollution measured?
   (d) What methods exist for controlling it?
   (e) What are some of the consequences of this control?
2. Find out how air quality is monitored in your municipality. Design a method of monitoring air quality in your classroom and keep a record over a period of time.

The Water We Drink

Key Ideas

- A clean supply of water on earth is essential for life.
- Being able to measure pollution is an important safeguard for health.
- Polluted water can be treated to make it safe for use.
- Water pollution can be controlled.

You know that the air we breathe is important to life on this planet. Water is also essential. The same kinds of pollutants that threaten the supply of clean air also threaten our lakes, rivers, and oceans. These threats come from industry, from our homes, and from the way we live. Some of the pollutants dissolve directly into the water from the air. Some are washed into the water from factories and our homes. No matter how they get there, these substances can affect the safety of drinking water or harm fish and other sources of food found in the waters of our planet. These contaminated food supplies can then cause severe harm to the people and other organisms that depend on them.

In this chapter, you will look at several water pollutants, their sources, the problems that they cause, and what can be done to control water pollution.

Our Water Supply

Figure 19.1 shows the earth's water resources. Canada is fortunate because it has a large supply of fresh water in the thousands of rivers and lakes that cover the land. In fact, Canada has almost 10% of the world's supply of fresh water! It is this fresh water that we depend upon to sustain human life.

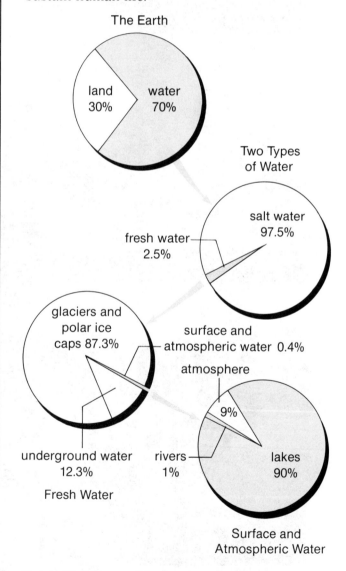

Figure 19.1 *The earth's water resources*

You have already learned in Unit One how water on earth circulates in a continuous **water cycle**. See Figure 19.2. Water travels through a cycle of *evaporation* (into air), *condensation* (into clouds), *precipitation* (as rain or snow), and *drainage* (through and over the ground). How do Canadians use fresh water? In Activity 19A, you will investigate this question.

Ideas and Applications

An aquifer is an underground body of water. The largest aquifer in the world, the Ogallala Aquifer, is located in the southwestern United States. It was left behind at the end of the last Ice Age, about 10 000 years ago. Vast quantities of water from this aquifer are used to produce crops and raise cattle. Scientists who are observing consumption patterns have estimated that this source may be dried up in less than forty years at the present rate of depletion.

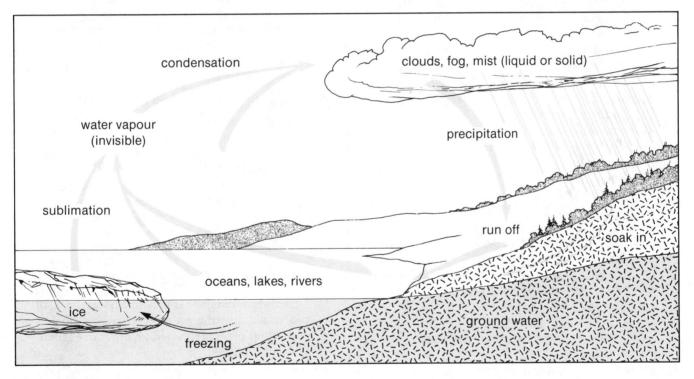

Figure 19.2 *The water cycle*

Problem

What is the estimated volume of water you (and all Canadians) use in one year?

Materials

You may find a ruler and calculator useful for this activity.

Procedure

1. Determine a logical value in litres for each of the quantities listed below. Describe how you made the measurements. Show your calculations wherever possible.
   (a) the volume of water that would fill a bathtub
   (b) the volume of water contained in the tank of a toilet
2. Estimate the volume of water (in litres) you use per week for each activity listed below. Show how you obtain your answers. For the last four activities, find your own portion of the family consumption.
   (a) personal washing (including baths and/or showers)
   (b) flushing the toilet
   (c) drinking
   (d) brushing your teeth
   (e) dish washing
   (f) clothes washing
   (g) watering plants and/or the lawn
   (h) other activities (explain)
3. Find the sum of your estimates in step 2. This will give you an estimate in litres for the water you consume personally each week.
4. Multiply your answer in step 3 by 52. This will give you the average volume of water you consume per year.
5. Multiply your answer in step 4 by the approximate number of people in Canada. This will give you an estimate for the consumption of water per year in our country. You will need to round off your answer.

Observations

1. (a) Compare your weekly water consumption with the volume of water used by a person living in a desert in Africa—about 15 L of water per week.
   (b) What does your answer in (a) suggest about the way our society uses water?
2. (a) Scientists estimate that each Canadian must be provided with about 160 000 L of treated or processed water per year. Compare your own annual consumption (Procedure step 4) with the amount of treated or processed water that scientists estimate each Canadian needs.
   (b) If your estimate is much smaller than the value found in (a), state possible uses of water that scientists would probably also include. If your estimate is larger, try to explain why.

Questions

1. Describe ways that you personally could reduce your consumption of fresh water.
2. Describe ways that all Canadians could reduce consumption of fresh water.
3. Why do you think it is important for people to be aware of patterns of water consumption?

Ideas and Applications

Scientists estimate that it takes about 5700 L of processed drinking water to produce a meal consisting of a hamburger, an order of French fries, and a drink.

Concerns about Maintaining Water Supplies

The water cycle provides us with a continuous supply of water. Why, then, are people concerned about maintaining water supplies? Consider the following:

- Measurements of annual rainfall indicate that water supplies are decreasing in some parts of the world. For example, the vast desert regions of northern Africa receive little or no rain, and the desert is slowly increasing in area. Also, in many countries, the supply of water below the ground is being used up. Water is therefore more difficult to find and obtain.
- The world's population is growing very quickly. Therefore, total water consumption is also increasing.
- In Canada's Prairie Provinces, scientists are finding increased concentrations of minerals in the underground water supply. These minerals, such as some compounds of calcium and magnesium, are naturally present in most water supplies. But increasing concentrations mean that the water is less useful for irrigating crops and for personal use. Remember, too much of an otherwise harmless substance can still cause harm.
- Humans are adding more and more harmful substances to the supplies of water they depend on. Some of these pollutants dissolve directly into the water from our polluted air. Some are washed in from factories and our homes. See Figure 19.3. No matter how they get there, these substances can affect the safety of drinking water and harm fish and other sources of food. The contaminated food supplies can then harm us and other organisms.

Later in this chapter, you will be finding out about the pollution that affects our water supplies and some methods for controlling it. But first you need to know a little more about the importance of water to the environment.

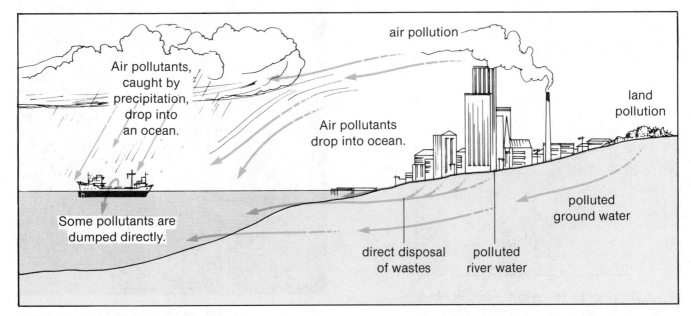

Figure 19.3 *Pollutants, no matter their source, eventually reach the oceans.*

Self-check

1. (a) What percentage of the world's fresh water is found underground?
    (b) What percentage of the surface and atmospheric water is found in rivers and lakes?
2. Describe the journey of one drop of water through the water cycle.
3. What factors are affecting the amount and quality of our water supplies?
4. Suggest four ways that you could improve your water consumption habits.

What Makes Water So Special?

One of the most important reasons why water plays such a large role in the environment is its properties as a *solvent*. Water has the ability to form solutions with more materials than any other solvent. This is because of the nature of the water molecule.

Figure 19.4 shows that water molecules act like tiny magnets. They attract the molecules of other substances to dissolve them. Some substances dissolve more easily in water than others. You know, for example, that sugar and salt dissolve very easily in water. Other substances, such as glass and oil, do not dissolve very much at all in water. Even though water cannot dissolve everything, it dissolves so many materials that it is called the "universal solvent." The existence of caves and rivers show that even rock and soil can be dissolved over many thousands of years (Figure 19.5).

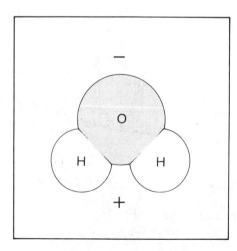

Figure 19.4 *Model of a water molecule. Note that one end is slightly positive and the other end is slightly negative.*

Figure 19.5 *Caves are the result of rainwater draining over and through rock.*

Substances Found Dissolved in Water

Water found naturally on earth is never absolutely pure. Its power as a solvent allows it to pick up solutes of many kinds as it travels through the water cycle. For example, normal precipitation is usually slightly acidic. Dissolved carbon dioxide gas in precipitation forms a dilute solution called carbonic acid. When this slightly acidic precipitation drains through limestone rock formations, it is able to dissolve compounds of calcium and magnesium from the rock.

Water that contains large concentrations of calcium and magnesium compounds is called **hard water**. Hard water reacts with soap to produce a curd-like precipitate which you may have seen as a ring in the bathtub. Remember that a precipitate is the solid, insoluble product of two solutions that have been mixed. Hard water also causes scale to build up on kettles and in hot water pipes.

Water that contains little or no calcium and magnesium compounds is called **soft water**. In Activity 19B, you will investigate the properties of both hard and soft water.

Problem

How can you demonstrate the properties of hard and soft water?

Materials

sample of *very* hard water (0.1 mol/L calcium chloride)
sample of *very* soft water (distilled water)
tap water
water samples from other sources
liquid soap in a dropper bottle
test tubes
test tube stand

Procedure

1. Prepare a table to record your observations. Your table should allow you to compare the amount of soap needed for each water sample to form a permanent lather.
2. Place about 2–3 cm of the soft water sample in a test tube.
3. Add two drops of liquid soap to the test tube.
4. Place a stopper in the test tube (or place your thumb over the end). Shake the test tube vigorously for about 30 s. If a lather forms, set the test tube aside in a stand and proceed. If a lather does not form, add two more drops of soap and shake. Repeat until a permanent lather remains. Record the number of drops of soap that you added.
5. Repeat steps 2–4 with each of the water samples. Remember to record the amount of soap used in each case.

Observations

1. Which water sample(s) formed a precipitate?
2. Describe the precipitate that formed.

Questions

1. What was formed in hard water samples before the soap suds appeared?
2. What will the dirt attach itself to when soap and hard water are used for washing?
3. Why is distilled water the best example of soft water?
4. A powdered cleaning agent is mixed with sample of well water. A white scum forms in the water. What does this suggest about the cleaning agent? What does this suggest about the type of water?

Challenge

Here is an interesting way to show what happens when molecules of soap are added to water. At home, rub a little soap on the end of your index finger. Fill a glass with water, and sprinkle pepper on the surface until it is evenly distributed. Touch the end of your soap-covered finger to the surface of the water. Explain your observations.

In some cases, substances dissolved in water can reduce the effect of acid precipitation on a body of fresh water. Certain forms of hard water can have this effect. This idea will be demonstrated in this activity.

Problem

How can acid precipitation be affected by hard water?

Materials

temporary hard water (calcium hydrogen carbonate solution)
sample of acid precipitation solution (sulphur dioxide solution or vinegar or any solution with a pH of 3–4)
universal indicator solution or pH meter
beaker, 250 mL
burette
magnetic stirrer

CAUTION Adequate ventilation is required when handling sulphur dioxide.

Procedure

1. Design a table that allows you to compare the colour of the acid precipitation solution with the pH and with the amount of hard water added.
2. Your teacher will set up the apparatus shown in Figure 19.6.
3. 100 mL of acid precipitation solution will be placed in a 250 mL beaker. The magnetic stirring bar and support will be added onto a magnetic stirrer.
4. The hard water solution will be placed in the burette. Your teacher will begin stirring the acid precipitation solution and adding 3–4 drops of indicator. If a pH meter is used, the electrode will be clamped so that it is not struck by the stirring bar.

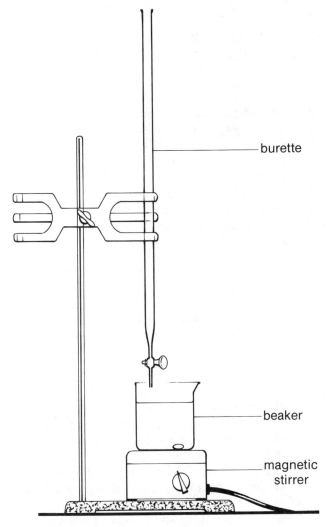

burette

beaker

magnetic
stirrer

Figure 19.6 *Set-up for Activity 19C*

5. Record the pH of the acid precipitation solution in your table.
6. Your teacher will begin to add the hard water to the acid precipitation solution, 10 mL at a time. In your notebook, record the pH of the solution in the beaker after each addition of hard water.
7. This procedure will end after 100 mL of the hard water has been added.

Observations

1. How did the addition of the hard water affect the pH of the acid precipitation solution?
2. Explain why your answer in question 1 is an example of neutralization. In your answer, identify which substance is the acid and which is the base.

Questions

1. What substance in the hard water is responsible for reducing the acidity of the acid precipitation solution?
2. (a) Where would water pick up this kind of substance during its passage through the water cycle?
   (b) Why do all lakes and rivers not have an adequate supply of this substance? Recall what you learned in Chapter 18.

Self-check

1. Why is water so important to the environment?
2. (a) What is hard water?
   (b) What is soft water?
3. (a) Where in the water cycle does water become hard?
   (b) Explain how this happens.
4. What test could you perform to identify a sample of water as either hard or soft? Explain your answer in detail.
5. How can the effects of acid precipitation be reduced by some forms of hard water?

Water Pollution

The tap water you use for drinking and washing has passed through several stages of cleaning and purification. You will learn more about water purification methods later in the chapter. But this water may still contain small amounts of several—or all—of the chemical pollutants shown in Figure 19.7.

How can we tell what pollutants are contained in water? Scientists have devised complex procedures to detect most pollutants and measure the quantity present. In Activity 19D, you will perform simple examples of these tests. The pollutants you will be looking for are chlorides, sulphates, and iron.

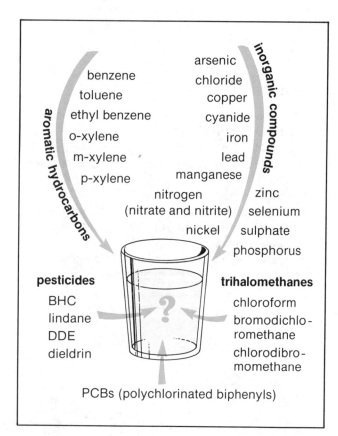

Figure 19.7 *Some of the many different pollutants that can find their way into drinking water.*

Activity 19D

Problem

How can certain substances be detected when they are dissolved in water?

Materials

dilute sodium sulphate solution
dilute potassium chloride solution
dilute iron(III) chloride solution
test solutions:
    silver nitrate solution
    barium chloride solution
    potassium thiocyanate solution
unknown solution containing one or
    more of the test solutions

test tube stand
test tubes

CAUTION Silver nitrate can stain skin and clothing. Handle this solution with care. Be sure to wash your hands after handling the chemicals in this activity.

Procedure

1. Test for Chloride
   (a) Place potassium chloride solution to a depth of 1 cm in a test tube. This is a solution you *know* contains chloride.
   (b) Place distilled water to a depth of 1 cm into another test tube. This is a solution you know does *not* contain chloride.
   (c) To each test tube, add 3–4 drops of silver nitrate solution. Record your observations.
2. Test for Sulphate
   (a) Prepare two more clean test tubes—one with 1 cm of distilled water and one with 1 cm of sodium sulphate solution.
   (b) To each of these test tubes, add 3–4 drops of barium chloride solution. Record your observations.
3. Test for Iron
   (a) Prepare two more clean test tubes—one with 1 cm of distilled water and one with 1 cm of iron(III) chloride solution.
   (b) To each of these, add 3–4 drops of potassium thiocyanate solution. Record your observations.

4. Testing an Unknown Solution
   (a) Place 1 cm of the unknown solution into a clean test tube.
   (b) Using the test solutions, find which pollutant(s) are present. If necessary, use more than one sample of the unknown to be certain of your results.

Observations

1. (a) What happens when silver nitrate solution is added to a solution containing chloride? Hint: Recall that a solid that forms when two solutions are mixed is called a precipitate.
   (b) What happens when silver nitrate solution is added to distilled water?
2. (a) What happens when barium chloride solution is added to a solution containing sulphate?
   (b) What happens when barium chloride solution is added to distilled water?
3. (a) What happens when potassium thiocyanate solution is added to a solution containing iron?
   (b) What happens when potassium thiocyanate solution is added to distilled water?
4. What pollutant(s) did the unknown solution contain? How do you know?

Questions

1. Describe in detail a test for each of the following solutions. Include observations you would expect when the substance is present and when it is absent.
   (a) chloride in water
   (b) sulphate in water
   (c) iron in water

Challenge

The tests in Activity 19D can tell you whether a substance is present or not in water. But they give no idea of the *quantities* of the substance present. Suggest a way to modify the procedure so you could measure the quantity of the substance present.

Common Water Pollutants

You know that water can dissolve a great variety of different substances. It would be unusual *not* to find other substances present in our water supply. Does that mean that all water is considered polluted?

Water is generally considered to be polluted if it is not fit to be used by humans, other animals, and plants. Water pollution is very difficult to control because there are so many types and sources. Table 19.1 on page 376 shows the types, sources, and effects of some of the more common water pollutants.

Self-check

1. It is impossible to find absolutely pure water in nature. Does this mean that all water is polluted? Explain.
2. A water sample is suspected of containing chloride, sulphate, or iron. Describe the procedures you would carry out to identify which are present.
3. Name three types of chemical pollutants that affect water.
4. For each pollutant you named in question 3, name one source and at least one effect on the environment.
5. Name two other types of pollutants that affect water.
6. For each pollutant you named in question 5, name one source and at least one effect on the environment.

Table 19.1 *Examples of Common Water Pollutants*

TYPE OF POLLUTION	EXAMPLES	SOURCES	EFFECTS
Chemicals	Oil	• Spills from oil tankers • Industrial waste	• Kills fish and water fowl • Unsightly
	Fertilizers, detergents	• Run-off from agricultural use • Human sewage	• Poisonous in large amounts • Causes increase in plant growth in water • Reduces amount of dissolved oxygen in water
	Pesticides	• Run-off from agricultural use • Improper spraying	• Passes through food chains • Poisonous to non-target organisms
	Acids, bases	• Industrial waste	• Alters pH of water • Causes effects similar to those of acid precipitation
	Mercury	• Industrial waste	• Passes through food chains • Attacks nervous system of organisms (Minimata disease)
	PCBs, dioxin	• Industrial waste	• Carcinogenic (cancer causing) • Causes birth defects • Causes long-term health problems
Solid Matter	Fine sand, silt	• Urban storm sewers • Run-off • Erosion due to poor agricultural practices	• Reduces transmission of light through water • Unsightly
	Sewage discharge	• Improper sewage treatment by municipalities and individuals	• Transfers bacteria to water • Unsightly • Has unpleasant odour
	Discarded containers, tires, etc.	• Careless and thoughtless humans	• Unsightly • Can dissolve in water • Encourages others to use water as a garbage dump
Thermal	Hot waste water	• Nuclear generating stations • Industries that need water for cooling purposes	• Raises water temperature • Threatens life of some aquatic organisms
Pathogens (Living Matter)	Bacteria, viruses, other single-celled organisms	• Dead animals • Human and animal waste • Sewage	• Source of disease for humans and other animals

Water Quality

In order to survive, most living things use or produce oxygen and carbon dioxide. Fish and other water organisms consume oxygen dissolved in the water. Some decomposers (bacteria and fungi) do the same. Wherever there is a great amount of dead material, such as a thick layer of black organic "ooze," the decomposers will use up most of the available oxygen. Polluted waters contain much organic material, and the reduced oxygen levels kill the organisms that inhabit these waters.

Scientists use a number of tests to determine whether water pollution is present in a body of water. They always check

1. the amount of dissolved oxygen in the water, and
2. the organisms that are present in the water.

For most forms of life, the oxygen levels need to be above 5 micrograms per gram (5.0 ppm) of water. This is the same as saying 5 parts of oxygen per million parts of water. In water with very low oxygen levels, only a few kinds of organisms such as bloodworms (midge larvae) and red sludge worms (*Tubifex*) can survive (Figure 19.8). These organisms are common in polluted streams and in the ooze at the bottom of lakes and ponds. Some fish, such as carp, are able to survive in as little as 1 ppm of oxygen in water, while trout require 10 ppm or more.

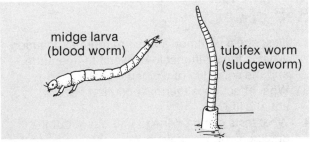

Figure 19.8 *These organisms can tolerate very low levels of oxygen in water.*

Industrial operations and power plants generate waste heat that may be either recycled or discarded. Some of the discarded heat goes into the atmosphere near the industry or power station. Most, however, is carried away by water dumped into a nearby river, lake, or ocean. This **thermal pollution** heats up the water and affects the oxygen level of the water. Consider what happens when you leave a glass of cold water standing for a short time. Air bubbles appear on the inside of the glass. This happens because heat from the room warms the water, making the oxygen less soluble. Oxygen, like other gases, is less soluble in warm water and more soluble in cool water.

Figure 19.9 shows the relationship between temperature and the solubility of oxygen in water. How do you think this would affect any fish living in the water?

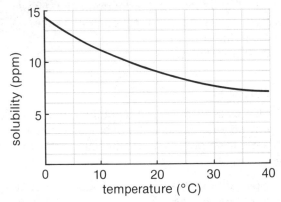

Figure 19.9 *The relationship between temperature and solubility of oxygen in water*

Measuring Water Quality

Scientists have devised tests that will give some indication of the quality of a body of water. One such test measures the quantity of dissolved oxygen in water. Other tests include measuring pH, hardness, the ability to absorb acids, and the amount of dissolved carbon dioxide. In Activity 19E, you will perform tests to compare the quality of tap water with the quality of stream water.

Note: *Alkalinity* refers to the "buffering" capacity of water. For example, water with a high alkalinity will be resistant to the effects of acid precipitation. Carbon dioxide levels in water are related to the dissolved oxygen content, the effects of acid precipitation, and the growth of aquatic plants.

Problem

How can we compare the quality of tap water and stream water in terms of dissolved oxygen, pH, hardness, dissolved carbon dioxide, and alkalinity?

Materials

commercial test kit for dissolved oxygen, carbon dioxide, alkalinity, hardness. Note: Hardness can also be compared using a procedure similar to the one in Activity 19B.

thermometer (preferably one able to be read remotely, so that the probe can be lowered to depth. An indoor-outdoor thermometer allows simultaneous measurement of air and water temperature.)

pH paper or pH meter

Procedure

Note: If a class field trip is not practical, your teacher will provide you with samples of stream water and with a modified procedure for measuring the quality of your sample.

1. Copy Table 19.2 into your notebook to record your observations.
2. At a convenient stream, find a pool 0.5–1m deep.
3. Measure the air temperature. Then measure the water temperature at the surface and at several depths. Calculate the average water temperature.
4. Use the test kit to measure the dissolved oxygen content at the surface and near the bottom.
5. On samples of water taken from the surface and near the bottom, measure pH, carbon dioxide content, hardness, and alkalinity.
6. Repeat the tests on samples of tap water from your municipality.

7. Use reference material from your resource centre or in your classroom to find the permitted values for the factors you are testing. Enter the values in your table.

Observations

Table 19.2 *Comparing the Quality of Stream Water and Tap Water*

TEST	STREAM WATER	TAP WATER	GOVERNMENT STANDARDS
Temperature			
Dissolved oxygen			
Carbon dioxide			
Hardness			
pH			
Alkalinity			

Questions

1. Compare the results of your tests with the government recommended values.
2. What other tests might be made to measure the quality of the water?
3. Make a statement about the quality of each water sample, based on the results of your tests.
4. What factor do you think is the most important to the quality of water? Explain your answer.

Self-check

1. Describe a common source of thermal pollution.
2. What is the relationship between temperature and the solubility of oxygen in water?
3. What effect does thermal pollution have on aquatic life?
4. What tests can be done to find out about the quality of a body of water?

Methods of Controlling Water Quality

Making Water Fit to Drink

Water distribution systems are needed to supply nearly 80% of Canada's population with water that is safe for drinking and washing.

Municipalities operate **water treatment plants** to purify water for use by large numbers of people. One or all of the processes shown in Figure 19.10 may be used in such plants. The processes involved depend on the quality of the water coming into the plant.

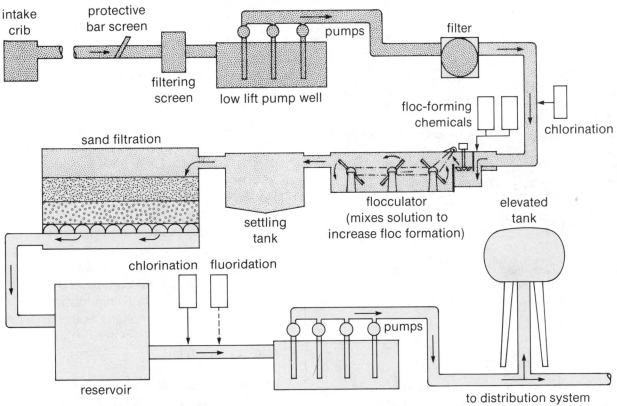

Figure 19.10 *Stages in a water treatment plant*

One of the most important steps in the water purification process is chlorination. Chlorine is added to the water to kill disease organisms (pathogens). Figure 19.11 shows the impact that chlorinating water supplies has had on the incidence of typhoid in North America. Typhoid is a serious disease that results in fever and an inflammation of the intestines. As you can see in Figure 19.11, typhoid claimed many thousands of lives before chlorination was introduced.

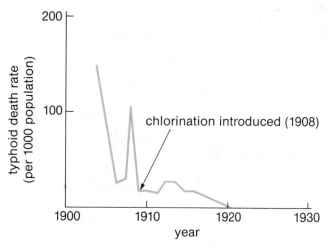

Figure 19.11 *The effect of chlorinating water on typhoid deaths in North America*

Ideas and Applications

Government health laboratories provide water sampling kits. These kits allow simple testing of water supplies for bacterial contamination. Individuals whose water is supplied not by municipalities, but from wells or springs, are encouraged to use this service. That way, they may find out what treatment, if any, is necessary for their water supplies.

Treating Wastewater

What do the following materials have in common?

- sour milk
- unfinished beverages (soft drinks, coffee, tea, juice)
- powdered or liquid cleansers
- paint thinner or old paint
- nail polish remover

These are examples of some of the many things people dispose of by pouring them down the drain. Does this mean that such materials are "out of sight, out of mind"? No. The same system that handles the wastewater from bathing and cleaning must also handle these other materials.

Figure 19.12 shows the stages in a **wastewater treatment plant**. This is a facility that cleans wastewater before it is returned to the environment. Wastewater from houses, apartments, office buildings, and many industrial operations travels through underground pipes that lead to the treatment plant.

There are three stages of wastewater treatment: primary, secondary, and tertiary (third) treatment. Not all communities have the complete three-stage system. Some large cities both in Canada and elsewhere still have only primary treatment.

PRIMARY TREATMENT

The wastewater is screened to remove large solids. It is also allowed to settle in large tanks or ponds so that dust, grit, and other smaller particles may settle out. To remove organic (living) matter in the water, micro-organisms that do not need oxygen may be added. As these micro-organisms digest organic matter, they produce methane gas. This gas is the major component in natural gas, and it can be collected for other uses. If only primary treatment is given to the wastewater, it will now be chlorinated to kill all micro-organisms before the water is released into the environment.

SECONDARY TREATMENT

Air is mixed with the water to encourage the action of helpful bacteria to decompose solid waste. More small solid matter is removed at this stage also. Solids removed here are rich in nutrients and can be used as fertilizer. Then chlorine is added to kill the micro-organisms. If this is the last stage of treatment, the water is released into the environment.

Dissolved substances such as nitrates, phosphates, cadmium, and lead are not removed by primary or secondary treatment. Tertiary treatment is needed to remove these and other harmful substances.

TERTIARY TREATMENT

Dissolved chemicals are removed. One method involves distillation. Another method involves adding other substances to cause precipitation reactions. Tertiary treatment of wastewater is expensive. The cost is much greater than that of primary and secondary treatment combined. That is why many communities omit this stage.

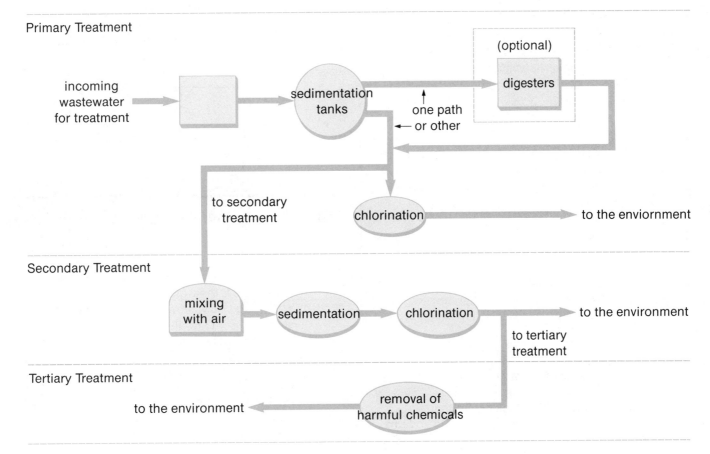

Figure 19.12 *Stages in a wastewater treatment plant*

Activity 19F

This activity provides three examples of the processes involved in water treatment.

Problem

How do water purification methods work?

Materials

soil
solid aluminum potassium sulphate (alum)
graduated cylinder, 250 mL
very dilute potassium permanganate solution
activated charcoal
calcium hydroxide (limewater) solution
beaker, 250 mL
filtration apparatus (Figure 19.13)
dilute sodium phosphate solution

CAUTION Be sure to wash your hands after handling the soil and chemicals in this activity.

Procedure

1. Put 200 mL of water in the graduated cylinder. Add a small amount of soil, shake well, and allow the mixture to settle. Then add 5–10 g of alum to the water. Shake once more, and allow the mixture to settle.
2. Obtain 100 mL of the sodium phosphate solution. Add calcium hydroxide solution to it until you observe a change.
3. Set up the apparatus shown in Figure 19.13. Then pass 50–100 mL of very dilute potassium permanganate solution through the filter.

Observations

1. Describe the effect of the alum in Procedure step 1.
2. Describe the change that took place when calcium hydroxide solution was added to sodium phosphate solution.

3. Describe the changes in colour that occurred as the potassium permanganate solution passed through the filter.

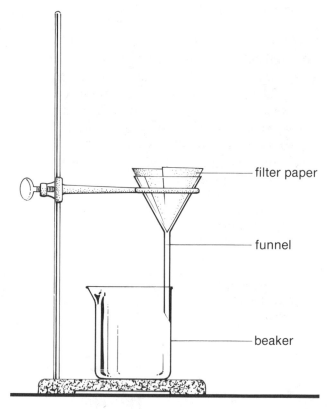

Figure 19.13 *Set-up for Activity 19F*

Questions

1. (a) How does the addition of alum to dirty water help to clear the water?
   (b) What stage of wastewater treatment does this step represent? Explain.
2. What stage of water treatment is represented in Procedure step 2?
3. (a) What effect does activated charcoal have on the colour of the wastewater you used in Procedure step 3?
   (b) What stage of water treatment does this represent?

Wastewater and Industry

Table 19.3 shows that industries use tremendous volumes of water for their operations. The water supplied to industry is usually the same water supplied to your home. Some industries actually require chemically pure water. Therefore, they must further treat water before it can be used. Industrial wastewater travels along with the wastewater from homes and offices to a wastewater treatment plant.

Table 19.3 *The Volume of Water Used Per Year by Selected Industries*

TYPE OF INDUSTRY	WATER USED (MILLIONS OF LITRES)
Brewery	660.0
Dairy	88.0
Meat packing	2100.0
Waste management company	15.5
Bakery	35.7
Cannery	3.4
Pop bottler	2.2
Appliance manufacturer	47.3
Potato chip manufacturer	910.0
Carpet dye house	200.0
Towel manufacturer	425.0
Automobile parts manufacturer	180.0

Industrial wastewater is often contaminated with pollutants. For example, the wastewater from a potato chip manufacturer may contain oil that was used to cook the potato slices. Of greatest concern, however, is wastewater that contains hazardous wastes.

Hazardous wastes are wastes that cause severe, sometimes long-lasting damage to the environment. Examples of such wastes include pesticides, mercury, lead, dioxins (by-products of pesticides), PCBs (cooling oils), and wastes from nuclear reactors.

These wastes are difficult to remove from water. Refer again to Figure 19.7. However, wastewater is not the only source of these wastes in the environment. Figure 19.14 shows that even hazardous wastes buried years ago can and still do threaten water supplies. In addition, the sad truth is that some industries illegally allow their wastewater to flow directly into nearby bodies of water. This crime allows higher concentrations and greater amounts of untreated, hazardous wastes to enter aquatic ecosystems.

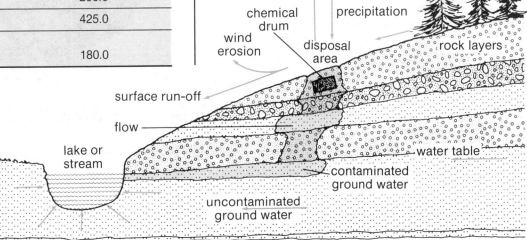

Figure 19.14 *What dangers are associated with this method of disposing of hazardous wastes?*

Treatment of Hazardous Wastes

It is now illegal in the province of Ontario to take hazardous wastes to open dump sites, landfill sites, and wastewater treatment plants. Instead, these wastes must be handled at an industrial hazardous waste treatment plant developed by the Ontario Waste Management Corporation (Figure 19.15). At this single location, hazardous wastes throughout the province will be inspected and disposed of by massive incinerators and/or chemical treatment. Any residue will be solidified to trap any components that could leach out into the environment. This material will then be taken to *sanitary landfill sites* where they will be buried. A sanitary landfill site is one that prevents contamination of the surrounding environment. Relatively clean solid wastes are buried there. Is this the safe solution to hazardous waste disposal? Only time will tell.

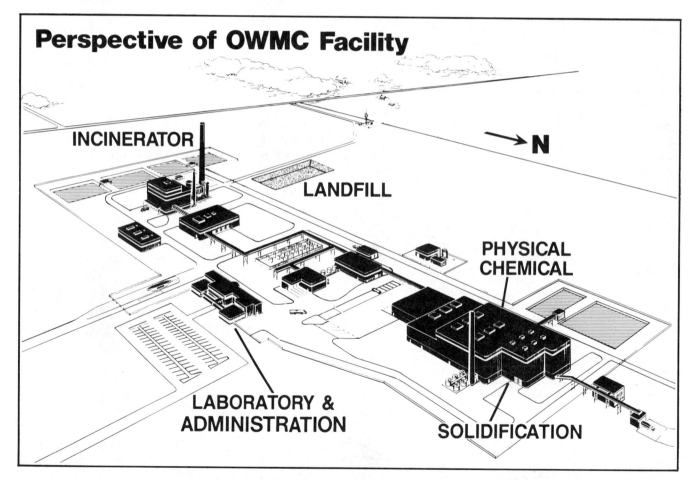

Figure 19.15 *This Ontario Waste Management Corporation facility will handle hazardous wastes from industries throughout the province.*

Science at Work

Recently, one wastewater treatment plant was receiving so much organic material that it could no longer treat the waste properly before releasing it to the environment. Upon examination, the bulk of the material was found to be starch, cooking oil, and potato scraps—the wastes of a local potato chip manufacturer. The local municipality obtained money to improve the wastewater plant by charging the company for its wastewater treatment. However, the potato chip manufacturer was simply producing too much waste. Another solution was needed.

The problem was solved by having the manufacturer recover its organic waste. Equipment was purchased to collect, compact, and dry the waste. This dried waste—several hundred tonnes a year—was hauled away by a farmer who purchased it to use as animal feed. The wastewater plant's operations soon returned to normal.

In the short term, the manufacturer had to shoulder the expense of paying for the recovery equipment. But in the long term, all parties involved benefited from this solution.

Self-check

1. What is the difference between a water treatment plant and a wastewater treatment plant?
2. Why is chlorine added to drinking water and to wastewater before it is released back into the environment?
3. (a) What are the three stages of wastewater treatment?
   (b) Which stage of wastewater treatment is often not performed?
   (c) Why is this stage often not performed?
   (d) Do you think the reason you gave in (c) is a good one? Explain.
4. (a) What are hazardous wastes?
   (b) What is the greatest source of hazardous wastes?
   (c) Why are hazardous wastes dangerous?
5. (a) Why are industries the greatest source of water pollution?
   (b) Do you think this means that individuals and society in general have little or no responsibility for the pollution caused by industry? Think carefully before explaining your answer to this question.

Pollution—and carrots? This sounds like an unlikely combination. Let's examine the facts to get to the *root* of this story.

Carrots grown in a home garden, and proudly brought fresh to the kitchen, are certainly no threat to the environment. But wait. The carrots pictured here weren't just picked. In fact, they might have been picked over a year ago. The process of preparing carrots (and many other vegetables) for canning or freezing holds the key to our headline. The connecting link is water.

When you prepare fresh carrots, you wash off any soil, trim the tops, and peel the root. The soil may be washed off into the garden, or into the kitchen sink. The peels and tops may be composted or tossed into a garbage container. Already this tasty and nutritious vegetable has become a potential pollutant.

Imagine not one, but millions of carrots being prepared. Until recently carrot-processing plants used water during the peeling process. Washed carrots were dipped in a strong solution of sodium hydroxide (lye) to soften and loosen their skins. High pressure jets of water then blasted the skins free and rinsed them away. This type of carrot-processing plant used 6880 m³ of water per day. This is the same as the wastewater from 2000 people!

Regardless of its source, wastewater must be cleansed of its organic waste before it can be safely returned to the environment. The more cleansing that is needed, the greater the cost and the greater the chance that the treatment plant can be overloaded. This overloading can result in polluted water being spilled into streams and waterways.

Carrots Found to Cause Pollution

Environmentalists Outraged!

Famous Vegetable Guilty

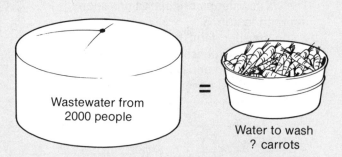

If it takes 500 mL to wash one carrot, how many carrots could you wash with the wastewater from 2000 people (6880 m³)?

Is this another strange headline? Not at all. Rubber is a vital part of the technology that has been developed to reduce wastewater from the industrial processing of carrots. Basically, the problem is how to remove the carrot's skin without using water. The solution is to dip the carrots in lye (as in the old process) and then send them through moving rubber discs. These discs rub off the softened peel, leaving the useful portion of the vegetable. The result is that up to 75% less water is used by the carrot- processing industry, and 85% less organic waste in the water is sent to the treatment plant.

A Happy Ending

This technological solution to a particular pollution problem has had benefits beyond those expected. The dry-peeling process actually improves the quality of the final prepared carrots. The carrots keep nutrients that would otherwise be rinsed away in the water. The dry peeling is more efficient and leaves 10% more carrot for use. The dry peel is easily collected for high quality animal feed once the lye is removed.

Rubber Offers Solution to Carrot Pollution!

Chapter Objectives

NOW THAT YOU HAVE COMPLETED THIS CHAPTER, CAN YOU DO THE FOLLOWING?	FOR REVIEW, TURN TO SECTION
1. Explain why people are concerned about maintaining supplies of clean water.	19.1
2. List the properties of water that make it so special.	19.2
3. Explain how hard and soft water are formed, and list their properties.	19.2
4. Describe how water pollution may occur.	19.3
5. Identify at least three common water pollutants and list their sources and effects.	19.3
6. Describe the effect of thermal pollution on water and water organisms.	19.4
7. Perform physical and chemical tests to determine water quality.	19.5
8. Explain the difference between a water treatment plant and a wastewater treatment plant, and describe how each works.	19.5
9. Explain the effect of industry on water pollution.	19.5
10. State the dangers posed by hazardous wastes.	19.5

Words to Know

water cycle
hard water
soft water
thermal pollution
water treatment plant
wastewater treatment plant
hazardous waste

Tying It Together

1. Why does Canada have a particularly good supply of fresh water?
2. If you are given a test tube filled with a clear, colourless liquid, describe how you would establish whether chlorine particles are present or not.
3. Why is water called the universal solvent?
4. What is hard water and how is it formed?
5. Why is it more difficult to wash in hard water than in soft water?
6. (a) Name three water pollutants.
   (b) For each water pollutant you named, give its source(s) and its effects.
7. What is the relationship between temperature and the solubility of oxygen in water?
8. (a) What is thermal pollution?
   (b) What are the possible effects of thermal pollution on aquatic organisms?
9. Explain how you could determine the quality of the water in a creek.
10. (a) What is a water treatment plant?
    (b) What is a wastewater treatment plant?
11. Name the three stages of wastewater treatment, and explain what occurs during each stage.
12. Agree or disagree with the following statement and give your reasons: "Industry has little effect on water pollution."
13. What are hazardous wastes?
14. Why is it so difficult to remove hazardous wastes from water?

Applying Your Knowledge

1. Consider a typical school day in your life.
   (a) List three actions that result in pollutants that may reach water systems.
   (b) Suggest possible changes in your lifestyle that could reduce the amount of pollution you are responsible for.
2. There is a large, marshy area behind a chemical plant. It has been found that chemical wastes are being dumped into this marsh. A disagreeable odour has begun to bubble up from the mud of the marsh.
   (a) Why is this marshy area not an appropriate place to dispose of chemical waste?
   (b) As a citizen living nearby, why do you want this situation cleaned up?
   (c) Suggest what might be done by you, your community, local government, and the industry itself to clean up this problem. Be sure to consider the possible responses for or against that each group could have.
3. In an effort to stop thermal pollution, three cooling towers have been installed beside a nuclear power plant. Each tower is 133 m high, 100 m wide, and can evaporate 14 000 L of water each minute. Suggest some problems these towers may cause in the area in which they are located.
4. You are a farmer with a pond located beside a road. This pond is used to irrigate your crops as well as to water your animals. In a traffic accident, a truck containing sulphuric acid ends up in your pond and spills its contents into the water. Sulphuric acid is a very strong acid used in many industrial processes. What do you do now?
5. You live in a small community situated near a river used mainly for recreation. You are also a member of a municipal council that must evaluate a proposal to allow a steel refining company into the community. What would be the advantages of accepting the proposal? What would be the disadvantages? Be specific. What guarantees do you want from the steel refining company before you can make your decision?

Projects for Investigation

1. Even if your home is supplied with hard water, there are ways to soften the water. Find out about home water softeners and how they work.
2. In the days before detergents and home water softeners, a substance called washing soda was often used to help soften water. Find the chemical name for washing soda. How did it work to soften the water used for washing?
3. During the 1960s, chemicals called *phosphates* were used in detergents. From research in your resource centre and/or through government environmental agencies, find out
   (a) why phosphates were originally added to detergents;
   (b) what effect phosphates had on the water quality and fish populations of the Great Lakes;
   (c) when the Canadian government imposed restrictions on the use of phosphates and how the decision came about; and
   (d) whether the water quality and fish populations have improved since restrictions on phosphate use were imposed.
4. In Toronto, Ontario, many beaches on the shore of Lake Ontario were closed to the public during the summers of 1985, 1986, and 1987.
   (a) Why were the beaches closed?
   (b) What was the source of the pollution affecting the beaches?
   (c) What steps are being taken to improve the situation?

Unit 6: Environmental Chemistry

MATCH

In your notebook, write the letters (a) to (h). Beside each letter, write the number of the word in the right column that corresponds to each description in the left column.

(a) component of air used by plants for photosynthesis

(b) most plentiful component of air

(c) compounds made up of hydrogen and carbon atoms

(d) gas involved in producing acid precipitation

(e) common acid

(f) calcium carbonate

(g) water that contains calcium compounds

(h) substance added to water to kill bacteria

1. hard water
2. sulphur dioxide
3. carbon dioxide
4. vinegar
5. chlorine
6. hydrocarbons
7. water
8. nitrogen
9. limestone
10. radiation

MULTIPLE CHOICE

In your notebook, write the numbers 1 to 10. Beside each number, write the letter of the best choice.

1. Which is *not* a component of pure air?
   (a) nitrogen
   (b) oxygen
   (c) sulphur dioxide
   (d) carbon dioxide

2. Which is not usually considered to be a pollutant?
   (a) nitrogen dioxide
   (b) particulates
   (c) water vapour
   (d) sulphur oxides

3. A solution with a pH of 8.5 is
   (a) acidic
   (b) basic
   (c) neutral
   (d) battery acid.

4. Which is a common nutrient for plants?
   (a) calcium carbonate
   (b) carbon monoxide
   (c) phosphorus
   (d) sodium chloride

5. Which gas is limewater used to test for?
   (a) carbon dioxide
   (b) nitrogen
   (c) carbon monoxide
   (d) ozone

6. Many people use water softeners in their homes because soft water
   (a) cleans better with soap
   (b) doesn't leave a deposit in water heaters
   (c) doesn't require as much detergent
   (d) all of the above.

7. The first step in most water treatment facilities is
   (a) screening and settling
   (b) adding chlorine
   (c) aeration
   (d) removal of dissolved chemicals.

8. Why is dissolved oxygen important in fresh water lakes and streams?
   (a) It makes the water look clear and refreshing.
   (b) It is important for the photosynthesis of water plants.
   (c) It is important for the survival of many fish species.
   (d) none of the above.

9. Thermal pollution harms aquatic life by
   (a) lowering the dissolved oxygen content of the water
   (b) attracting too many human swimmers and divers
   (c) causing the water to evaporate too quickly
   (d) none of the above.

10. Which of the following is important in the control of pollution?
    (a) government
    (b) industry
    (c) individual people
    (d) all of the above

TRUE/FALSE

Write the numbers 1 to 10 in your notebook. Beside each number, write T if the statement is true and F if the statement is false. For each false statement, rewrite it as a true statement.

1. Clean air contains no carbon dioxide.
2. Air pollutants stay in the immediate area of their source.
3. Acid precipitation raises the pH of lakes and rivers.
4. Litmus paper turns blue in the presence of acids.
5. Carbonated beverages are basic.
6. Carbon dioxide is a common product of combustion.
7. The greenhouse effect is caused by a buildup of water vapour in the atmosphere.
8. The ozone layer is being threatened by chlorofluorocarbons from thermal pollution.
9. Sulphur and oxygen are two elements that form water.
10. Hard water contains calcium and magnesium ions.

FOR DISCUSSION

Read the paragraphs below and answer the questions that follow.

Eurasian water milfoil is an aquatic weed that grows on lake bottoms. In Canada, it is found primarily in Ontario and British Columbia. Dense populations of the weed grow on various types of lake bottoms: silt, sand, gravel, and broken rock. Floating plant fragments of Eurasian water milfoil produced by waves and boating are spread rapidly by currents and winds. New plants grow when the fragments sink to the bottom, and they grow very quickly, making the plant difficult to contain. Since the weed was first identified in British Columbia in 1971, it has spread over 1200 ha of water area.

Eurasian water milfoil presents the following problems:
 (a) the dense growth affects prime recreational areas, preventing swimming, boating, water skiing, and fishing
 (b) the weeds are unattractive, and when decaying plant fragments wash up on shore, they have a foul odour
 (c) in some areas, irrigation and water drainage are affected by the dense growth
 (d) the economic and environmental costs are high, particularly in areas that rely on recreation and tourism
 (e) efforts to control the growth of the weeds using herbicides, erecting barriers, and dredging have had only limited success

Recently, scientists in Ontario have observed that milfoil appears to be on the decline. They have linked this observation with the discovery of a moth caterpillar that lives underwater and eats the weeds. This caterpillar has been found in all areas of Ontario where milfoil grows.

1. Why has it been easy for Eurasian water milfoil to spread quickly?
2. Why is the weed considered to be a problem?
3. (a) Is it safe to conclude that the decline of the weed is a result of the caterpillars? Explain.
   (b) Suggest ways that the caterpillars could be used to control the spread of the weeds. Think of these as plans for a "milfoil-control business" you want to start up.

The Metric System

The metric system of measurement was originally designed by French scientists in 1791. The system is based on multiples or fractions of ten. It is used throughout the world for scientific purposes and in almost every country for everyday measurement.

As techniques for measurement improved, many of the original metric definitions had to be changed. In 1960, the metric system was modernized to form an international system known by its French name, *Le Système International d'Unités*, or SI. In SI, there are seven base units from which all other units can be derived. Table A.1 shows these units.

Table A.1 *SI Base Units*

QUANTITY	UNIT	SYMBOL
Length	metre	m
Mass	kilogram*	kg
Time	second	s
Electrical current	ampere	A
Temperature	kelvin	K
Amount of substance	mole	mol
Luminous intensity	candela	cd

*The kilogram is the only base unit with a prefix. The gram was too small for practical usage.

Once a base unit has been chosen, it can be multiplied or divided by different multiples of 10 to give larger or smaller units. A prefix is used to denote each new unit. For example, the prefix *kilo* means "multiply by one thousand." Thus, *kilometre* is one thousand metres, and *kilogram* is one thousand grams. Kilogram is the *base* unit but gram is the *standard* unit. Table A.2 lists the metric prefixes and the factor by which the unit is to be multiplied. Table A.3 shows some derived units that you may use in this course.

Table A.2

PREFIX	SYMBOL	FACTOR BY WHICH BASE UNIT IS MULTIPLIED	
exa	E	$10^{18} =$	1 000 000 000 000 000 000
peta	P	$10^{15} =$	1 000 000 000 000 000
tera	T	$10^{12} =$	1 000 000 000 000
giga	G	$10^{9} =$	1 000 000 000
mega	M	$10^{6} =$	1 000 000
kilo	k	$10^{3} =$	1 000
hecto	h	$10^{2} =$	100
deca	da	$10^{1} =$	10
standard unit		$10^{0} =$	1
deci	d	$10^{-1} =$	0.1
centi	c	$10^{-2} =$	0.01
milli	m	$10^{-3} =$	0.001
micro	μ	$10^{-6} =$	0.000 001
nano	n	$10^{-9} =$	0.000 000 001
pico	p	$10^{-12} =$	0.000 000 000 001
femto	f	$10^{-15} =$	0.000 000 000 000 001
alto	a	$10^{-18} =$	0.000 000 000 000 000 001

Table A.3 *Common Derived SI Units Used in This Course*

QUANTITY MEASURED	UNIT PREFIX MULTIPLE	milli $\frac{1}{1000}$	centi $\frac{1}{100}$	deci $\frac{1}{10}$	UNIT 1	deca 10	hecto 100	kilo 1000
Length		millimetre mm	centimetre cm	decimetre dm	metre m			kilometre km
Area			square centimetre cm²		square metre m²			
Volume (solid)			cubic centimetre cm³	cubic decimetre dm³	cubic metre m³			
Volume (liquid)		millilitre mL			litre L			kilolitre kL
Mass		milligram mg			gram g			kilogram kg
Energy					joule J			kilojoule kJ

These units are related by the factor 1. Converting one unit to another involves moving the decimal point:

1. When the new unit is smaller, move the decimal to the right.
2. When the new unit is larger, move the decimal to the left.

Graphing

B.1 DRAWING A GRAPH

A graph is a special kind of diagram that shows information (*data*) in the form of a picture. Graphs make it easy to see how one experimental factor relates to another. Graphs also show patterns that you might not observe if the data was in a table or chart. Graphs are used in many areas such as business, economics, technology, and science.

When drawing a graph, you must first decide which quantity goes along the horizontal axis (*x*-axis) and which goes along the vertical axis (*y*-axis). Because quantities in an experiment usually change, they are called *variables*. The *independent variable* is the quantity for which the experimenter chooses the values. It is usually written first in a data table or ordered pair and is graphed along the horizontal axis. The *dependent variable* is the quantity that is to be studied. Its value depends on the value chosen for the independent variable. The dependent variable is written second on a data table or ordered pair and is graphed along the vertical axis. A title should always be given to the graph.

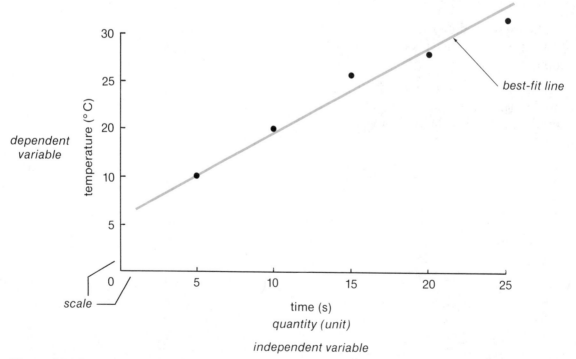

Figure B.1 *Temperature versus time*

B.2 TIPS FOR DRAWING A GRAPH

1. Identify the horizontal axis and vertical axis.
2. Decide which is the independent variable. Label the horizontal axis with this quantity and its units.
3. Label the vertical axis with the dependent variable and its units.
4. Label the graph.
5. Choose suitable scales for both quantities, keeping in mind that
   (a) all data must fit on the graph paper
   (b) most of the available space should be used up
   (c) the two axes can have different scales
   (d) the scales do not have to start at the origin
   (e) it should be easy to estimate intermediate values from the scale.
6. Plot the data from your table.
7. If a pattern is obvious, draw a best-fit line to show the relationship. The best-fit line can be a straight line or a smooth curve. It does not have to touch every plotted point.
8. If there is more than one graph on the page, include a legend to identify the points.
9. Once the graph is drawn, the slope of the line can be calculated using one of the following equations:

$$\text{slope} = \frac{\text{rise}}{\text{run}} \quad \text{or} \quad \text{slope} = \frac{\Delta x}{\Delta y}$$

where y is the change in the value plotted on the vertical axis, and
x is the change in the value plotted on the horizontal axis

Always include the units when calculating the slope. This will indicate the meaning of the slope.

Practical Tips on Microscope Use

The microscope is one of the most important instruments used by scientists today. We use it to investigate objects that are otherwise too small to be seen. The compound light microscope that you will use is an expensive tool. Handle it with care at all times.

Before you begin to use the microscope for any activity, please review carefully the following basic rules for handling and caring for the microscope.

HINTS FOR HANDLING A MICROSCOPE

1. Use both hands to carry the microscope. Carry it by the arm, and use your other hand for additional support under the base.
2. Keep the microscope in an upright position when using liquids or when it is not in use.
3. Keep the stage clean and dry. If any liquids are spilled on the microscope, wipe them up immediately with a piece of tissue.
4. Focus with the low-power lens first, before using any of the other lenses.
5. Focus by moving the lens away from the slide. In other words, focus by increasing the working distance (the distance between stage and objective lens).
6. Call your teacher if the lenses are dirty.
7. Call your teacher if the adjustments do not work freely.
8. Remove the slide from the microscope stage when you are not using it.
9. When putting the microscope away, place the stage clips parallel to the arm, and place the low-power objective lens over the opening.
10. Keep your microscope covered when it is not in use, and keep your area clean and tidy.

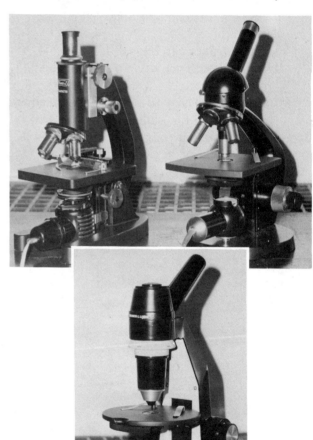

Figure C.1 *You may use a compound microscope like one of these.*

DETERMINING MAGNIFICATION

To determine the *magnifying power* of a microscope, you need to know two things:

1. The magnifying power of each objective lens. This is engraved on the side of the objective. Refer to Figure C.2.
2. The magnifying power of the eyepiece. This is also engraved on the side of the lens. Again see Figure C.2.

Magnification is the product of the magnifying power of the objective and eyepiece lenses. For example, if the low-power objective's magnifying power is 5x and the eyepiece's magnifying power is 10x, the total magnification at low power is as follows:

$$5 \times 10 = 50x$$

In other words, the total magnification at low power is 50x.

USING A COMPOUND LIGHT MICROSCOPE

A slide prepared for viewing with water and a coverslip is called a *wet mount*. In this activity, you will have a chance to review your skill in preparing a wet mount and using a microscope. Then you will be ready to review how to measure the *field of view*—the area that can be observed through the eyepiece.

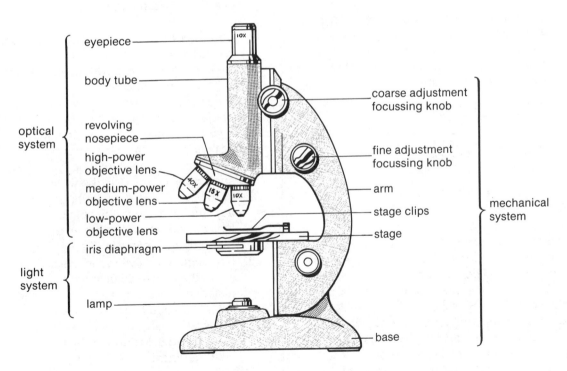

Figure C.2 *Parts and systems of the microscope*

PART 1

Problem

How can you prepare and view a wet mount of a newspaper letter?

Materials

letter "a" or "e" cut from a newspaper
beaker of water
dropper
coverslip
cleansing tissue
microscope slide
compound microscope

Procedure

1. Using the dropper, place a drop of water on a clean glass slide.
2. Place the prepared letter carefully on top of the drop of water (Figure C.3). Be careful not to smudge the slide with your fingers.

prepared letter on drop of water

Figure C.3 *Place the prepared letter carefully on top of the drop of water.*

3. Take a clean coverslip. Hold it between your thumb and forefinger, and touch the edge of the coverslip to the slide. The water will spread along the edge. Hold the coverslip to the slide as shown in Figure C.4. Lower the coverslip onto the slide so that it covers the object. If you have done this correctly, there will be no air bubbles between the slide and coverslip. The slide you now have is called a wet mount.

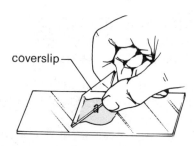

Figure C.4 (a) *Holding the slide between thumb and forefinger, touch the edge of the coverslip to the drop of water.*

Figure C.4 (b) *There should be no air bubbles between the slide and the coverslip.*

4. Turn on or adjust the light source on the microscope.
5. Make sure the low-power objective lens is "clicked" into position.
6. Place your prepared slide on the centre of the stage under the stage clips. The letter should be over the centre of the opening. Make sure the coverslip is on the top side of the slide. The letter on the slide should be facing you. You should be able to read the writing.
7. With your eye at stage level, use the coarse adjustment to bring the object and objective lens as near to each other as possible without touching the coverslip (Figure C.5).
8. Now, with your eye to the eyepiece, slowly move the coarse adjustment to increase the distance between the letter and the lens (Figure C.6). Continue this process until the image is focussed clearly. If the image is not clear, repeat steps 7 and 8. Make sure the letter is centered over the opening.

Figure C.5 *With your eye at stage level, use the coarse adjustment to decrease the working distance.*

Figure C.6 *Slowly move the coarse adjustment to increase the working distance and focus the object.*

9. Adjust the diaphragm so that the letter can be seen as clearly as possible.
10. To observe the letter under medium and high power, follow the steps listed in Table C.1. Move the revolving nosepiece to bring the next higher lens into position. Make sure that you hear the "click" sound to ensure that the objective lens is in place. *When using the medium- and high-power objectives, you should only use the fine adjustment.*

> CAUTION If your microscope has an oil immersion lens, get instructions from your teacher.

Table C.1 *Focussing Your Microscope—The Basic Rules*

— To find the object, always begin your examination with the low-power objective lens.

— To bring the object into focus, increase the working distance between object and objective lens.

— Never allow the objective lens to come in contact with the coverslip. If you have difficulty focussing under a higher power, start over again with the lower power.

— Always centre the object in the field of view before turning to a higher objective lens.

Part 2

Problem

How can you determine the diameter of the field of view?

Materials

compound microscope
clear plastic ruler

Procedure

1. Place a clear plastic ruler on the stage of the microscope.
2. Using the low-power objective, focus and view the ruler through the eyepiece.
3. Move the ruler so that one of the markings is at the left edge of the field of view (Figure C.7). Measure the field of view across the diameter.

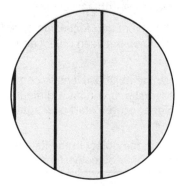

Figure C.7 *The diameter of the field of view shown here is 3.5 mm.*

4. Calculate the diameter of the field of view for the medium- and high-power objectives using the following formula:

diameter of
medium-power or = diameter of low-power x magnification at low power / magnification at medium or high power
high-power field field

DETERMINING THE ACTUAL SIZE OF AN OBJECT

You can find the actual size of objects under the microscope if you know the diameter of the field of view. Line up the object in the centre of the field of view. Count the number of times you think it would fit across the diameter. For example, in this illustration the letter fits across the field of view seven times.

Figure C.8

To determine the actual size of the object, use the formula below. This will give you the actual size of the object, whether it is seen under low, medium or high power.

actual size of object = diameter of field of view (mm) / number of times object fits across the field of view

A

abiotic component Those things in the community that are non-living

absorption The act of taking the products of digestion into the cells lining the small intestine

acid A substance that usually dissolves in water, neutralizes bases, and has a pH of less than 7

acid-base indicator A chemical that changes colour in response to the acidity of a substance

acid precipitation Rain or snow that is unusually acidic due to the presence of air pollution such as sulphur dioxide

air pollutant Substance in the air that is harmful to animals, plants, or people

algal bloom A population of algae

alternating current (AC) Current in which the electrical charges move back and forth instead of in one direction

alveoli (singular: alveolus) Tiny grape-like sacs within the lungs in which gas exchange occurs

ammeter A device used to measure current in a circuit

amniocentesis A procedure that obtains cells from a developing fetus for examination

ampere (A) A unit used to measure current

anabolism The production and storage of energy (as food) within a cell

aorta The large vessel at the top of the heart that carries oxygenated blood from the heart to the arteries

aquaculture The farming of fish, shellfish, or other aquatic organisms

aquatic ecosystem A water area that includes biotic and abiotic components interacting together; may be freshwater or marine

artery Any vessel that carries blood away from the heart

artificial insemination The fertilization of female organisms using sperm collected from males with desirable traits (frequently done in cattle breeding)

artificial respiration The act of assisting someone who has stopped breathing to inhale and exhale

asexual reproduction Reproduction in which a single organism produces offspring that are identical to itself

asthma A condition that causes bouts of coughing and wheezing resulting in great difficulty in breathing

atom The smallest particle of an element

attract To pull toward

B

base A substance that dissolves in water, neutralizes acid, and has a pH of more than 7

battery A group of electrochemical cells connected in series to produce or store energy

bile A green-coloured liquid produced in the liver that acts to separate clumps of fat

bile duct The tube through which bile from the liver passes into the small intestine

biomass energy Chemical potential energy stored in plants and animal wastes

biome A large area with the same climate and a characteristic group of plants and animals

biosphere The part of the earth where all life exists

biotic component Those things in the community that are alive or were once alive

birth rate The number of organisms born into a population over a period of time

blood The transport fluid of the body, consisting of a liquid portion called plasma and several kinds of cells

blood plasma The straw-coloured liquid portion of blood, consisting of water, blood proteins, serum proteins, and ions

blood pressure The force exerted by blood upon the walls of the blood vessels

bronchi (singular: bronchus) First two branches of the respiratory system following the trachea

bronchiole Branch of the bronchi within the lungs

bronchitis A disease that affects the region of the bronchioles characterized by a buildup of fluids in the trachea and the bronchi

budding A type of asexual reproduction in which an offspring grows out of the body of the parent

C

capillary The smallest blood vessel in the body

carbohydrate A molecule formed of carbon, hydrogen, and oxygen, which is one of the types of nutrients needed by living things

carbon cycle The circulation of carbon and oxygen on earth through the processes of respiration and photosynthesis

carbon dioxide The atmospheric gas used by plants in photosynthesis and released by cellular respiration

carbon monoxide An odourless, invisible, and poisonous gas produced by the incomplete combustion of fuels

carnivore A consumer that eats other animals

cartilage Flexible reinforcing material, particularly important as a support to the trachea

catabolism The release of energy within a cell

cell (1) The basic unit of life which has a cell membrane, a nucleus, and a cytoplasm
(2) An apparatus that produces current through chemical reactions

cell membrane Outer living surface of a cell

cellular respiration A specific form of catabolism that takes place in cells to release energy from food

chemical digestion The chemical breakdown of food, involving the action of enzymes

chemical potential energy Energy stored in molecules of matter

chlorophyll The chemical which gives leaves their green colour and which enables plants to carry on photosynthesis

chromosome The structure within the nucleus that contains the genetic instructions passed from parent to offspring

chromosome error Results when a cell does not receive the correct number or parts of chromosomes following cell division

chronic bronchitis A condition where the trachea and bronchi are irritated, often as a result of smoking

cilia Tiny hair-like structures that trap particles within the respiratory system

circuit The complete path through which current travels, including the source

circuit breaker An apparatus that prevents too much current from flowing through a circuit by popping open when the current exceeds a certain value

circulatory system Consists of all the vessels that carry blood

cirrhosis A serious liver condition with symptoms that include nausea, weight loss, weakness, and abdominal pain

community Several different populations of plants and animals living in the same area

conception The fertilization of the egg by sperm (usually referring to humans)

conductor A material that allows electrons to flow through easily, for example, gold and copper

conserver society One in which all parts of the society (individuals, industries, public institutions) are concerned about the use of energy today and conserving energy for the future

consumer An organism that obtains its energy by eating other organisms

coronary blood vessel The blood vessel that supplies the muscle of the heart with blood

coulomb (C) An amount of electrical charge equal to 6.02×10 electrons

crop Part of the digestive tube of a bird that allows food to be gulped, then stored and moistened without chewing it first

current electricity Current in which the electrical charges move from one place to another

cytoplasm The part of a cell outside the nucleus

D

DDT A chemical pesticide that was used to kill insects but is now known to be harmful to other organisms

death rate The number of organisms that die in a population over a period of time

decomposer An organism that eats and digests dead organic material, thus releasing nutrients that are used by other living things

diaphragm A thin sheet of muscle that separates the chest region from the abdomen and is used in breathing

diastolic pressure The lowest blood pressure; occurs just before the ventricles contract again.

digestive system Includes the digestive tract and related organs

digestive tract The tube through which food passes during the processes of digestion

diploid number The number of chromosomes in each body cell, twice the number in a gamete. See **haploid**

direct current (DC) Current in which the charges move in one direction only

DNA (deoxyribonucleic acid) The chemical substance within chromosomes that contains the genetic code for each trait

domain A group of atoms whose magnetic fields are all lined up in the same direction

dominant gene The gene that affects the appearance or behaviour of the individual

E

ecology The study of the relationships among organisms and their environment

ecosystem An area that includes biotic and abiotic components all interacting together

egg The gamete produced by the female parent

elastic potential energy Energy stored in stretched or compressed objects

electrical energy Energy of charged particles such as electrons and protons

electric potential difference The difference between the energy an electron has at two different points in a circuit

electromagnet A magnet produced by passing electrical current through a conducting wire or coil of wire

electron The negatively charged particle found orbiting the nucleus of an atom

electroscope A device used to detect static electrical charge

electrostatic precipitator A device used to attract dust and other small particles

embryo The stage in an organism's development in which the zygote has divided into many cells which continue to grow and divide

emphysema A disease of the lungs in which the walls of the cells of the alveoli are changed so that gas exchange may be prevented

energy The ability to do work

energy conversion The changing of energy from one form to another

energy input The amount of energy used to operate an energy system

energy output The amount of useful energy obtained from an energy system

energy resource A raw material from nature that can be converted to useful energy

energy system A device that converts one form of energy into one or more other forms of energy

environment The surroundings of an organism, including the air, water, climate, habitat, and other organisms

enzyme In digestion, a complex chemical that breaks down large molecules into smaller molecules without itself being changed

epiglottis A flap of tissue deep in the pharynx that prevents swallowed food or liquid from entering the trachea

exhale To breathe out

extinct Referring to a particular species that has died out

F

fat A nutrient needed by living things

feces Waste material eliminated from the body

fertilization The process of joining egg and sperm cells together to form a zygote

fetus A human embryo after the eighth week following conception

fibre Made up of a mixture of cellulose and other large complex carbohydrates

food additive Any chemical added to a food in order to preserve it

food chain The connections between consumer and prey organisms showing the transfer of energy from one organism to the next

food web Several food chains linked together

fossil fuel A non-renewable energy resource formed from plants and animals that died millions of years ago

fraternal twins Twins that result from two eggs being fertilized by two sperm cells during conception

frequency Number of vibrations per second

fuse A device with a thin metal strip that is inserted into a circuit. If the current flowing through the circuit becomes too large, the metal strip melts and breaks the circuit.

G

gall bladder A sac that stores the bile produced by the liver before its release into the bile duct

gallstone A hard lump of bile pigments and calcium salts that develops in the gall bladder

galvanometer A device used to measure very small electrical currents

gamete Special cell contributed by each parent in sexual reproduction

gene The portion of a chromosome that codes for one particular trait

generator A device that uses mechanical energy to produce electricity

gene splicing A technique where a gene is taken from the chromosome of one individual and joined to a chromosome of another organism

genetic counsellor Person who gives people advice on the chances that they might bear a child with a genetic defect

genetic engineering The application of genetic knowledge for practical purposes

genetics The science of heredity

genotype The kind of genes present in an individual

geographical North Pole The northernmost point of the earth

geothermal energy Heat energy available beneath the earth's surface

gizzard A muscular sac which, in birds, acts as a grinding stomach

gravitational potential energy Energy stored in raised objects

greenhouse effect The phenomenon that occurs when increasing amounts of carbon dioxide may act like the glass of a greenhouse, causing the earth's atmosphere to become warmer

grounding The process of making an object electrically neutral by placing it in contact with the ground

H

habitat The physical space where an organism lives

haploid number The number of different chromosomes in a gamete. See **diploid**

hard water Water that contains large concentrations of calcium and magnesium compounds

hazardous wastes Wastes that can cause severe, sometimes long-lasting, damage to the environment

hemoglobin The oxygen-carrying protein contained in red blood cells

hemophilia A sex-linked trait in which a person's blood does not form clots

hepatitis A disease of the liver with symptoms that include jaundice, a yellowing of the skin

herbivore A consumer that eats plants

heredity The tendency of offspring to resemble their parents

hertz (Hz) The unit used to measure frequency

hormone A chemical secreted by glands in the body to regulate or control the functions of body organs

host An organism that is affected by a parasite

hybrid A product of cross-breeding two different varieties; when each of the pair of genes for a particular trait is different

hydraulic energy Kinetic energy of falling water

hydrocarbon Compound made up of hydrogen and carbon

hydro-electricity Electricity generated from moving water

hypothetical population An assumed population of organisms suggested for the purpose of reasoning the effects of changes in a population

I

identical twins Twins that develop from the same fertilized egg and have identical genes

incinerator A device that burns solid waste at high temperature

induction (of electrical charge) The movement of electrons, caused by a nearby charged object

ingestion The act of taking food into the mouth

inhale To breathe in

insulator A material that does not allow charges to move freely, for example, rubber and styrofoam

J

joule (J) The unit used to measure both energy and work

K

kidney Organ responsible for changing the concentration of water and chemicals in the blood, as well as for the formation of urine

kilowatt hour (kW·h) The unit used to measure electrical energy consumption

kinetic energy Energy of moving objects

L

large intestine The portion of the digestive tract that follows the small intestine

laryngitis A condition where the mucus membranes lining the larynx become inflamed

larynx Voice box, located in the upper portion of the trachea

left-hand rule (for straight conductors) If you point the thumb of your left hand in the direction of the electron flow, the fingers wrapped around the conductor will point in the direction of the magnetic lines of force.

lodestone Also known as magnetite; a naturally occurring mineral that was the first known magnet

M

magnet A body that can attract iron, nickel, and cobalt if they are within its magnetic field

magnetic field The region around a magnet where its effect can be detected

magnetic North Pole The point to which the needle of a compass will be drawn

magnetite See **lodestone**

mechanical digestion The physical breaking down of food

megajoule (MJ) One megajoule is equal to one million joules

meiosis A special type of cell division used to produce gametes by reducing the double set of chromosomes being reduced to a single set of chromosomes per gamete

Mendel, Gregor The discoverer of the basic pattern of the inheritance of traits

menstrual period The time during which there is a flow of blood from the uterus

menstruation The periodic flow of blood from the uterus

metabolism All of the energy-storing (anabolic) and energy-releasing (catabolic) processes within a cell

migration rate The movement of organisms into or out of a specific area

mineral One of the groups of nutrients which includes, for example, calcium and iron

mitosis The duplication of the chromosomes and the division of the nucleus prior to cell division

mucus Fluid secreted by the cells lining the walls of the respiratory system

murmur An extra heart sound that results when a valve in the heart does not close properly and blood leaks back into a chamber

mutation A sudden change in a trait between a parent and its offspring

N

nasal passage First portion of the respiratory system

natural material Manufacturing material found in nature, such as iron, wool, and cotton

negatively charged When an object has more electrons than protons

neutron An uncharged particle found in the nucleus of an atom

niche An organism's role (or job) in the community

nitrogen The atmospheric gas that is an important nutrient to plants once fixed in soil

nitrogen oxides Gases formed when fuels are burned at high temperatures. Nitrogen oxides react with oxygen and sunlight to produce poisonous ozone gas

non-renewable resource A resource from nature that takes so long to renew that once it is used it is essentially gone forever

north-seeking pole (N-pole) The pole of a magnet that will point toward the magnetic North Pole

nostril Opening in the nose through which air enters the nasal passages

nuclear fission The splitting of a large atomic nucleus into smaller nuclei in order to release large amounts of energy

nuclear fusion The joining together of one small atomic nucleus with another in order to release large amounts of energy

nuclear potential energy Energy stored in the central part (nucleus) of an atom

nucleus (1) The core of an atom that contains neutrons and protons
(2) control centre of a cell, containing its chromosomes

nutrient The components of food that the body needs in order to maintain good health

nutrition The science of food and nutrients and their relation to health

O

offspring The next generation of organisms

omnivore A consumer that eats both plants and other animals

oxygen The atmospheric gas used in cellular respiration

ozone An unstable, toxic form of oxygen that forms an essential layer of protection against the sun's damaging ultraviolet radiation in the upper atmosphere

P

parallel An electrical connection in which the electrons move in two or more independent paths

parasite A consumer that lives in or feeds on another organism (called a host) for its own benefit, without killing that organism

particulate One general kind of air pollutant consisting of tiny particles

peristalsis The movement of food through the digestive tract by co-ordinated muscle contractions

permanent magnet A substance that keeps its magnetic properties over a long period of time

pesticide A chemical used to kill anything considered to be a pest, for example, certain insects

pharynx Common passage for air entering the respiratory system and for material entering the digestive system

phenotype The appearance of a trait in an individual

pH scale A description of how acidic or basic a substance is, with distilled water having a pH of 7

piezo-electric effect Electricity produced from the squeezing or vibrating of crystals

pistil The central part of a flower that consists of stigma, style, and ovary

platelet Smallest cell in the blood, involved in blood clotting

pneumonia A general term that applies to serious lung infections characterized by fluid buildup in the lungs

pole One of two regions of a magnet that displays the greatest magnetic force

pollen A powdery substance containing sperm cells produced by the stamen of a flower

pollination The process by which pollen is transferred from an anther to a stigma (from the stamen to the pistil) of a flower

pollutant A harmful substance that enters the environment

pollution Anything added to the environment that causes harm to living things

population A group of individuals living in the same area that are of a single species

positively charged When an object has more protons than electrons

potential difference See **electric potential difference**

predator A consumer that hunts and kills other animals for its food

prenatal period The time spent by the baby in the uterus of the mother

primary sexual characteristics Differences between the female reproductive organs and the male organs

producer An organism, such as a green plant, that uses inorganic forms of energy to produce its own food

protein A nutrient important as a building material for living things

proton The positive particle of an atom, located in the atom's nucleus

pulmonary artery Carries blood, low in oxygen, from the heart to the lungs

pulse rate Heart rate detected as rhythms within arteries

pure strain When both of the pair of genes for a particular trait are the same

Q

quadrat Section of regular size (for example one metre by one metre, or ten centimetres by ten centimetres) used to divide an area so that random samples can be obtained

R

radiant energy Energy that travels in the form of high-speed waves, for example, visible light

random sample A sample that is scattered by chance and not selected deliberately

recessive gene The gene that, although it does not affect the appearance or behaviour of the individual if a dominant gene is present, is still passed on to the next generation

recycling The collection of waste material in order to make more of the same product

red blood cell Cell in the blood that carries hemoglobin

relationship Interrelationship between two living things

renewable resource A resource that renews itself within a normal human lifespan of about 75 years

repel To push apart

reproduce To produce offspring

reusing Using an item more than once before discarding it as waste

S

saliva A watery fluid produced in the mouth

salivary gland Group of cells that secrete saliva

scavenger An animal that eats dead and decaying material

secondary sexual characteristics A visible difference between mature males and females resulting from the action of hormones on various parts of the body during growth

selective breeding A procedure by which only animals and plants with desirable traits are allowed to reproduce

series An electrical connection in which the electrons must flow through each part of the circuit in turn

sex-linked trait Trait coded by genes located on the sex-determining chromosomes

sexual reproduction Reproduction that requires two parents

small intestine The portion of the digestive tract that follows the stomach, consisting of the duodenum, the jejunum, and the ileum

soft water Water that contains relatively small concentrations of calcium and magnesium compounds

solar cell A device that converts light energy into electrical energy

solar energy Radiant energy from the sun

solenoid A coil of wire that produces a magnetic field when electrical current passes through it

sound energy Energy produced by vibrating objects

south-seeking pole (S-pole) The pole of a magnet that will point towards the magnetic South Pole

sperm The gamete produced by the male parent

stamen The male part of a flower

static electricity The presence of an electric charge that is stationary, not flowing

steady state A condition that fluctuates to produce an average situation

sterile Any organism that cannot reproduce itself

stethoscope A device used for listening to sounds occurring within the body

storage battery Apparatus for storing electrical energy in a chemical form

succession A sequence of changes in a biotic community, usually increasing its complexity

sulphur dioxide A highly corrosive gas formed when oxygen and sulphur combine; a major cause of acid precipitation

synthetic material A manufacturing material made by chemical processes, such as plastic

systolic pressure The blood pressure created by the contracting of the ventricles

T

technology The development of tools, machines, or processes that help people make use of resources

temporary magnet A substance that loses its magnetic properties after a short period of time

terrarium A model of a terrestrial ecosystem

terrestrial ecosystem A land area that includes biotic and abiotic components, interacting together

thermal energy Internal energy of an object (possessed by molecules)

thermal pollution Heating up of natural waterways by waste heat from industry or power plants

thermocouple A device consisting of two different metals joined together that will produce electrical current when heated

tidal energy Kinetic energy of water moving in and out of coastal regions

trachea Windpipe made of cartilage; reinforced portion of the respiratory system following the pharynx

trait Characteristic of the parents that is passed to the offspring

U

ulcer A crater-like wound in the skin or lining of the digestive tract

ultrasound Technique using sound waves to produce an image of a developing fetus

universal donor A person with Type O blood, whose blood can be donated to people of any other blood type

universal receptor A person with Type AB blood, who can accept any other blood type in a transfusion

V

valve A flap of tissue that prevents the backward flow of blood in veins or within the heart

vein Any vessel that carries blood to the heart

villi (singular: villus) Tiny finger-like projections or folds lining the surface of the small intestine

vital capacity The amount of air a person's lungs will hold

vitamin One of the groups of nutrients consisting of several important compounds that bodies cannot make for themselves and which must be eaten

vocal cord One of two string-like cords stretched across the larynx which produce different sounds when air is forced over them

volt (V) The unit used to measure potential difference

voltmetre A device used to measure the potential difference between two parts of a circuit

W

wastewater treatment plant A facility that cleans wastewater before it is returned to the environment

water cycle How water circulates on earth through evaporation, condensation, precipitation, and drainage

water treatment plant A facility that cleans water for human use, especially by removing pathogenic (disease-causing) organisms

white blood cell One of several types of large cells in the blood, for example, disease-fighting leucocyte and lymphocyte

wildlife sanctuary An area set aside for plants and animals to live unmolested by hunting or other human disturbance

wind energy Kinetic energy of moving air

Z

zygote The newly formed cell that arises from the fertilization of an egg cell by a sperm cell

Colour Section: Bill Ivy
Unit One: NASA, Chapter 1: Bill Hause, Don Galbraith, 1.1: National Museum of Canada, 3.4: Ontario Ministry of Natural Resources, 3.5: Lorne Scott, 3.7(b): Supply and Services Canada, 3.8: Agriculture Canada, 3.13: A.W. Andrews, Chapter 4: Miller Services, Ontario Ministry of Natural Resources, Miller Services, Chapter 5: Miller Services, 5.18: Vern Freer, 5.19: Miller Services, Chapter 6: Vern Freer, Ontario Ministry of Natural Resources, 6.17: Vern Freer. Chapter 7: Toronto General Hospital, Chapter 8: Vern Freer, Unit Three: The Globe and Mail, Chapter 9: Mary Kay Winter, 9.2: M.E. Browning, 9.5: Murray Lang, 9.6: Mary Kay Winter, 9.7: Don Galbraith, 9.22: Toronto General Hospital, Canapress, Chapter 10: University of British Columbia, Faculty of Medicine, 10.2: Dr. B.P. Kaufman, University of Michigan, 10.9, Smith Collection, Center for History of Chemistry, 10C: Windfield Farms, 10D: Canapress, 10.18: Murray Lang, 10.19: Blandchris Kennels Reg'd., 10.21: Ontario Ministry of Agriculture, 10.23: Ontario Ministry of Agriculture, 10.24: Sheridan Nurseries, Chapter 11: Mark Antman/Stock, Bos., 11.2: Ontario Science Centre, 11.3: The Red Cross Society, 11.8: YMCA of Metropolitan Toronto, 11.9: General Electric Medical Systems Limited, 11.10: Southam Communications, 11.11: Sheila Camer, 11.12(a): Vancouver General Hospital, 11.12(b): Frank Cloutier, 11.13: Vancouver General Hospital, 11.14: Seneca College, 11.14: Connaught Laboratories, Unit 4: Gordon R. Gore, Chapter 12: Bill Hause, 12.1: Gordon R. Gore, 12.2: Burndy Library, 12.3: Gordon R. Gore, 12.9: Alcan Canada Products

Limited, 12.10: Gordon R. Gore, 13.1: Alan J. Hirsch, 13.2: Bill Hause, 13.3: Gordon R. Gore, 13.4: Bill Hause, 13.6: Bill Hause, 13.9: Derek Bullard, 13.17: Gordon R. Gore, Chapter 14: Gordon R. Gore, 14.1: Alan J. Hirsch, 14.13: Smith Collection, Fisher Scientific Company, 14.20: Gordon R. Gore, 14.30: Gordon R. Gore, Unit 5: US Wind Power Inc./ Ed Linton, Chapter 15: NASA, 15.19(c): Los Alamos National Laboratory, 15.2(a): Royal Ontario Museum, 15.2(b): Deborah MacNeill, 15.2(c): Imperial Oil, 15.4: Indal Technologies, 15.5: Geological Survey of Canada, 15.7: Nova Scotia Power Corp., 15.8: Ontario Hydro, Chapter 16: Donald Plumb, 16.1: Netherlands Board of Tourism, Chapter 17: E.I. Dupont de Nemours & Co., 17.2(b): Ford Motor Co., 17.2(c): Shell Canada Ltd., 17.6: R.H. Czerneda, 17.7: R.H. Czerneda, Unit 6: Derek Bullard, 18.1: Miller Services, 18.7: Miller Services, 18.12: Don Galbraith, 18.13: Donald Plumb, 18.16: Chris Hannell, Chapter 19: W.H.O./ P. Almasy, Information Canada Phototech, Brigitte Nelson, 19.5: Derek Ford, 19.15: Ontario Waste Management Corp.

Colour section: Page 1: bald eagle, shaggy mane mushroom, lynx, Page 2: spotted salamander, great tiger moth, red baneberry, grizzly bear, barred owl, Page 3: American toad, garter snake, yellow lady slipper, ruffed grouse, porcupine, Page 4: common loon, wild bergamot, yellow touch-me-not, woodland caribou, white-footed mouse, Page 5: rounded earth star, musk ox, ladybug, American goldfinch, red squirrels, Page 6: polar bear, wild columbine, little brown bat, Blanding's turtle, *Amanita citrina*, Page 7: fiddlehead, great blue heron, deciduous forest, red-spotted purple butterfly, sea anemone, Page 8: Courtesy of NASA.